D1268395

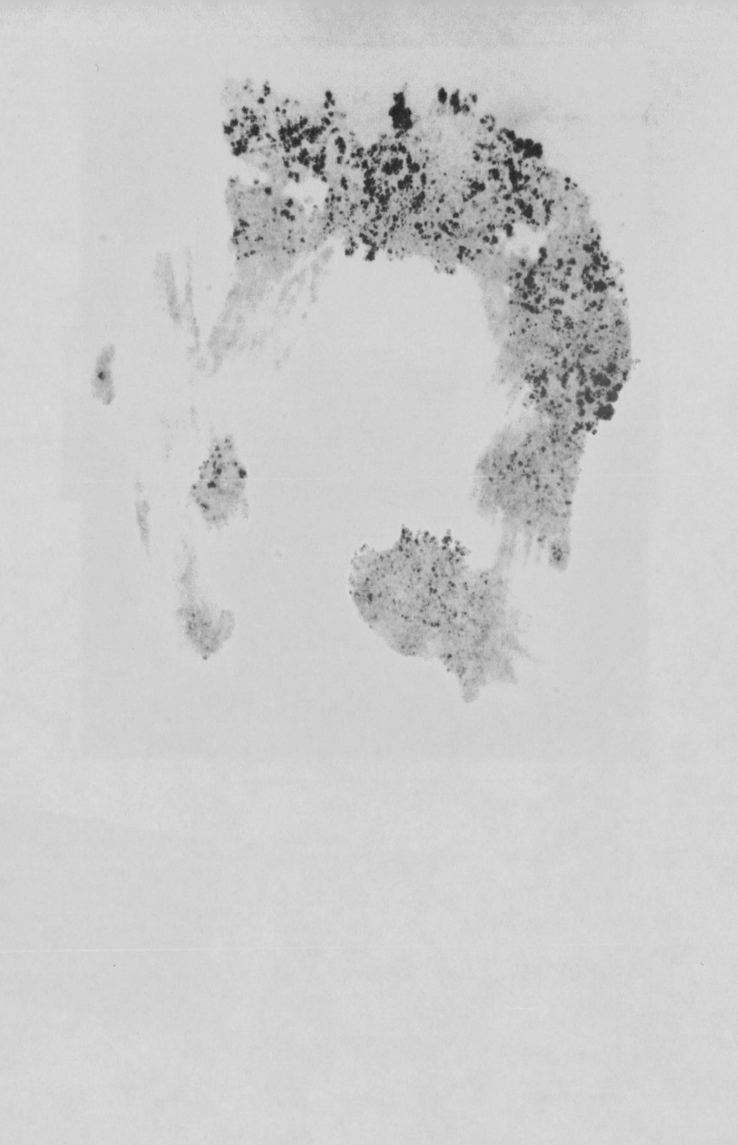

ART IN ITALY,

1600–1700

GUIDO RENI *81. The Meeting of David and Abigail*
Collection of Walter P. Chrysler, Jr.

ART IN ITALY, 1600–1700

Organized by
FREDERICK CUMMINGS

Introduction by
RUDOLF WITTKOWER

Commentaries by
Robert Enggass · Bertina Suida Manning · Robert Manning · Dwight C. Miller
Alfred Moir · Donald Posner · Olga Raggio

THE DETROIT INSTITUTE OF ARTS

Distributed by Harry N. Abrams, Inc., New York, N.Y.

Library of Congress Catalogue Card Number 65-20153

DESIGNED BY WILLIAM A. BOSTICK

COMPOSED IN GARAMOND TYPES BY MICHIGAN TYPESETTING COMPANY, DETROIT, MICHIGAN

PRINTED IN THE UNITED STATES OF AMERICA BY OFFSET LITHOGRAPHY BY FLEXITYPE
AND DOUGLAS OFFSET COMPANY, DETROIT, MICHIGAN

CONTENTS

PREFACE

THIS BOOK is a result of the collaboration among the distinguished group of young American scholars who constitute the Consulting Committee, and the honored master of the Italian Baroque, Rudolf Wittkower. Denis Mahon has also proffered advice and assistance almost from the moment of inception.

Our primary purpose has been to illustrate the seventeenth century in Italy with works representing each noteworthy artist at a high level of accomplishment. We have not presumed to define "Baroque." Works of art have been included which might be called late Mannerist, proto-Baroque, early-high-late Baroque, and proto-Rococo. It has been our concern to demonstrate the multiplicity and variety in the art of the age and so to characterize it by juxtaposition rather than to limit it by forced selection. To this end we have organized the material broadly by schools, placing Roman and Bolognese works at the beginning and closing with Genoese and Venetian.

To produce this book and the exhibition (April 6—May 9, 1965) which it commemorates, we have worked *a la italiana* with specialists offering suggestions at every point. Commentaries and documentation have been prepared by Donald Posner (D. P.) for early Roman and Bolognese Schools, Robert and Bertina Suida Manning (R. L. M. and B. S. M.) for the Genoese and Venetian Schools, Alfred Moir (A. M.) for Caravaggesque and Neapolitan artists, Dwight C. Miller (D. M.) for later Bolognese and Florentine Schools, Robert Enggass (R. E.) for later Roman Schools, Olga Raggio (O. R.)

(Opposite page)
DONATO CRETI
119. Musical Group
Collection of Walter P. Chrysler, Jr.

for sculpture, Rudolf Wittkower (R. W.), and Frederick Cummings (F. C.). Thus entries have been written by outstanding scholars who have generally made special studies in their assigned area. Yet these authors not only have worked arduously to procure the most pertinent data and to produce pithy sketches for each object and artist, they also had a hand in selecting the works of art. In so controversial and volatile an area as the Italian seventeenth century, and in a field in which American museums and private collectors are rapidly adding new acquisitions, this has been an essential corollary of our method. Nonetheless, it should be stressed that the Consulting Committee has not uniformly agreed on every selection, and this happily is reflected in the individual commentaries. If the principle behind our approach has been to work in the Italian way, it has not always been possible in practice. Rather than gathering around a conference table with Malvasia's *Felsina Pittrice* at hand and the great European scholars all around, we have worked far from each other, attempting to bridge distances with an elaborate programme of letterwriting. Although unwieldy, this has not been an altogether insupportable burden. Throughout the period of preparation letters containing photographs and detailed scholarly data constantly sped between Detroit and the university seats of the Consulting Committee. In this way a number of new attributions have been put forward. Certain of these are reflected in the commentaries; still others are found in the changed attributions attached to individual objects.

Our second purpose was to evaluate the extent and significance of the collecting of Italian seventeenth century art in America. It has become increasingly apparent that the acceptance of the Italian Baroque is a deeply rooted and extensive one, as Rudolf Wittkower makes clear in his introduction. However, it has come as something of a surprise that with notable exceptions the Italian seventeenth century can be illustrated in great detail from American collections. Where gaps existed or where pictures of outstanding quality were essential to demonstrate the stature of certain artists, we have been able to draw on the superb resources of one European collection, that of Denis Mahon. Only in a very few cases were we unable to obtain a major work by an important artist.

This remarkable fact suggests that something new and vibrant has subtly penetrated the American spirit. Like a silent visitor who has stayed to occupy the house and, yeastlike, has leavened it with a Mediterranean richness, the Baroque has remained in America. Among cement walls and Mies van der Rohe piers, the human figure, the rich and subtly nuanced in color, the intricate and curvilinear, rather than the rectilinear and spare in formal arrangement, have found their way. The ascetic sophistries and obviousness of our current cultural diet, the childlike witticisms and momentary titillations of much of our visual fare have left the vast reaches of the intellect without satisfaction. It is to slake this deep and aching thirst that the most dynamic and sophisticated of artistic forms has slowly and determinedly suffused our culture.

Numerous individuals have given graciously of their time and energy in order to make this undertaking possible. To the lenders who have so generously taken paintings and drawings from their living-room and gallery walls, we extend our warm expressions of gratitude. A special note of thanks is due the administration of the Wadsworth Atheneum and the Nelson Gallery-Atkins Museum for making special exceptions to allow certain pictures to come to Detroit.

Special acknowledgment and the sincere appreciation of all those who worked on the exhibition go to Denis Mahon. Apart from allowing his pictures to brave the hazards of crossing the sea, he has made suggestions at every point which have been fundamental to the success of this undertaking.

To all of the members of the Consulting Committee, to Dr. Wittkower, and to Stephen Pepper, who worked arduously to produce original and noteworthy material, our sincere appreciation. We wish also to thank Erwin Panofsky for identifying the subject of Guericino's *Salome Visiting St. John the Baptist*. Janos Scholz has been more than generous not only in lending a major group of drawings but in providing information and making available rare catalogues which have greatly facilitated the compilation of data. Francis H. Dowley has generously provided information and opinions which have aided us greatly in the later Roman section.

We are also grateful to many individuals who have given their time and special assistance. Anthony M. Clark, Jacob Bean, John Maxon, Otto Wittmann, Stephen E. Ostrow, Michael Mahoney, Klaus Lankheit, Charles C. Cunningham, Laurence Sickman, Bob Jones, Jr., Perry Rathbone, Sigmund Vigtel, Sherman Lee, Mary M. Davis, Richard P. Wunder, Thomas C. Colt, Jack M. McGregor, René Taylor, Agnes Mongan, Basil Petrov, Charles Sawyer, Felice Stampfli, R. H. Hubbard, Justus Bier, E. R. Hunter, Kneeland McNulty, Donald G. Humphrey, Robert O. Parks, Richard E. Fuller, Helene Muensterberger, Charles E. Buckley, Edward S. King, Mr. Young of Day & Meyer, Murray & Young, and numerous individuals on museum staffs throughout the country have helped greatly to make this exhibition a success.

Without the constant assistance of the staff of the Detroit Institute of Arts, the consummation of the exhibition would have been impossible. We wish to thank especially Charles H. Elam who has read through the entire manuscript and made helpful suggestions. Anne Kerney deserves a special measure of thanks for typing innumerable letters and much of the manuscript. William A. Bostick designed the book, saw it through the press and gave professional assistance in all stages of preparation. We are grateful to Audley Grossman who was responsible for the decor of the exhibition galleries. To Harold Shaw and his staff who have so ably installed the exhibition goes a warm measure of appreciation. A very special expression of thanks goes to the Women's Committee of the Founders Society and especially to Mrs. J. Merriam Barnes, Chairman of the opening reception.

A note about the editing will facilitate the use of this book. The sizes of works of art are indicated with height preceding width. No attempt has been made to cite all references (Ref.) and many titles of works are frequently given in shortened form. The biographies of artists have been written by the persons preparing the entry for their paintings or sculptures, rather than by the author of the drawings entries. Exceptions are indicated with brackets.

WILLIS F. WOODS

FREDERICK CUMMINGS

INTRODUCTION

by Rudolf Wittkower

IT IS INTERESTING to speculate on what an Italian Baroque exhibition at Detroit might have been like thirty or even fifteen years ago. In 1935 a Baroque exhibition would have been focussed on a few great names of the Roman and Bolognese schools, on Caravaggio, the Carracci, Domenichino, Reni, Guercino, and one might have surrounded these major stars by some 'embroideries,' a few pictures by provincial masters, who had always maintained a reputation, a Strozzi, a Ribera and a Salvator Rosa. An exhibition in 1950 would still have been not unlike that in 1935.

After the second world war many things happened. Such painters as Antonio Balestra, Francesco del Cairo, Giovanni Maria Canuti, Giulio Carpioni, Valerio Castello, Donato Creti, Marcantonio Franceschini, Francesco Maffei, Sebastiano Mazzoni, Mastelletta and Tanzio da Varallo, all represented in the exhibition, virtually unknown not so many years ago, have become well defined personalities. Others, among them Giovanni Benedetto Castiglione, Cerano, Giovanni Battista Gaulli, Luca Giordano, Giovanni Lanfranco, Carlo Maratti, Morazzone, Mattia Preti and Francesco Solimena—once again all shown here—have been intensely studied and re-evaluated.

This conquest of a vast new artistic territory surely reflects a shift of taste among active scholars, to which curators of museums and private collectors responded. But without the response of the interested public, the curator's efforts and the scholar's discoveries remain locked up in the proverbial ivory tower. It is to the credit of Frederick Cummings, Curator of European Art at the Detroit Institute of Arts, that he courageously planned this exhibition, organized within the *Great Ages of Art* program of the Museum, so as to convey to the public our new and expanded vision of the Italian art of the seventeenth century. Large numbers of people will be exposed to this experience, and if they share our enthusiasm, not only will those who participated in realizing this exhibition be amply rewarded, but the event will also be memorable in the annals of the public esteem of Baroque art.

Until recently the appreciation of Baroque art suffered from the eclipse brought about by nineteenth century critics like Ruskin, and the public, particularly of the Anglo-American world, has not yet fully overcome prejudices deeply rooted in aesthetic, social and religious traditions. To a certain extent we all are, however, beneficiaries of a reversal of aesthetic values accomplished within living memory. We may, perhaps, distinguish three phases in the modern vindication of the Italian Baroque. The phase of the pioneers, among whom the names of Gurlitt, Woelfflin, Schmarsow and Riegl are still gratefully remembered by many, dates from the mid-1880s to the first world war. These pioneers opened the way to an unbiased approach to the Italian Baroque, repudiated the stigma of decadence attached to the period, hammered out the categories of vision which they believed specific to the Baroque age, introduced psychological criteria of interpretation and attempted a differentiated history of the style.

The second phase is bounded by the end of the first and the beginning of the second world war. It is the era during which Baroque studies acquired respectable academic status. A new generation with such eminent scholars as Fiocco, Longhi, Marangoni and Muñoz among the Italians, and Brinckmann, Frey, Pevsner, Posse, Voss and Weisbach among the Germans accomplished an immense widening of the field. This development could hardly have been predicted in view of the militant opposition of world authorities of Bernard Berenson's calibre, for whom great art died about the mid-sixteenth century, and of a philosophically buttressed anti-Baroque attitude epitomized in Benedetto Croce. Add to this the general infatuation with the various facets of post-Impressionist art, and it is all the more remarkable that Baroque art began to find favor with the public.

At the beginning of the second world war scholars in the Baroque field looked back to a large mass of solid achievement. Nevertheless, as I have indicated, more remained to be done than we ever dreamed of in the 1920s and '30s. During the third and most recent phase of Baroque studies, comprising roughly the last two decades, scholars have been working in a firmly established field with deft assurance on an immense variety of problems. Instead of the small coterie active in Baroque studies thirty or forty years ago, the number of devotees has swelled to hundreds. Above all, Anglo-American scholars, who in the twenties and thirties had kept aloof, now take a passionate part and to them we owe some of the most significant Baroque studies in recent years. But I cannot leave unmentioned that one scholar, one museum director, and one collector pioneered in this country the taste for Baroque art more than a generation ago. Arthur McComb published the first English study on Italian Baroque painters in 1934; A. Everett Austin, Jr., arranged the first Baroque exhibition in 1930, at the Wadsworth Atheneum; the collection of the

John and Mable Ringling Museum at Sarasota, Florida, was formed from the late twenties onward and to this day it remains the foremost Baroque museum in America. Two of the important Ringling pictures, Agostino Carracci's *Susanna* (no. 68) purchased as early as 1927, and Pietro da Cortona's magnificent *Hagar* (no. 34), bought shortly later, are here on view.

Most of the other American museums acquired their Baroque pictures, of which the visitor will see a good sampling, in recent years. The main challenge today comes from a few inspired collectors. This exhibition would not have been possible without the impressive achievements of Mr. Walter P. Chrysler, Jr., Mr. and Mrs. Paul H. Ganz, Mr. and Mrs. Robert Manning, all of New York, and Mr. Denis Mahon, who enriched the exhibition with some of the treasures assembled in his London house.

Drawings play a steadily growing part within the purview of Baroque studies and a fair number of drawings are included in the exhibition. This is as it should be, for from the late sixteenth century on the preparatory drawing and even the rapid sketch were increasingly valued as works of art in their own right and became collectors' items. In fact, hardly at any other period of the history of art were drawings equally vital for the interpretation and understanding of artists' intentions. In this field, too, private initiative has outwitted the more conservative public institutions as many gems from Mr. Janos Scholz' unrivalled collection in New York go to show.

The visitor to the exhibition may well be perplexed by the kaleidoscopic variety of styles he encounters, and he may ask himself whether the term "Baroque Age" is not devoid of meaning. This question has, of course, been much discussed and is still being discussed among scholars, and there are those who advocate limiting the term "Baroque" to a specific but no doubt fundamental trend: the dynamic and emotive art which arose in Rome in the 1620s and which we associate primarily with the names of Bernini, Cortona, and Lanfranco in sculpture and painting and with Borromini in architecture. But this 'contractionist' approach does not take into account that stylistic designations such as Gothic, Renaissance, Mannerism are primarily terminological signposts erected by us to facilitate communication. Every work of art has its own specific character and style, and its uniqueness can never be penetrated by a generic term. This is even true if two pictures by the same artist are considered. In Luca Giordano's *Adoration of the Shepherds* (no. 163) the divine light issuing from the Child magically attracts the surrounding garland of human and angelic devotees; the painter needed the dramatic contrast of dark and light areas and virtual spacelessness to convey his message forcefully. In *Miriam's Song* (no. 164) the country stretches far to the horizon and in the distance appears, not unexpectedly, the Red Sea. It is the deliverance from its perils that the prophetess celebrates. She stands amid a female choir loosely arranged in a spatial circle around her. What is Baroque? Is it the spatial or planar figure composition, the vast open space or spacelessness, the natural light of the evening sky or an irrational chiaroscuro?

The Luca Giordano pictures have obviously many features in common. It is not easy, on the other hand, to discover formal bonds in such approximately contemporary works as the paintings by Pietro da Cortona and Sassoferrato (nos. 16, 17). Although the differences between seventeenth-century paintings can be enormous, no self-appointed art-historical pontiff should be allowed to decree barricades between Baroque art, non-Baroque art and anti-Baroque art and thus play havoc with the inherent dialectics of the age. The generic term 'Baroque Age' has come to stay, but this does not preclude the narrower differentiation between 'Baroque,' 'classical,' and 'naturalistic' trends within the Baroque Age.

Polarities are not only the characteristics of our own time; they existed in the seventeenth century as well as in other historical periods. The visitor will notice that spiritual and sensuous values, religious surrender and secular rationality, formal exuberance and restraint appear side by side in Baroque works. It is timely to remind him that the history of art does not roll along as a 'linear' history of styles, from the fullness and equilibrium of the High Renaissance to the frozen contortions and contradictions of Mannerism, to the unbridled movement and loud effects of the Baroque, to the grace and sophistication of the Rococo and on to the formal and expressive discipline of Neo-classicism. To be sure, the simultaneity of contrasting formal characteristics belongs to all epochs and is increasingly manifest from the Renaissance onward. Moreover, it is often possible by an analysis in depth to unravel the structural affinity between various seemingly contradictory artistic and cultural emanations of the same age. Thus the religious division brought about by the Reformation led to a self-consciousness of religious experience: henceforth religious imagery could hardly be 'naive.' It vacillates between two extremes, ecstatic rapture and hypocritical piety.

One might claim that the new self-consciousness also had other roots. The seventeenth century was not only the age of the restored vitality of the Catholic Church, to which the enormous artistic production commissioned by the Church bears witness, but it was also the cradle of modern science, the age of Galileo and Descartes. A rift between emotive surrender and self-awareness, leading on to self-criticism and even self-mockery can be observed in many works of the period. As an extreme example of this dualism I may

mention that Bernini, the most devoted servant of the seventeeth century papacy, did not shrink from drawing a jesting caricature of a reigning pope.

In attempting to transmit their emotive experience, seventeenth century artists often chose a language (directly or indirectly derived from Roman antiquity) of conventional gestures and expressions, thus assuring easy communication with the greatest number of beholders. But, at the same time, artists from the late sixteenth century onward began to ponder over the meaning of artistic creation; their growing awareness of the uniqueness of personal style and of the moment of inspiration led to a heretofore unknown appreciation of the drawn, painted, and sculpted sketch as well as to a highly individual rendering of figures and subject matter at the farthest remove from rhetorical conventions. The exhibition offers ample material for the study of this dichotomy (compare, for instance, the works by Sirani and Mazzoni, nos. 114, 198).

A purely formal analysis can never resolve the pictorial realization of such contrasts as mysticism and hypocrisy, extrovert sensuality and introvert reserve, conventional style elements and unfettered freedom of expression. While this fact needs to be stressed, it is obvious that none of the Baroque artists could dissociate himself from the living pictorial tradition to which he belonged or to which he became exposed in the course of his career. Those who allow themselves sufficient time in the exhibition will discover regional differences between Florence, Bologna, Naples and Venice and note the impact of intra-Italian cross-currents on artists of different fibre and training. The following remarks may help to stimulate the visitor's own exploration.

The new era opens, as has long been acknowledged, with Caravaggio and Annibale Carracci working side by side in Rome in the 1590s. These artists differed less in their convictions than modern art historians sometimes try to make out. Both revolted against the facile tradition of the immediate past, both interpreted religious imagery again in simple and human terms; both represented the world of mystery and revelation with palpable, majestic figures, figures of flesh and blood; both owed much directly or indirectly to the great sixteenth century painters of Venice. But while Annibale was painstaking in the preparation and execution of his pictures, while he visibly acknowledged his debt to a variety of inspirational sources, to classical antiquity, Raphael, Correggio and Titian, Caravaggio—a man of a wild and anarchic character—set out on a less trodden path. He usually painted *alla prima*, without Annibale's craftsmanlike preparation; he chose low-class models and cast them in semi-darkness. His celebrated *tenebroso*, to which painters reacted in many different ways, always strikes upon solid form and hides as much as it reveals. The two Caravaggios in the exhibition expose the idiosyn-

CARAVAGGIO 3. *St. John the Baptist*
Nelson Gallery—Atkins Museum, Kansas City, Mo.

crasies of his style. The earlier of the two, the Wadsworth Atheneum *Ecstasy of St. Francis* (no. 2) shows the saint in a carefully observed state of trance, and mystery is suggested by the glimmer of natural light breaking through the dark evening sky. More remarkable even is the Nelson Gallery *St. John the Baptist* (no. 3). Never before had St. John been represented as a brooding young proletarian, nor had a body ever been painted as a pattern of light and dark areas with the eyes, "the windows of the soul," cast in deep shadow.

Caravaggio's and Annibale Carracci's influence on the further course of seventeenth century painting was immeasurable. Luigi Lanzi, the learned author of a still useful history of Italian painting published at the end of the eighteenth century, was not so wrong in declaring: "To write the history of the Carracci is equivalent to writing the history of painting of the last two centuries." Annibale's fully developed Roman grand manner, of which the Mahon *Coronation of the Virgin* (no. 72) gives a foretaste, struck a balance between the Roman tradition of compact form on the one hand, and Venetian color and Correggesque *sfumato* on the other; between the scholarly study of expression and movement, and subjective emotionalism. His frescos in the Farnese Gallery in Rome were revered by artists of the most diverse convictions, by Bernini and Rubens, Cortona and Lanfranco, Poussin and Lebrun, Domenichino, Albani and Sacchi.

Artists tending toward a luxuriant Baroque took up and developed the coloristic, tactile, and subjective qualities inherent in Annibale's manner. The more specifically classical and objective components of the style were enhanced by Annibale's Bolognese followers, above all by Domenichino (nos. 77, 79), and had a formative influence on Poussin and his French successors. In his landscapes of the Roman period Annibale clothed emotions in a carefully conceived heroic form. A straight line of influence leads from these landscapes to those of Domenichino (no. 78) and Claude Lorrain (nos. 21-23) who, like Poussin, spent most of his life in Rome. Of no less importance were Annibale's portraits, closely observed character studies, the impressive bulk of which often fills the entire frame (no. 75). They also taught Bernini a lesson, but his 'speaking' likenesses are usually more actively engaged and seem to converse with the beholder (no. 28).

Although some members of the clergy protested against Caravaggio's 'vulgarity,' the directness of his approach no less than his *tenebroso* found eager partisans, not only in Italy, but also in the rest of Europe. Velasquez and Rembrandt, the German Elsheimer and the French brothers Le Nain—they all were deeply indebted to him. Nearer home, painters from all parts of Italy came under his influence for longer or shorter periods. We may mention Carlo Saraceni (no. 187), Orazio and Artemisia Gentileschi (nos. 6, 8), Bartolomeo Manfredi (no. 9), the Frenchman Vouet in his Roman years (no. 10), the early Strozzi in Genoa (no. 199), Tanzio da Varallo in Lombardy (no. 140), Caracciolo and Ribera in Naples (nos. 146, 144); but the classically inclined Bolognese were the first to pay homage to his genius: most of them passed through a brief Caravaggesque phase soon after their arrival in Rome in the early years of the century.

The generation maturing around 1650 saw Caravaggio with new eyes. Individualists such as Valerio Castello in Genoa (no. 178) and Maffei, Mazzoni and Langetti in Venice (nos. 197, 198, 208) imbued the Caravaggesque tradition with the painterly tradition coming from the late Titian. Their work with the loaded brush (*pittura di tocco*) and with sketchy juxtapositions of small areas of color was worlds apart from the smooth handling of paint by the contemporary classicists. Still later, the Genoese Magnasco (no. 182) and the Bolognese Giuseppe Maria Crespi (no. 118), one of the greatest artists of the Italian Seicento, passed on this painterly Caravaggism to Marco Ricci, Piazzetta and the young Tiepolo. Wherever in the seventeenth century the free brush-stroke prevailed, we are certain to move in the orbit of the Venetian painterly tradition, a tradition first revitalized by Fetti, Liss and Strozzi (nos. 189, 190, 193, 199, 200) and handed down through them to the artists working at the mid-century. Poussin himself, in later years the champion of a rigid classicism, was fascinated by this tradition in his early period, around 1630 (no. 14). In any case, the Venetian *pittura di tocco*, ensuring a distinctly personal liberty in handling paint bold and uninhibited, always appears allied to progressive trends in contradistinction to the academic tendencies with their insistence on the preservation of solid form, on balance and control and their opposition to diversionary proclivities.

It hardly needs mention that throughout the history of western art the classical tradition had always remained alive, but it was not until the rise of the Italian Renaissance that it was buttressed by an explicit theory. Contracted to the briefest statement, this theory held that art was based on rules which can be taught, that (in the wake of Aristotle) the synthesis aimed at in a work of art must result from a rational and selective process and that the ancients (and later, Raphael) had done the selection for us and therefore set objective standards of beauty. Giovanni Bellori (1615-96), a friend and counsellor of the classical circle of artists in Rome, intimate of Poussin and Duquesnoy, made the supreme statement of this theory in a lecture read to the Roman Academy of St. Luke in 1664. Thus, at the height of the Baroque Age a rational doctrine advocating the imitation of the ancients and of Raphael was universally acclaimed: no artist aspiring to the highest distinction in the profession, not even Bernini, could or would want to escape its authoritative call. The classical theory, however, was far from static, and those who adhered to it vigorously responded, also in practice, to the other artistic trends of their time.

In a first phase, the early decades of the seventeenth century, 'Baroque Classicism' (as we should term the specific classicism of this period) turned against the *maniera*, i.e. against the facile and stereotyped formulas of picture-making of the Mannerists, as well as against the representation of 'accidental nature' as practised by Caravaggio and his followers. Domenichino's paintings of the second decade most fully conform to this theoretical position. In the twenties the predominance of Bolognese classicism was broken, mainly owing to Guercino's and Lanfranco's work. Characteristically, they as well as others were exposed to the strong impact of Venetian colorism. In the course of the thirties the classical tradition began to re-assert its strength. In the forties and fifties a comparatively chaste form of classicism prevailed in Rome and was also in vogue up and down the peninsula. The upholders of this position now turned against the redundant rhetorics of the Baroque and violently condemned the practitioners of the lower genre (nos. 12, 13), whose ever-growing popularity was, in their view, detrimental to the dignity of the profession. But the classicism of the mid-century was not as solid and statuesque as that of the first phase: it was often tinged with the painterly and form-dissolving Venetian influence as well as enlivened by tangible links with the extrovert Baroque trend. An illuminating comparison may be made between two works separated by a generation, Domenichino's and Cortona's *St. Jerome* (nos. 77, 33), the latter picture, as so many others by Cortona, being tied in many ways to the classical tradition.

In a third phase beginning in the 1670s the upholders of the classical doctrine began to be on the defensive. But now the initiative shifted from Rome to Paris, the stronghold of academic indoctrination. The art theoretician Roger de Piles (1635-1709) led the attack. He exalted Rubens, the master of the great Baroque sweep and the colorist *par excellence*, at the expense of Poussin and even turned against the authority of classical antiquity itself. Before the end of the century the heated controversy between the 'Poussinists' and the 'Rubenists,' as they were called, had been decided in favor of the 'Rubenists.' At least temporarily the way was open for a free development of painting and sculpture, relatively unencumbered by the intellectual ballast of the classical doctrine. These events were not lost upon the Italians. But in Rome the importance of the revolution brought about in Paris was never fully grasped. Carlo Maratti, reared in the classical tradition, though himself anti-dogmatic and opposed to theoretical speculations, was regarded by Bellori as the legitimate heir to his own classical philosophy. But in his paintings Maratti steered in fact a middle course between the Baroque and the classical (nos. 54-7). It was this style, a competent and sincere recapitulation of Sacchi and Cortona, Reni and Lanfranco, rather than Gaulli's intense, spiritualized Late Baroque (no. 49) that determined the artistic climate in Rome at the beginning of the eighteenth century.

Other Italian centres were more fully awake to the new call. Witness the marvellous ascendancy of Venice where the painters of the free and easy touch arose after the turn of the century; a few pictures in the exhibition foreshadow this development, among them the *Martyrdom of SS. Cosmas and Damian* by Antonio Balestra (no. 211), who remained, however, essentially a master of the seventeenth century, tied to a large extent to Marattesque precepts. Witness also the rich and elegant Baroque decorations in Genoa and, above all, the explosive vitality of the Neapolitan school. With Mattia Preti, Luca Giordano and Solimena (nos. 150-52, 163-67), first rate masters belonging to three consecutive generations, Naples became for a time the most vigorous Baroque centre in Italy.

Enough has been said to indicate the give and take between the classical, Baroque and 'naturalistic' (Caravaggesque) trends and their changing aspects. Clearly, terminological rigidity would prevent us from grasping the complex tissue of events. Though remaining true to themselves, many artists helped to create, or participated in, the prevailing temper of the moment. Thus the great Reni veered through Caravaggesque, classical and Baroque phases (nos. 80-86) to end his career in a tender and sensitive form of classicism entirely his own which, nevertheless, found a large following. A much less formidable artist, Simon Vouet, submitted to both the Caravaggesque and Baroque idioms in Rome (nos. 10, 11), but found an easily digestible classicism a more appropriate idiom after his return to France. Painters like Castiglione and Salvator Rosa and to a certain extent also Pier Francesco Mola, belonging by natural endowment essentially to the small group of 'romantic' individualists of the mid-century, vacillated between Baroque verve and classical restraint (nos. 18-20).

Rather than continue the endless list of the shifting allegiance of individual artists, I want to end by returning to the less variable regional characteristics. While the Venetians always cherished free painterly values, the Florentines kept up their traditional emphasis on bright local colors, on the rhythmic line and the clear silhouette through most of the seventeenth century (nos. 126, 127). For more than 150 years Bologna remained the stronghold of classicism, and Naples, through her connection with Spain prone to a radical naturalism, lay wide and persistently open to the influence of Caravaggio's art. Perhaps less distinct are the native tendencies in Milan and Genoa, the former exhausting her strength in a solemn and intense counter-reformatory art at the beginning of the century (nos. 135, 140); the latter, a great international mercantile centre, giving rise to a fusion of Flemish and intra-Italian regional traditions.

Through most of the century Rome's pre-eminence was unchallenged. Only in Rome with her imperial and artistic past and with the concentration of papal power and of wealth could the Baroque Age take on clearly circumscribed contours. But the Roman Baroque, summed up in its greatest artist, Gianlorenzo Bernini (nos. 25-29), is truly revealed only in the countless cycles of frescoes, the churches, palaces and fountains. Moreover, the highest achievement of the Roman Baroque, the union of painting, sculpture and decoration for one overwhelming effect, is inseparable from the original setting and can never be transplanted to a museum 5000 miles from the Eternal City.

COMMENTARIES ON THE WORKS OF ART

I. Rome

Giuseppe Cesari, called the *CAVALIERE D'ARPINO*
1568 Rome 1640

Although his style is essentially Mannerist and old-fashioned for a contemporary of Caravaggio, Giuseppe Cesari had an important part in Roman art history of the first decade of the seventeenth century. The favorite artist of Clement VIII (1592-1605), he was given the most important commission of the period, the cartoons for the mosaic of the inner dome of St. Peter's, completed in 1612. With the accession of Paul V (1605-1621), he also received the important directive to head the decoration of the Capella Paolina in S. Maria Maggiore where he painted the dome and its pendentives. However, in the reign of the Barberini Pope, Urban VIII (1623-44) Giuseppe Cesari fell behind the younger Bolognese and Roman artists, although he still received important commissions outside Rome in Perugia and Reggio among others. Cesari accepted neither of the predominate styles of his day, that of Caravaggio or that of the Carracci. No doubt this was not due to any theoretical position on his part but rather to his own late Mannerist training and his personal predilection to maintain an older tradition.

1. The Expulsion of Adam and Eve

Genesis 3, 23.

The Pierpont Morgan Library, New York, N.Y.

Red Chalk, 13 15/16 x 9 9/16 in.

Coll.: Henry Reveley (Lugt 1356); Charles Fairfax Murray.

Ref.: C. Murray, *Collection of Drawings by the Old Masters*, London, 1912, IV, no. 161. [F.C.]

(Opposite page)
GIUSEPPE MARIA CRESPI
118. The Continence of Scipio
Collection of Walter P. Chrysler, Jr.

Michelangelo Merisi, called

CARAVAGGIO

1573 Caravaggio—Porto Ercole 1610

Trained in Milan, not far from his birthplace, by Simon Peterzano, Caravaggio went while yet an adolescent to Rome where at first he had a difficult time. But by about 1600 he had established himself as a brilliant, if controversial, new force in the city's artistic life, and he had begun to be awarded one important commission after another. His Roman successes were brought to an abrupt end, however, in

1606 after he murdered a tennis opponent and was forced to flee, first to the Alban hills and then to the South. The rest of his life he wandered, to Naples, to Malta, to Syracuse and Messina in Sicily, and again to Naples, finding generous and enthusiastic patronage, and leaving major work in each city. Finally he was pardoned and set out to return—by sea—to Rome, but at Porto Ercole he fell sick with fever, and died.

His maturity and public career lasted little more than ten years, almost half of which was spent traveling. Yet for a decade after his death his manner was tremendously influential in Rome, hardly—if at all—less than that of Annibale Carracci. And from Rome it spread all over Italy, to Spain, France, and particularly to the Low Countries. But this success was short-lived. Already going out of style in Rome by the early 1620's, Caravaggesque painting subsisted scarcely more than another decade there, and by 1650 had, with few exceptions, ceased to be of importance anywhere in Europe.

2. *Ecstasy of St. Francis*

The painting represents the moment in which St. Francis, praying at Mount Alverno, has just received the stigmata. In the middle ground, faintly seen, is his companion, Brother Leo; and in the background, on a meadow beside a lagoon, dimly illuminated by a bonfire, are three figures, perhaps shepherds, who are obviously perturbed and gesticulate to the left, as if to a vision. Although the saint is supported by a winged angel, as Friedlaender has pointed out, the usual apparition in the sky of the six-winged Christ is absent. Friedlaender suggests that "the shimmer of golden light on the horizon" represents the Divinity, and notes that this conception of an extraterrestrial force as a "magic light" is in keeping with Caravaggio's later works.

Wadsworth Atheneum, Hartford, Conn., The Ella Gallup Sumner and Mary Catlin Sumner Collection.

Canvas, 36⅜ by 50¼ in.

Coll.: Probably purchased from Caravaggio by the Genoese gentleman-collector-dealer Ottavio Costa who, with his brother, was one of Caravaggio's patrons in Rome; given by him in 1597 or before to the Abbot of Pinerolo (Piedmont), Ruggiero Tritone da Udine; presumably in Udine after 1612, when the abbot died; in 1938 it belonged to Dr. Guido Grioni, Trieste, reportedly acquired from a private collection in Malta; purchased for the Wadsworth Atheneum in 1943 from Arnold Seligmann, Rey and Company, New York.

Ref.: A. Venturi in *L'Arte*, 1928, XXI, 58; Marangoni in *International Studio*, 1929, vol. 94, pp. 34-35, 106; Naples, Palazzo d'Anjou, *Neopolitan Paintings*, 1938, no. 4; *Art News*, 1940, XXXVIII, 8; Hartford, Wadsworth Atheneum, *Night Scenes*, 1940, no. 5; New York, Durlacher Brothers, *Caravaggio and the Caravaggisti*, 1946, no. 1; Hartford, Wadsworth Atheneum, *In Retrospect—Twenty-one Years of Museum Collecting*, 1949, no. 3; Voss in *Kunstchronik*, 1951, vol. 7, p. 169; Milan, Palazzo Reale, *Caravaggio e i Caravaggeschi*, 1951, no. 17; Hinks, *Caravaggio*, New York, 1953, pp. 21, 44, 95; Seattle Art Museum, *Caravaggio and the Tenebrosi*, 1954, no. 1; Friedlaender, *Caravaggio Studies*, Princeton, 1955, pp. 131, 145, 148-149; Hartford, Wadsworth Atheneum, *A. Everett Austin, Jr.: A Director's Taste and Achievement*, 1958, no. 15; Pearce, *Studies in Conservation*, 1959, vol. 4, pp. 129, 131; Richmond, Va., Museum of Fine Arts, *Treasures in America*, 1961, p. 59.

This painting from its provenance must antedate 1597, and stylistically is clearly a very early work. The similarity of the angel in type and in costume to the youths in Caravaggio's "Bohemian" phase is particularly striking, as is the reminiscence of North Italian painting in the nocturnal landscape. The strong chiaroscuro is, like the outright religious subject matter, a rarity in Caravaggio's earliest years, and seems in this painting to look back to his antecedents as much as forward to the monumental night-scenes of his maturity. The painting has been associated with the *Rest on the Flight to Egypt* (Rome, Doria Collection). It shows the artist somewhat more self-assured, and might postdate the St. Francis by a year or so, but belongs to the same pastoral mode, uses much the same composition (reversed), and even includes very similar flora.

Two other versions of the subject exist, one in the Museo Civico, Udine, and the other, reported Friedlaender, in the possession of a New York dealer. The Udine painting is identical to the Hartford one which, however, is of superior quality; the New York painting adds the silhouette of a town in the background on the left. Although Voss questioned the Hartford painting, it is now universally accepted as the original, and as an autograph Caravaggio. [A.M.]

3. *St. John the Baptist*

(Illustrated on page 16)

The saint, still presumably undergoing the years of wandering and retreat in the desert which he spent in preparation for high calling as one of the protomartyrs as well as the last prophet and the herald of the Messiah, is represented as contemplative—if we may be permitted to use so modern a word—even moody. He is thus kin to the meditative *St. Jerome* which Caravaggio painted several times, and to the pensive and melancholic *David* (Rome, Galleria Borghese). Carvaggio treated these subjects less as members of a heavenly hierarchy than as interesting human beings; he carried what he had begun in the St. Francis (no. 2) to its logical extreme, and entirely eliminated the trappings of sainthood (except for an occasional very discreet halo) and the actual representation of divine beings and apparitions, for the sake of skillful manipulation of outward appearances to evoke the effects of inner states of mind.

Nelson Gallery-Atkins Museum, Kansas City, Mo. (Nelson Fund)

Canvas, 68¼ x 52 in.

Coll.: to 1844, Lord Ashton of Forfar Collection; to 1951 Chichester-Constable Collection, Burton Constable;

Ref.: Longhi in *Proporzioni*, I, 1943, 15, pl. 18; *Mostra del Caravaggio e i Caravaggeschi*, Milan, 1951, p. 24; Mahon in *Burlington Magazine*, XCIII, 1951, 234; Venturi, *Il Caravaggio*, Novara, 1951, p. 41, note 35; Mahon in *Burlington Magazine*, 1952, XCIV, 19; Longhi, *Il Caravaggio*, Milan, 1952, pl. XXIII; Hinks, *Caravaggio*, London, 1953, no. 37, pls. 58, 68; Berenson, *Caravaggio*, London, 1953, pl. 54; Baumgart, *Caravaggio*, Berlin, 1955, no. 29; Friedlaender, *Caravaggio Studies*, Princeton, 1955, no. 20D; Wagner, *Caravaggio*, Bern, 1958, pp. 106-109, 207; *Art News*, Feb. 1953, vol. 51, p. 31; Valsecchi, *Caravaggio*, Milan, 1951, pl. 53; *Gallery News*, Nelson Gallery-Atkins Museum, Feb. 1953; *Handbook Nelson Gallery of Art-Atkins Museum*, 4th ed., Kansas City, 1959, p. 71; *Portraits by the Masters*, Fort Lauderdale, Fla., 1963, p. 13.

Several paintings of St. John the Baptist by Caravaggio are mentioned in seventeenth century sources: in the Ciriaco Mattei, Cardinal Pio, and Borghese Collections, in the possession of Martino Longhi (inherited from Caravaggio's friend Onorio Longhi), and in the possession of the Viceroy of Naples, after Caravaggio's death. Which, if any, of these is the Kansas City painting, is unknown; it is however generally accepted as an unquestionable work of Caravaggio's Roman maturity, perhaps antedating the Borghese *David* by a year or so, *i.e.*, 1604/1605.

A copy exists in Naples at Capodimonte, and a copy-variant in the Palazzo Corsini, Rome, but neither is of quality equal to the Kansas City painting. The *St. John* which has been in the Galleria Borghese in Rome since 1613 may also be an autograph Caravaggio, but is so damaged as to prohibit definitive judgment. [A.M.]

4. *Sleeping Eros*

An often-repeated *motif* in ancient sculpture, the theme seems merely "window-dressing" for the representation of a 4- or 5-year old boy who, while he sleeps so soundly, has been transported into pagan mythology by the addition of a few props: a pair of wings (the like of which we know Caravaggio borrowed from a friend in 1603), an unstrung bow and an arrow.

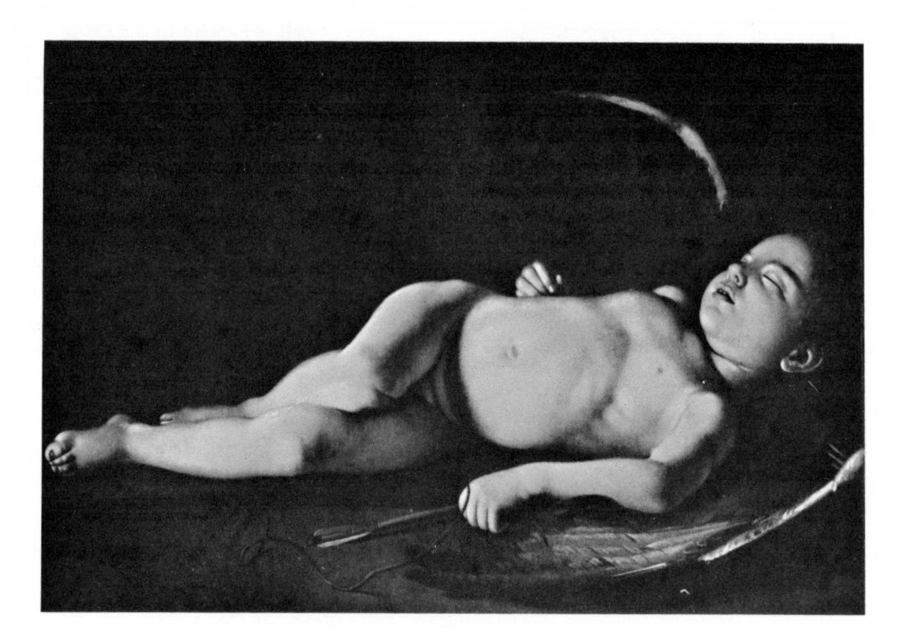

The Clowes Fund Collection, Indianapolis, Indiana.

Canvas, 25¾ x 41½ in.

Coll.: A private collection, Ireland; then a dealer in New York.

Ref.: Friedlaender, *Caravaggio Studies*, Princeton, 1955, p. 220; John Herron Art Institute, Indianapolis, *Paintings from the Clowes Collection*, 1959, no. 13; Indiana University Museum of Art, Bloomington, *Italian and Spanish Paintings from the Clowes Collection*, 1962, no. 22.

Friedlaender, who first attributed the painting to Caravaggio, believes that it is not a copy of the identical version in the Palazzo Pitti in Florence (which bears on the back an inscription "Opera di Michelanglo Marese Da Caravaggio in Malta 1608"), but rather was "painted on the commission of one of the Knights of Malta" and then "a duplicate [the Pitti version] was ordered from Caravaggio to be sent to the Grand Duke of Tuscany." Except possibly for the two versions of the *St. John with a Ram* (both in Rome, one in the Capitoline Galleries, the other in the Doria Collection), as Friedlaender points out "there are no definite examples of Caravaggio's repeating himself literally." Friedlaender also notes that X-rays have shown many *pentimenti* and, beneath the existing painting, a foreshortened head "similar to the head of St. Lucy in the *Martyrdom of St. Lucy*, painted at about the same time in Syracuse."

It should be observed that the St. Lucy head might argue in favor of attributing the painting to a highly skilled imitator of Caravaggio, inasmuch as the *Martyrdom* (properly *Burial*) of *St. Lucy* was not painted until after Caravaggio had left Malta. Hesitant as one may be to question the opinion of Friedlaender, who speaks with the greatest authority on all Caravaggio subjects particularly in this instance when his attribution was supported by the late Lionello Venturi, nonetheless the rather flimsy evidence of the inscription on the Pitti painting combined with the *pentimenti*, with Caravaggio's customary practice, and with such stylistic lapses as the rather clumsily painted left foot in the Clowes version (cf. the feet of St. Francis and the angel in the Hartford painting no. 2), indicate that the attribution to Caravaggio himself should be made with caution at best.

The *motif* was repeated in a number of early 17th century Italian paintings: G. B. Caracciolo's *Sleeping Boy* (Museo Nazionale, Palermo), a *Cupid* (Hampton Court) also attributed to Caracciolo, and Bartolomeo Schedoni's *Cupid* (Ringling Museum, Sarasota). [A.M.]

FOLLOWER OF CARAVAGGIO

Il Pensionante del Saraceni

5. *The Fruit Vendor*

Apparently this is a straightforward genre painting without concealed allegorical meaning. With the exception perhaps of some of his earliest "Bohemian" works, Caravaggio's own paintings usually had some religious or allegorical meaning; the conversion of his manner to pure genre was generally accomplished by his North European followers.

The Detroit Institute of Arts, gift of Edsel B. Ford, 1937.

Canvas, 51¼ by 38½ in.

Coll.: 1696, apparently in the collection of the Duke of Pembroke; ca. 1930 in London.

Ref.: Richardson in *D.I.A. Bull.*, vol. 16, 1937, pp. 86-91; Longhi in *Proporzioni*, I, 1943, p. 23; Milan, Palazzo Reale, *Caravaggio e i Caravaggeschi*, 1951, no. 136; Seattle, Art Museum, *Caravaggio and the Tenebrosi*, 1954, no. 4; von Halldor Soehner in *Zeitschrift für Kunstgeschichte*, vol. 18, 1955, p. 18; Gilbert, *Figures at a Table*, Sarasota, 1960, no. 3; New Orleans, Delgado Museum of Art, *Fêtes de la Palette*, 1962, no. 58.

The evolution of research on Caravaggio and his followers during the past quarter-century is interestingly demonstrated by this painting, which was originally attributed to Caravaggio himself, presumably on the basis of its similarity to *St. Peter and the Maidservant* (Vatican Pinacoteca), then also attributed to Caravaggio. Roberto Longhi, the great authority on Caravaggio's followers, in 1943 reatrributed it to an unidentified associate of the Venetian Carlo Saraceni to whom he gave the name "Pensionante [Roomer] del Saraceni," adding that this young artist was very close to Jean Le Clerc (ca. 1587-1632), a native of Nancy, documented as Saraceni's assistant.

The basket and the fruit it contains are intimately related to Caravaggio's *Basket of Fruit* (Milan, Ambrosiana). They are also reminiscent of the work of Tomaso Salini called Mao, a Roman Caravaggist who specialized in still-life painting, but they are tighter and smoother in handling than Mao's work. The melons are similar to those in a *Still-Life* (Kress Collection, National Gallery, Washington) which has been very questionably attributed to Caravaggio, but they are painted with more impasto and seem closer to the version of the Manfredi *Four Seasons* (no. 9) which was in the collection of Feodor Chaliapin. As for the figures, apart from their kinship to those in the Vatican painting, their drapery recalls the work of another Frenchman, Jean Tassel (1608-1667) who, however, was too young to have painted the Detroit canvas, which was almost surely done in Rome during the 1610s; but in physiognomies, poses, and drapery they are most similar to such of Le Clerc's works as his *Adoration of the Shepherds* (Langres, Musée des Beaux-Arts). Charles Sterling is recorded in the Detroit Institute of Arts archives as having, in 1947, suggested that Le Clerc was in fact the artist. With the possibility of collaboration by another still unrecognized hand in the still-life, this hypothesis seems now sufficiently convincing to justify the reattribution of the painting to Le Clerc. [A.M.]

ORAZIO GENTILESCHI
1563 Pisa—London 1639

He was trained in Pisa by his half-brother Aurelio Lomi, a skilled Mannerist painter, and went to Rome in 1576 or 1578. Around 1600 he became friendly with Caravaggio, and from ca. 1605 to ca. 1620 was very much influenced by him. Working also in fresco, he was active in Rome and the Marches until 1621, when he went North—to Genoa, perhaps to Turin, to Paris, and finally to London where he settled for the rest of his life. Long underestimated, Orazio Gentileschi appears now to have had very considerable influence on his juniors in Rome, particularly on artists who were also from Tuscany or had been trained by Tuscans, and on a group of young Frenchmen.

6. *Judith with the Head of Holofernes*

The painting represents a moment later than that appearing in Artemisia Gentileschi's version of the subject (no. 8); Judith and her maid are apprehensively concealing Holofernes' head in a bag to take home with them. Presumably this was the direct inspiration for Artemisia's versions of the subject.

Wadsworth Atheneum, Hartford, Conn., The Ella Gallup Sumner and the Mary Catlin Sumner Collection, 1949.

Canvas, 52 7/16 by 61 3/4 in.

Coll.: 1780, in the Palazzo Pietro Gentile, Genoa; later collection of Sir Hugh Cholmely, England; 1948, Koetser Gallery, New York.

Ref.: Soprani-Ratti, *Le Vite dei Pittori Genovesi*, Genoa, 1780; Bertolotti in *Giornale di Erudizione artistica*, Perugia, vol. 5, 1876, p. 201; Longhi in *L'Arte*, 1916, p. 312; Voss, *Malerei des Barock in Rom*, Berlin, 1925, p. 461; Redig de Campos in *Rivista d'Arte*, vol. 21, 1939, pp. 311-323; Wadsworth Atheneum, *In Retrospect, Twenty-one Years of Museum Collecting*, 1949, no. 8; *Handbook of the Wadsworth Atheneum*, 1958, p. 63; *Emporium*, Feb. 1959, p. 87; *Apollo*, LXVII, 1958, 397.

There are at least three versions of this subject, relations among which have been somewhat confused. A document of 1612 mentions a *Judith* of some size by Orazio belonging to Artemisia; whether the same or not, the Hartford painting is surely an autograph original. The other versions are inv. no. 1059 (Vatican Pinacoteca), and an inferior copy which was in the possession of the Italian art dealer Ugo Jandolo in 1922.

In the van Dyck sketchbook at Chatsworth there is a drawing of this composition, presumably made by van Dyck from this painting in Genoa during the 1620s.

The Hartford work is very close to Orazio's *Mary and Martha* (Munich, Staatsgemäldesammlungen), which also has been attributed to Artemisia; both paintings date from the early 1610s.[A.M.]

7. *Head of a Youth*

A preparatory drawing by Orazio for his *St. Cecilia* (Brera, Milan).

Janos Scholz Collection, New York, N.Y.

Black and white chalk on gray paper, 14 5/8 by 10 11/16 in. Inscribed on the reverse, probably in the late 17th century, with the name of the artist.

Coll.: Zoomer; private collection, Stockholm.

Ref.: Janos Scholz Collection exhibitions: Mills College, 1961;

6.

Columbia, S. C., 1961; Hamburg and Cologne, 1963; Vitzthum, *Master Drawings*, I, 1963, 58.

This drawing is a great rarity, inasmuch as it is one of the very few by a follower of Caravaggio which is authenticated by its relation to an unquestionably autograph painting. Other drawings have been attributed to Orazio, notably two at Windsor Castle, but none with the assurance possible in this case. [A.M.]

ARTEMISIA GENTILESCHI
1597 Rome—Naples 1652/53

Hardly less romantic a figure than Salvator Rosa, Artemisia was the daughter of Orazio, and through him one of Caravaggio's circle. Artemisia had a precocious talent, and was trained by her father and his associate, Agostino Tassi, who was accused in 1612 of raping her. By 1615 she had established such a reputation as a painter that she was invited by the Grand Duke of Tuscany to work in Florence, where (except for a probable, brief trip to Rome in 1619) she stayed until the mid-1620s. Then she returned to Rome and, about 1630, went on to Naples. She visited her father in England just before his death, but otherwise she remained in Naples for the rest of her life. There she had a considerable influence on artists of such importance as Stanzione and Cavallino, who seem to have responded particularly to the bright colors and elaborate draperies typical of her work.

8. *Judith and Holofernes*

The story, from the *Apocrypha*, relates how a beautiful and virtuous Hebrew widow deceived an Assyrian general whose army was menacing the Israelites. Allowing him to believe that he could seduce her, she got him so drunk that she was able to behead him, thus saving her people. Judith and her maidservant escaped untouched. The maid is believed by some to be a self-portrait of the artist.

Caravaggio painted the subject, which was very appealing to

seventeenth century taste and was often repeated by his followers. It was something of a favorite of Artemisia's, a fact which has not escaped the fascinated attention of 20th century psychologically-oriented writers. Artemisia represented it in three forms: the actual decapitation (Uffizi), the moment after the deed (Detroit and Capodimonte, Naples), and the flight from the Assyrian camp (Pitti, Florence).

The Detroit Institute of Arts, gift of Leslie H. Green, 1952.

Canvas, 72½ by 55¾ in.
Coll.: Prince Brancaccio, Rome.
Ref.: Richardson in *D.I.A. Bull.*, vol. 33, 1952, p. 81; *Art Quarterly*, vol. 16, 1953, pp. 91-92.

It was believed, until recently published documents proved that Artemisia was in Florence from 1615, that the painting dated from the early 1620s. Now, however, it seems more likely to be a work of the late teens, relatable to such painters associated with the "Tuscan enclave" in Rome as the Genoese Domenico Fiasella and the mysterious Cecco del Caravaggio. The presence of the lighted candle should be noted. This is a typical Caravaggesque device derived, however, not from Caravaggio himself, but from the German Adam Elsheimer and (probably in this instance) the Dutchman Gerrit van Honthorst, who popularized it in Rome during the 1610s. [A.M.]

BARTOLOMEO MANFREDI
c. 1580 Ostiano near Mantua—Rome 1620/21

One of Caravaggio's closest and most skillful followers, Manfredi, significantly enough, was born and had his early education, like the master, in Lombardy. He went to Rome when he was quite young and was associated with Cristoforo Roncalli called il Pomarancio; just possibly he can be related to Caravaggio as early as 1603. By 1615 he was recognized as an important painter who was already attracting to him, in his personal variation on Caravaggio's style, a group of young artists, particularly from France and the Low Countries, who were later characterized by the German painter-art historian, van Sandrart, as forming the *Manfredi Maniera*. This consisted of raffish subject matter, sometimes with no religious reference whatsoever, treated as contemporary genre in dramatic chiaroscuro. It should also be noted that Manfredi apparently not only subsisted but was even highly successful without receiving any public commissions.

9. The Four Seasons

An alternative title for this allegorical painting has been suggested as *The Five Senses*. But the four figures do clearly refer to the seasons: the flowering of spring, the fruit of summer, the harvest of autumn and the withering cold of winter.

The Dayton Art Institute, Dayton, Ohio, gift of Mr. and Mrs. Elton F. MacDonald, 1960.

Canvas, 53 x 36 in.
Coll.: Lt. Commander R. Riggs; Pietro Tozzi; H. Schaeffer; Mr. and Mrs. Elton F. MacDonald, Grosse Pointe Park, Mich.
Ref.: Longhi in *Proporzioni I*, 1943, 24-25; *Dayton Art Institute Bulletin*, vol. 18, no. 6, 1960; Smith College Museum of Art, *Italian Baroque Painting*, 1947, no. 4.

This painting is one of several versions of the subject. The first one, published by Longhi in 1943, was then in the estate of the great Russian *basso* Feodor Chaliapin; it has since apparently dis-

appeared. Longhi also noted an "autograph replica" in a Florentine private collection, which he later stated (letter to the New York dealer H. Schaeffer) might be the Dayton painting. Still another version was in the Rebora Collection in Rome before World War II; judging from a photograph it must have been a copy of inferior quality.

An early work, like Manfredi's major surviving youthful painting, *Mars Punishing Amor* (Chicago, Art Institute), *The Four Seasons* is datable around 1610. [A.M.]

SIMON VOUET
1590 Paris 1649

Vouet is reported to have been in England painting portraits in 1604. In 1611 he began the travels which took him to Constantinople and in 1613 to Venice, before he settled in 1614 in Rome. There he had great success, even being elected Principe (President) of the Academy of St. Luke in 1624. He traveled extensively in Italy, and in 1627 returned via Venice to Paris where he became *Premier Peintre du Roi*. He had many commissions for decorations in the royal palaces and in noble houses and for tapestry cartoons, and he developed a large *atelier* including not only his brother Aubin, his wife Virginia, a son and two sons-in-law, but also most leading French artists of the latter part of the century. During his later years he was somewhat overshadowed by Poussin, even though the younger painter spent almost all his mature life in Rome.

10. The Fortune Teller

This kind of picaresque subject derives from Caravaggio's *Fortune-Teller* (Paris, Louvre) and his lost *Cardsharks* (formerly in the Sciarra Collection, Rome). Little developed by Italians except Manfredi, who had a direct influence on Vouet, these subjects were particularly popular among North European painters.

The National Gallery of Canada, Ottawa.

Canvas, 47¼ x 67 in.

Coll.: Dal Pozzo, Rome (?); provincial French collection.

Ref.: Nicolson in *Burlington Magazine*, 1955, XCVII, 129; Longhi in *Paragone*, 1955, p. 63; Galerie Heim, *Caravage et les peintres francais*, Paris, 1955, no. 13; Musée des Beaux-Arts, *L' Age d' Or*, Bordeaux, 1955, no. 103; Revel in *Connaissance des Arts*, 1958, p. 66; Manning in *Studies in the History of Art Dedicated to William E. Suida*, London, 1959, p. 294; Crelly, *Painting of Simon Vouet*, New Haven, 1962, pp. 23, 190-191; Chatelet and Thuillier, *French Painting*, 1963, p. 180.

For some time attributed to a French contemporary of Vouet's in Rome, Nicolas Regnier, this painting was reattributed to Vouet by Longhi, who noted that a study in oil of the woman on the left was in a private Roman collection about 1915. An anonymous 17th century French print, reversing the image, was included in a volume (Paris, Cabinet des Estampes, Bibl. Nat.) devoted to the works of Vouet; and Robert de Cotte's manuscript (also Bibl. Nat.) describing the collection of the great French patron and connoisseur in Rome, the Cavaliere dal Pozzo, attributes "Une Egipienne qui Dit la Bonne Fortune," which is possibly this painting, to Vouet. (A related drawing in red chalk is in the Print Room of the Yale University Art Gallery.) According to Longhi and Manning, the painting should be dated 1620, but probably Crelly's placement of

it "in the years just prior to 1620" when Vouet was most involved in Caravaggism, is more exact. [A.M.]

11. St. Cecilia

A Roman lady, resident in Trastevere where there is a church traditionally supposed to be on the site of the house of her husband, St. Valerian, St. Cecilia was martyred during the time of the Emperor Marcus Aurelius. Since the 15th century she has been the patroness of music and musicians. She is usually represented at an organ, presumably listening to a celestial choir.

Robert and Bertina Suida Manning, New York, N.Y.

Canvas, 52¾ x 38½ in.
Coll.: James Whatman.
Ref.: Colnaghi's *Paintings by Old Masters*, London, 1951, no. 9; Nicolson in *Burlington Magazine*, 1951, XCIII, 276; Manning in *Studies in the History of Art Dedicated to William E. Suida*, London, 1959, pp. 296-97; Crelly, *Painting of Simon Vouet*, New Haven, 1962, pp. 188-89.

There are several other versions of this painting, including one in the Louvre, and three, cited by Manning, in New York. Probably it can be dated by an engraved version which is signed 1627. It represents the latest phase of Vouet's Italian stay, when his earlier Caravaggism had evolved into a much more ideal, if rather less arresting, style. Particularly evident in this painting are the conventionally sentimental prettiness of the physiognomy, at least partially derived from Bolognese sources, and the luxuriousness of the draperies, always a predilection of the artist (possibly encouraged by the example of the Gentileschis) and here carried almost to the point where they seem to wear the model rather than the other way around. [A.M.]

Pieter van Laer, called
IL BAMBOCCIO
1592/95 Haarlem 1642

Nothing is known of the artist's work before 1625, when he arrived in Rome, where he stayed until 1639. The name *Bamboccio* (which may be roughly translated "big baby") was given to him by the society of Netherlandish artists in Rome, the "Bentveughels," because he was deformed and ridiculously disproportioned.

In Rome, basing his work on Netherlandish traditions and on some aspects of Caravaggism, he developed the "bambocciata," a type of small picture that depicts scenes of popular, everyday life. He and his followers, who came to be called the "Bamboccianti," were much despised by adherents of the "grand manner" in contemporary art. However, the influence of

the Bamboccianti was considerable, especially in the Netherlands, but also in France as well as in Italy.

12. A Roman Street Scene with Card Players

Denis Mahon, Esq., London.

Canvas, 17 x 13½ in.

Coll.: Joseph Gillot, until 1872; acquired by the present owner in 1958.

Ref.: Nicolson in *Great Private Collections* (ed. D. Cooper), London, 1963, pp. 120, 124.

Very similar to Bamboccio's *"Ciambelle" Vendor* (National Gallery, Rome) and to his *Blacksmith* (Busiri-Vici Collection, Rome), the painting recalls the words of the seventeenth century writer Passeri that Bamboccio "was excellent in representing the plain truth in all its purity, so that his pictures seemed an open window, through which events were seen without distortion or alteration." (*Vite de' pittori* [ed. J. Hess], Leipzig, 1934, p. 74.)

The painting was attributed to Karel du Jardin when it was sold in 1872. A copy, paired with another copy of a lost Pieter van Laer, is in the Museum at Capodimonte, Naples. [D.P.]

ANGELUCCIO
active around 1650
and
MICHELANGELO CERQUOZZI
(Michelangelo delle Battaglie)
1602 Rome 1660

Of Angeluccio one knows only that he was a pupil of Claude Lorrain and that he died young.

Cerquozzi studied with Cavaliere d'Arpino and the Flemish artist Jacob de Haase. He was influenced by

Pieter van Laer, and he began painting *bambocciate* as early as 1630. He also painted battle pictures; hence his sobriquet. Cerquozzi frequently collaborated with other artists, like Angeluccio, and Codazzi and Saluzzo, painters of architectural vistas.

13. Blind Man's Buff

The Detroit Institute of Arts, gift of Mr. and Mrs. Henry Reichhold, 1942.

Canvas, 38 x 33½ in.

Ref.: Valentiner in *D.I.A. Bull.*, XXI, 1942, 58; Valentiner in *Art Quarterly*, V, 1942, 186, 190, 194; Detroit Institute *Catalogue*, 1944, p. 27; Briganti, in *I Bamboccianti* (Organizzazione Mostre d'arte "Antiquaria"), Rome, 1950, p. 40; Briganti in *Proporzioni*, III, 1950, 198, no. 28; D. Sutton, *Artists in 17th Century Rome*, London, 1955, p. 1; Carpegna in *Paesisti e Vedutisti a Roma*, Rome, 1956, pp. 7-8; Marabottini in *Il Seicento Europeo*, Rome, 1956, pp. 62-63; Röthlisberger, *Claude Lorrain*, New Haven, 1961, I, 519-20.

The painting was sold at Christie's in 1938 (July 25) as Claude Lorrain. Valentiner attributed it to Claude and Pieter van Laer. The present attribution was first made by Briganti in 1947 (letter to Detroit Institute).

In quality the painting is one of the best of a stylistically coherent group of pictures representing very similar scenes. The attribution of the group is based on a description in an old Chigi inventory of two of them (Incisa della Rocchetta Collection, Rome) as collaborative works of Angeluccio and Cerquozzi, the former responsible for the landscapes and the latter for the figures. (Cf. Briganti in *I Bamboccianti*) [D.P.]

NICOLAS POUSSIN
1594 Les Andelys (Normandy)—Rome 1665

Poussin had little, if any, formal training in France, but by about 1622 he was beginning to have some professional success in Paris. In 1623 he set out for Rome, where he arrived, after a stop in Venice, early in 1624. He soon became associated with the erudite circle of Cassiano dal Pozzo. For a time he shared quarters with the sculptor Francesco Duquesnoy. In the late 1620s and early 1630s Poussin contributed to the neo-Venetian movement in Rome; in the 1630s he turned away from his earlier, Baroque manner and began to develop a grand, classical style.

In 1640 Poussin went to Paris, where he was appointed *Premier Peintre du Roi*. However, he was displeased by his official responsibilities and by court intrigues, and in 1642 he returned to Rome, where he remained until his death. While in Paris Poussin had strengthened his ties with French patrons and, from that time on, most of his works were destined for France. Thus, Poussin's role in the history of Italian art belongs mainly to the period 1624-40.

14. Diana and Endymion

Diana (or Selene, the Moon), in love with the shepherd Endymion, must leave him when Night pulls back her curtain to reveal the chariot of the Sun, preceded by Dawn, rising into the sky. (Ovid, *Ars Amandi*, III, 82)

The Detroit Institute of Arts, gift of the Founders Society, 1936.

Canvas, 48 x 66½ in.

Coll.: Cardinal Mazarin; Cassirer, Berlin, 1922; Julius H. Haass, Detroit; Mrs. Trent McMath, Detroit.

Ref.: G. Jules, Comte de Cosnac, *Les Richesses du Palais Mazarin*, Paris, 1885, p. 318; Grautoff in *Gazette des Beaux-Arts*, VII, 1932, 328; Friedlaender in "Thieme-Becker," Leipzig, 1933, XXVII, 325; Valentiner in *D.I.A. Bull.*, XV, 1936, 96; Friedlaender in *Gazette des Beaux-Arts*, XXIII, 1943, 26-30; *D.I.A. Catalogue*, 1944, p. 104; Bertin-Mourot, *Bulletin Société Poussin*, I, 1947, 56; Toledo Museum and Minneapolis Institute of Arts, *Nicolas Poussin*, 1959, no. 12;

Blunt in *Exposition Poussin*, Paris, 1960, p. 65; Mahon in *Burlington Magazine*, CII, 1960, 300, 352, 354; Mahon, *Poussiniana*, Paris, 1962, pp. 55, 57, 78; Mahon in *L'Ideale classico del Seicento*, Bologna, 1962, pp. 173-74.

Neo-Venetian color, idealized forms, and harmonious compositional rhythms here combine to create one of the most beautiful and poetical paintings of Poussin's early career. The date, as Denis Mahon has argued, must be about 1632. At that time Poussin, along with the sculptor Duquesnoy and the painter Andrea Sacchi (by whom he was influenced at this moment), was revising the Baroque manner that had dominated in Rome in the late 1620s and formulating a new "classical" style.

Miss Judith Colton, in a study of Endymion iconography being prepared for publication, stresses the importance of contemporary French and Italian literature and book illustration, and of antique sculpture as formal and iconographic sources for Poussin's painting. (Verbal communication.) [D.P.]

15. The Holy Family

The Detroit Institute of Arts, gift of Harriet Wilkinson, 1954.

Canvas, 28 x 21⅞ in.

Coll. : Stefano Roccatagliata; Bailli de Breteuil; Robert Ansell, until 1771; Peniston Lamb, 1st Lord Melbourne, and heirs; Edgar B. Whitcomb, Detroit; Harriet Wilkinson, Detroit.

Ref. : Jouanny, *Correspondance de Poussin*, Paris, 1911, pp. 57, 112, 124, 137, 153, 159, 163, 165, 169; Smith, *A Catalogue Raisonné of the Most Eminent Painters*, London, 1829-37, VIII, no. 68; Andresen, *Poussin nach Kupferstiche*, Leipzig, 1863, no. 119; Grautoff, *Nicolas Poussin*, Munich, 1914, pp. 255-56; Friedlaender, *Nicolas Poussin*,

Munich, 1914, pp. 117, 214; Magne, *Nicolas Poussin*, Paris, pp. 122, 134; Borenius in *Art in America*, XIII, 1925, 92; Friedlaender and Blunt, *Poussin Drawings*, London, 1939, I, nos. 41, 42; Bertin-Mourot, *Bulletin Société Poussin*, II, 1948, p. 47; Toledo Museum and Minneapolis Institute of Arts, *Nicolas Poussin*, 1959, p. 27; Blunt in *Exposition Poussin*, Paris, 1960, pp. 99-100; Mahon, *Poussiniana*, Paris, 1962, pp. xiii, 110; Mahon in *L'Ideale classico del Seicento*, Bologna, 1962, pp. 190-91.

Painted in France between April 1641 and May 1642 for the Roman art dealer Roccatagliata, the picture is one of the purest statements of the classical style that Poussin had recently achieved. Indeed, it seems to forecast nineteenth century "neo-classicism."

Two drawings in Windsor Castle are possibly studies for this painting (cf. Friedlaender and Blunt, 1939), which was engraved in the eighteenth century by Carlo Faucci. [D.P.]

Giovanni Battista Salvi, called *IL SASSOFERRATO*

1605 Sassoferrato—Rome 1685

It is not known when Sassoferrato came to Rome. He was deeply influenced by Domenichino and may have studied with him. Sassoferrato created a kind of rarified, sentimentalized classicism that refers back directly to the pictorial traditions of his native Umbria around 1500.

16. The Madonna and Child

The Detroit Institute of Arts, gift of James E. Scripps, 1889.

Canvas, 29½ x 23¾ in.
Coll. : Joseph Gillot, until 1872.
Ref. : *D.I.A. Catalogue*, 1944, p. 119.

Many of Sassoferrato's paintings are based on compositions by Perugino and Raphael, especially the early works of the latter. This one is a copy of the lost *Virgin with the Pink* from Raphael's Florentine period, known today from several copies. (Cf. Rosenberg, *Raffael* [Klassiker der Kunst], Stuttgart, 1909, p. 201.) The present painting may be identical with a copy by Sassoferrato that Passavant listed as in the Haeglin Collection in Basle (*Raphael d'Urbin*, Paris, 1860, II, 63). [D.P.]

17. Head of a Monk

Janos Scholz Collection, New York, N.Y.

Black and red chalks on blue paper, 10½ x 7½ in.
Coll. : Piancastelli (Lugt 2078a); Brandegee (Lugt 1860c).
Ref. : Janos Scholz Collection exhibitions: Staten Island, N.Y., 1961; Columbia, S.C., 1961; Hamburg, Germany, 1963; Cologne, Germany, 1963-64; New Haven, Conn., 1964.

This beautifully drawn head shows well how Sassoferrato's draw-

ing style is characterized by the restraint, the careful attention to detail, and the purity that is also found in his paintings. There are excellent examples by this artist which compare favorably to the style and technique of this drawing in the Art Institute of Chicago and in the collections at Windsor Castle. [F.C.]

PIER FRANCESCO MOLA

1612 Coldrerio (Como)—Rome 1666

Mola is especially interesting because of the wide range of his artistic culture. He seems to have gone to Rome as a young man and entered the shop of Cavaliere d'Arpino. However, he was deeply impressed by the art of Guercino and, about 1635, he went to Bologna to study that master's work. In Bologna he was also influenced by Albani. He traveled to Venice, where he copied works by Titian and Veronese and evidently studied Bassano. In 1637, through Pietro Testa in Lucca, he came in contact with the "romantic" trend that stemmed in large part from Poussin's work around 1630. In the 1640s Mola settled in Rome and came under the influence of Pietro da Cortona. The chronology of Mola's work remains largely problematic.

18. Mercury Putting Argus to Sleep

Jupiter, in an effort to conceal his affair with Io from his wife Juno, transformed Io into a heifer. Juno, suspecting the truth, forced Jupiter to make her a present of the cow/Io, which she gave into the keeping of the hundred-eyed, never-sleeping Argus. Grieved by Io's suffering, Jupiter sent his son Mercury to slay Argus. Mercury, disguised as a herdsman, lulled Argus to sleep with music and story and then decapitated him. (Ovid, *Metamorphoses*, I, 601-721.)

Allen Memorial Art Museum, Oberlin College, Oberlin, Ohio. Samuel H. Kress Study Collection.

Canvas, 23⅛ x 39⅛ in.
Coll. : Samuel H. Kress Collection, 1950.
Ref. : Stechow in *Allen Mem. Art Mus. Bull.*, XIX, 1961, 39; London County Council (Iveagh Bequest, Kenwood), *An American University Collection*, 1962, no. 27; *Burlington Magazine*, CIV, 1962, 310.

The romantic treatment of the scene links the picture to works by Testa and to Poussin's early Roman paintings. The handling, which is very Venetian, also reveals, like the figures, the influence of Guercino. The painting probably dates after 1640. [D.P.]

19. St. Bruno and another Carthusian in the Wilderness

Toward the end of his life St. Bruno refused to become Archbishop of Reggio and withdrew into a wilderness in Calabria. St. Bruno, the eleventh century founder of the Carthusian order, was canonized in 1623, and he became a popular subject in seventeenth century art.

Denis Mahon, Esq., London.

Canvas, 20¼ x 26¾ in.
Coll. : Ingram, Temple Newsam House, Leeds; Earl of Halifax; acquired by the present owner in 1947.

Ref.: Ms. inventory of pictures at Temple Newsam, Dec. 5, 1808, no. 26 (Yorkshire Archaeological Society, Deposited Deeds, DD.N.S.R. 54); Waagen, *Treasures of Art in Great Britain*, London, 1854, III, 332; Briganti in *Connoisseur*, CXXXII, 1953, 12, 18.

In the brilliance of their handling, and in their romantic atmosphere, Mola's landscapes parallel those of Salvator Rosa, but they seem to have been independently developed. The influence of Venetian art, as well as the influence of Guercino, is evident in this landscape. [D.P.]

20. The Sonnet Vendor

In this vignette, drawn from the daily life of Rome's artist colony, a poor poet, who is selling his verses by the sheet from the box he carries on his shoulder (labelled "Sonnetti"), pauses to glance at a canvas set out on the street by a painter who is apparently without regular patrons so that he too must sell what he can to passersby. The square in front of the Pantheon often served as a market for such wares.

Janos Scholz Collection, New York, N.Y.

Pen and brush, dark brown ink on white paper, 8⅞ x 6½ in.
Coll. : Savoia-Aosta (Lugt 47a).

Ref.: Janos Scholz Collection Exhibitions: Oakland, Cal., 1957 (as Guercino); Hagerstown, Md., 1960; Staten Island, New York, 1961; Columbia, S.C., 1961.

This drawing is far more spirited than is customary for Mola—close to Guercino yet unlike him. Denis Mahon, whose work on Guercino is definitive, proposed the attribution to Mola working in the style of Guercino, as he is known to have done. [R.E.]

Claude Gellée, called
CLAUDE LORRAIN
1600 Chamagne (Vosges)—Rome 1682

Claude may have arrived in Rome as early as 1612/13. Before 1625 he studied with Agostino Tassi, a painter of landscapes and architectural perspectives. Around 1618 he probably went to Naples and worked with the Flemish artist Goffredo Wals. In 1625 Claude returned to his native Lorraine, where he was an assistant to the artist Claude Deruet. He returned to Rome in 1626/27 and remained there until his death. The main influences on Claude's art were Tassi, Bril, the Bamboccianti, and Domenichino. Thus, although Claude's personal vision of nature was surely in large part molded by his French heritage, his art must be understood in terms of artistic developments in Italy.

By the mid-1630s Claude found it necessary to protect himself from imitators and forgers, and he began the *Liber Veritatis*, a systematic record of his paintings, generally giving the name of the patron, destination, and date. The book, now in the British Museum, contains 195 drawings made by Claude after his paintings. One of the greatest landscapists of the seventeenth century, Claude enjoyed international patronage. In the eighteenth century his "idyllic" views of the Roman *campagna* began to exercise an especially great influence on art and taste in England.

21. Pastoral Landscape

The Detroit Institute of Arts, gift of Edsel B. Ford, 1941.

Canvas, 30¾ x 45½ in.

Inscribed on the rock in the center foreground: *CLAVDIO I.V. 163(7?)*.

Coll.: Lord Grenville (1759-1834), Dropmore, Bucks.

Ref.: Richardson in *D.I.A. Bull.* XX, 1941, 67; *D.I.A. Catalogue*, 1944, p. 26; Constable in *Gazette des Beaux-Arts*, XXVI, 1944, 308; Cahen in *Bulletin des Musées Royaux des Beaux-Arts*, Brussels, 1957, p. 224; Kitson and Röthlisberger, "Claude and the Liber Veritatis," *Burlington Magazine*, CI, 1959, 23; Röthlisberger, *Claude Lorrain*, New Haven, 1961, I, 119-20.

Claude recorded the picture in the *Liber Veritatis* (no. 12, inscribed: "*faict pour Napoli. Claudio fecit in V.R.*") The date of the painting has been read as 1631, but Kitson and Röthlisberger have convincingly proposed 1637. Röthlisberger (1961) relates the painting to a group of pictures made for Naples in 1637/39, possibly commissioned as a result of a short stay by the artist in Naples in 1636. He points out, furthermore, that the composition is connected with an etching by Claude dated 1635 (previously read as 1633; Blum, *Les eaux-fortes de Claude Gellée*, Paris, 1925, no. 7).

The rays of the low-lying sun at the left break through the misty atmosphere that fills the vast landscape. The painting has generally been called "Evening," but Kitson and Röthlisberger consider it a morning scene. It was probably made as a pendant to the *River Landscape* in the possession of Wildenstein and Co. (Röthlisberger, no. 21). A drawing in the Tyler Museum, Haarlem (Hind, *The Drawings of Claude Lorrain*, London, 1925, pl. 3) contains four preliminary studies for the Detroit picture, which was engraved in 1774 by Richard Earlom. [D.P.]

21.

22. *Coast Scene*

The Detroit Institute of Arts, gift of Mr. and Mrs. Edgar B. Whitcomb, 1942.

Copper, 16 1/16 x 20 5/8 in.

Inscribed on the bale at the bottom right: *CLAVDIO I.V. 16(38?) ROMA*

Coll.: Barberini, Rome, until 1934

Ref.: Pattison, *Claude Lorrain*, Paris, 1884, p. 244; Lafenestre, *Rome, les museés*, Paris, 1905, p. 148; Valentiner, *Five Centuries of Marine Painting*, Detroit, 1942, no. 74; Richardson in *D.I.A. Bull.*, XXII, 1943, 70; *D.I.A. Catalogue*, 1944, p. 26; Röthlisberger, *Claude Lorrain*, New Haven, 1961, I, 468-69.

The date has been variously read: 1625, 1635, 1643, 1673, 1638. The last, proposed by Röthlisberger, is probably correct. This is one of about fifteen surviving works by Claude painted on copper.

In the 1630s Claude painted many scenes of coast and seaports, subjects that were particularly suited to his poetical renditions of light and atmosphere. The earlier seaport paintings of Paul Bril were an important source of inspiration for Claude. The genre scene in the foreground of the Detroit picture suggests Claude's connection with the Bamboccianti, and some features of the landscape at the left bring Elsheimer to mind. [D.P.]

23. *Landscape with the Rest on the Flight into Egypt*

See no. 161.

The Cleveland Museum of Art, Purchase, Leonard C. Hanna Jr. Bequest.

Canvas, 80¾ x 59½ in.

Coll.: Count Francesco Crescenzi or Giovanni Battista Crescenzi, Marquess de la Torre; Sir William Lowther, Holker Hall; Cavendish family, 1756—1960.

Bibliography: Smith, *A Catalogue Raisonné of the Most Eminent Painters*, London, 1837, III, nos. 47, 88; Waagen, *Treasures of Art in*

Great Britain, London, 1857, IV, 421; Pattison, *Claude Lorrain*, Paris, 1884, pp. 77, 230; Röthlisberger, *Claude Lorrain*, New Haven, 1961, I, 243-44; Francis in *Cleveland Mus. Bull.*, XLIX, 1962, 230-35.

Recorded in the *Liber Veritatis* (no. 88, inscribed: *quadro faict per ill mo Conte Crescence*). Another drawing by Claude, probably after the picture, is in the Lehman collection, New York. The painting's dimensions, which are unusually large for Claude, relate it to four pictures that he made in 1639/40 for the King of Spain (Röthlisberger, nos. 47-50). The landscape is, in fact, repeated from one of them, *Liber Veritatis* no. 47, the *Finding of Moses* (Prado, Madrid).

The painting can be dated c. 1645. It is a splendid example of the grand style that Claude developed around 1640, partly under the influence of Domenichino's "ideal" landscapes (cf. no. 78). Compared to Claude's earlier paintings, pictures like this, where the scene is made to extend by a clear progression of parallel planes into the far distance, are more constructed and "posed." [D.P.]

GASPARD DUGHET
(Gaspard Poussin)
1615 Rome 1675

Dughet, whose father was French, was the brother-in-law of Nicolas Poussin, whose name he adopted. He probably began his studies under Poussin about 1630. A landscape specialist, Dughet was evidently also influenced by Claude Lorrain. Major problems regarding Dughet's art, complicated by the fact that none of his works are dated, still remain to be solved. It is possible that the young Dughet was responsible for a group of paintings assigned by Blunt to "the Silver Birch Master" (*Burlington Magazine*, XCII, 1950, 69-73).

24. Landscape with a Lake

Mr. and Mrs. Eugene Victor Thaw Collection, New York, N. Y.

Canvas, 19¾ x 25½ in.
Coll.: Anon., Stockholm.

A date in the late 1650s seems probable for this work. Its structure is dependent on the example of earlier landscapes by Nicolas Poussin, such as *Landscape with a Snake* (National Gallery, London) and *Landscape with Orpheus and Eurydice* (Louvre). However, Dughet's handling here and his taste for wild, luxuriant aspects of nature are closer to Poussin's late landscape style, which was possibly influenced by Dughet.

Dughet used this small format in a number of paintings; for instance, in two landscapes in the National Gallery, London (*Plates, French School*, 1950, pls. 42, 44), one in the Mahon Collection and one in the Winter Collection (*L'Ideale classico del Seicento*, Bologna, 1962, nos. 111,117). [D.P.]

GIANLORENZO BERNINI
1598 Naples—Rome 1680

Born in Naples of a Tuscan father—the sculptor

24.

Pietro Bernini—and a Neapolitan mother, Bernini went to Rome with his parents as a small child and remained there, except for a short trip to Paris in 1663 when he was asked by Louis XIV to submit plans for the completion of the Louvre. His first works—the *Goat Amalthea* (1615), *St. Lawrence* and *St. Sebastian*—show him precociously master of his technique and deeply influenced by Hellenistic sculpture. Soon thereafter he produced the celebrated life-size groups of *Aeneas and Anchises*, *Apollo and Daphne*, and the *Rape of Proserpina* for his first patron, Cardinal Scipione Borghese. In 1624 the accession of Urban VIII to the papal Throne marked the beginning of Bernini's long and brilliant career in the service of the Church. From then on his activity expanded to embrace the greatest variety of sculptural and architectural commissions. To this period belong the spectacular *Baldacchino* in St. Peter's and the statues of *Santa Bibiana* (1624) and of *St. Longinus* (1631) where, for the first time, the draperies express the spiritual concept and the emotional life of the subject.

After a decade of temporary interest in classical compositional ideas—to which are due his design of the *Monument of Countess Matilda* (1633-37) and the relief of *Pasce Oves Meas* in St. Peter's—Bernini reverted to the unimpeded development of his High Baroque style. In 1647 he finished the *Tomb of Urban VIII*, and in 1652 the Cornaro Chapel with the famous group of the *Ecstasy of St. Teresa* in S. Maria della Vittoria. His life-long interest in the creation of fountains reached its climax with the prodigious *Fountain of the Four Rivers* (1648-51) and the *Fontana del Moro* (1653-55), both on the Piazza Navona. From 1657 to 1666 he created the *Cathedra Petri* and within the same years laid out the design of the square of St. Peter's.

In the last period of Bernini's activity, his sculptural style is marked by an increasing abandonment of classical form in order to emphasize spiritual intensity, religious fervor and dramatic expressiveness. When he died in 1680, Bernini's contemporaries rightly felt that with him disappeared "the greatest genius the century had produced."

25. *Model of the Chair of St. Peter*

A sketch for the sumptuous bronze throne designed by Bernini to encase as a precious shrine the most venerated relic of Saint Peter's in Rome: the old, wood and ivory chair of the Prince of the Apostles. Placed in the apse of the Basilica, the "Cathedra Petri" appears as if suspended against a background of clouds: to its side and slightly below it, stand the two Fathers of the Latin Church and the two Fathers of the Greek Church; above it, a glory of angels carrying the Papal Tiara and the Keys seems to dissolve in the golden light streaming from the oval stained glass window with the Dove of the Holy Spirit. "A Mystery given visual shape" (Wittkower), the Cathedra represents the apotheosis of the Catholic Church, a unique and supreme convergence of emotional and rational symbols.

On the *bozzetto* for the Chair as on the Cathedra itself, the reliefs referring to the most significant moments in the life of Saint Peter symbolize the Mandate of the Vicar of Christ: on the back, the scene where Christ resurrected bids Saint Peter "Feed my sheep" ("Pasce Oves meas", *John* 21:18); on the side, the "Handing of the Keys" (*Matthew* 16:19) and the "Washing of the Feet" (*John* 13:5-20); and on the front, the "Miraculous Draught of Fishes" (*John* 21:1-14)—a scene which appears only in the sketch-model, and was replaced in the finished version by a decorative panel with pierced floral design.

The Detroit Institute of Arts, The Ralph H. Booth Fund, 1952

Terracotta and tinted plaster, 23 x 11½ in.

Coll.: Cardinal Mattei di Pergola; Count Mattei di Pergola; C. A. de Frey, Luzern.

Ref.: R. Battaglia, *La Cattedra Berniniana di San Pietro*, Rome, 1943, pp. 244-49; Grigaut in *Art Quarterly*, XVI, 1953, 124-30, and *D.I.A. Bull.*, XXXII, 1952-53, 65-68; H. Comstock in *Connoisseur*, 1953, CXXXI, 137; R. Wittkower, *G. L. Bernini*, London, 1955, p. 220

On 3 March 1656 Alexander VII decided to transfer the old chair of Saint Peter from the Baptismal Chapel into the apse of the church of Saint Peter's. One year later a preliminary design by Bernini envisaging the chair set into a "magnificent bronze ornament" with "gilded metal statues" was given formal approval. Thereafter Bernini started to improve and expand his design, making numerous sketches and, apparently, small three-dimensional models. A first large-scale model was tried out *in situ* in 1660, only to be further enlarged and modified. In 1663 the chair itself was cast in bronze, and on 17 January 1666, after the relic had been transferred into it, the Cathedra was officially unveiled.

Several autograph sketches, two finished workshop drawings—one at Windsor Castle and the other known through an 18th century engraving by C. M. Metz—four large-scale models of the two angels flanking the Chair, and numerous surviving documents help us in following the gradual unfolding of Bernini's grandiose concept. (Brauer-Wittkower, *Die Zeichnungen des G. L. Bernini*, Berlin, 1931, pp. 108-10; and R. Battaglia.) The significant differences between the Detroit *bozzetto*, the Windsor and the Metz drawings and the final version of the Chair—such as the design of the base, the standing angels and the front panel—suggest that this sketch-model may reflect a working stage between 1658 and 1660, a conclusion supported by Battaglia (1943) and by Wittkower (1955).

The bold assurance and vivacity of the reliefs that enliven the architectural structure of the chair, still somewhat tight and hesitant in this study, recall the quality of some pen or charcoal sketches by Bernini with their searching abbreviations and their brilliant tempo. A problem still open to discussion is that of the authorship of the two standing angels modeled in plaster, from their ankles up, for their design is obviously more schematic and their quality weaker than that of the rest of the model. According to a careful analysis by P. L. Grigaut (1953) who pointed out that the two fluted pilasters on the back of the chair are also made of the same stucco, these angels should probably be thought of as restudies by the master himself, conceived in more summary terms and later somewhat obliterated in the course of washing or cleaning the entire *bozzetto*. This seems to be entirely plausible, for the contrast would also document a very characteristic stage in Bernini's way of developing a motif, starting from simplified rendering of forms and a study of planes and working up towards a more heightened Baroque expression. [R.O.]

26. Triton with a Shell

The Detroit Institute of Arts, The Ralph H. Booth Fund, 1952

Terracotta, H. 12⅜ in.

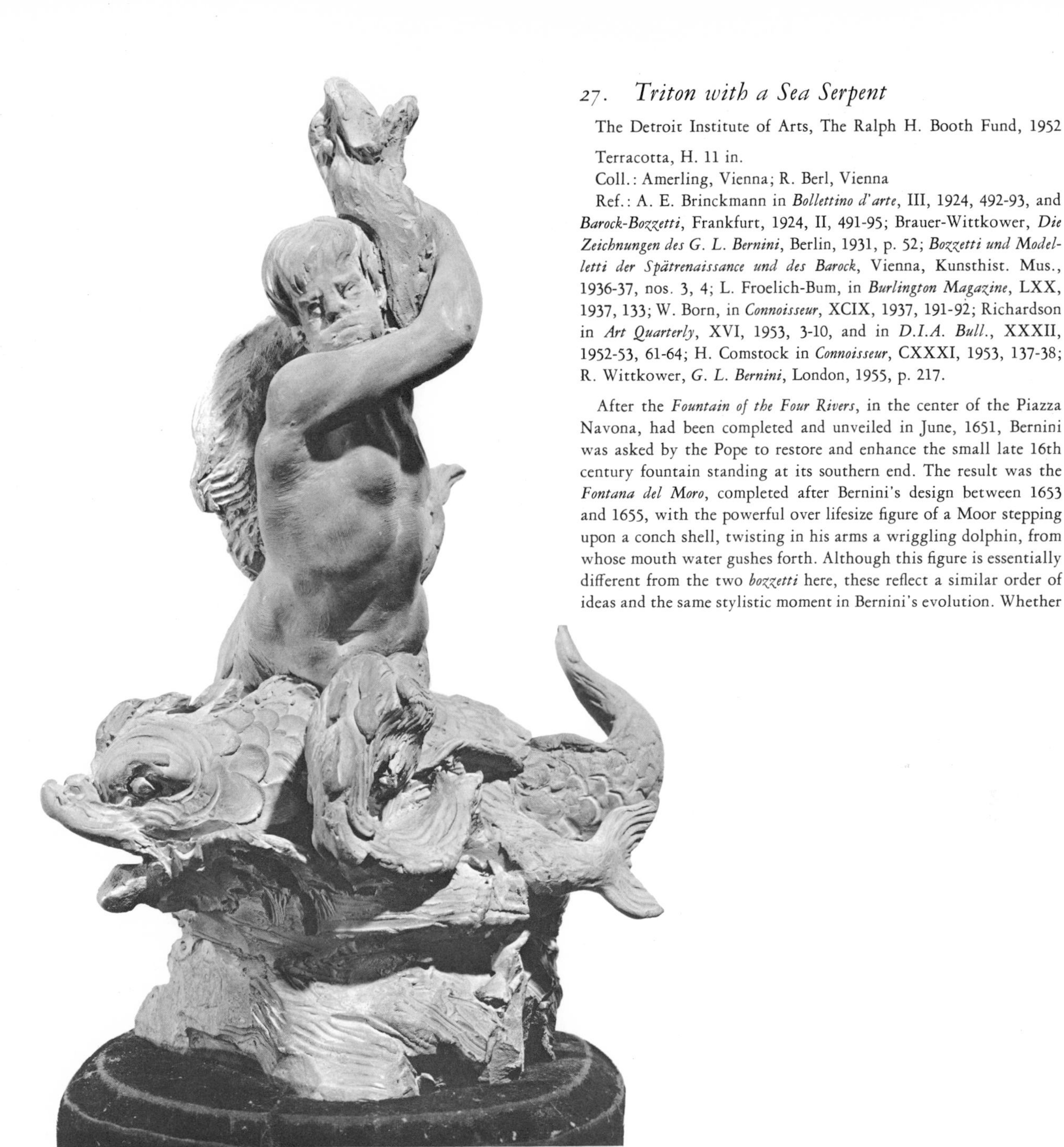

27. *Triton with a Sea Serpent*

The Detroit Institute of Arts, The Ralph H. Booth Fund, 1952

Terracotta, H. 11 in.

Coll.: Amerling, Vienna; R. Berl, Vienna

Ref.: A. E. Brinckmann in *Bollettino d'arte*, III, 1924, 492-93, and *Barock-Bozzetti*, Frankfurt, 1924, II, 491-95; Brauer-Wittkower, *Die Zeichnungen des G. L. Bernini*, Berlin, 1931, p. 52; *Bozzetti und Modelletti der Spätrenaissance und des Barock*, Vienna, Kunsthist. Mus., 1936-37, nos. 3, 4; L. Froelich-Bum, in *Burlington Magazine*, LXX, 1937, 133; W. Born, in *Connoisseur*, XCIX, 1937, 191-92; Richardson in *Art Quarterly*, XVI, 1953, 3-10, and in *D.I.A. Bull.*, XXXII, 1952-53, 61-64; H. Comstock in *Connoisseur*, CXXXI, 1953, 137-38; R. Wittkower, *G. L. Bernini*, London, 1955, p. 217.

After the *Fountain of the Four Rivers*, in the center of the Piazza Navona, had been completed and unveiled in June, 1651, Bernini was asked by the Pope to restore and enhance the small late 16th century fountain standing at its southern end. The result was the *Fontana del Moro*, completed after Bernini's design between 1653 and 1655, with the powerful over lifesize figure of a Moor stepping upon a conch shell, twisting in his arms a wriggling dolphin, from whose mouth water gushes forth. Although this figure is essentially different from the two *bozzetti* here, these reflect a similar order of ideas and the same stylistic moment in Bernini's evolution. Whether they are preliminary alternatives for this fountain (Brinckmann), or simply closely related to it in time and conception (Wittkower), their superb sculptural quality, the verve of their invention and the freshness of their surface—either finished with a ripping chisel or smoothed with the fingers, as if to convey an imaginary play of water and light—evoke the master's most inspired creations. [O.R.]

28. Portrait of Sisinio Poli

The Pierpont Morgan Library, New York, N. Y.

Black and red chalks heightened with white, $10\frac{9}{16}$ x $8\frac{1}{8}$ in.

Inscribed in a seventeenth century hand on wood, probably from the original mount of the drawing: "Eques Laurentius Berninus/ Die vigesimo octavo Aprilis 1638/ Delineavit/ Effigies Sisinii Poli aetatis suae/ Decimo octavo".

Coll.: Charles Fairfax Murray.

Ref.: *Collection of Drawings formed by C. Fairfax Murray, J. P. Morgan Collection*, London, 1912, IV, no. 174; H. Brauer and R. Wittkower, *Die Zeichnungen des Gianlorenzo Bernini*, Berlin, 1931, p.156

As the inscription indicates, Bernini made the drawing in 1638 when the sitter was eighteen years old. The casual pose—an instant caught in time—is characteristic of Bernini's portraiture. The young man turns to look directly at us, his lips parted, as if he is about to speak. Tousled hair and rumpled collar add to the informality. Bernini builds up the hair in thick, closely blended, curved tufts, while the chalk elsewhere is used to produce flocculent, painterly surfaces. As Brauer and Wittkower point out, Bernini's *Portrait of a Man* (perhaps Cassiano dal Pozzo, Windsor Castle, no. 5542) is almost identical to the Morgan portrait both in type of pose and in graphic technique, though the sitter is a good deal older. [R.E.]

29. Study for the Tomb of Cardinal Pimentel

Domenico Pimentel was a Spanish Dominican whom Innocent X Pamphili raised to the College of Cardinals in May of 1653. In December of the same year he was dead. The drawing shows him kneeling in prayer above his sarcophagus while below on the sides are allegorical figures of virtues who mourn his passing. To the right is Justice, identified by the fasces at her side. Bent over in grief, she buries her face in her hands. On the left is Charity nursing an infant.

The Pierpont Morgan Library, New York, N. Y.

Black lead and brown wash, $14\frac{13}{16}$ x $11\frac{1}{4}$ in.

Coll.: Inscribed lower right with stamp of B. Jolles (Lugt 381a)

Ref.: F. B. Adams *et al.*, *Ninth Report of the Fellows of The Pierpont Morgan Library*, New York, 1959, p. 97.

Pimentel's tomb was probably commissioned shortly after the cardinal's death in 1653. Bernini himself made the basic design, but entrusted its execution to his pupils. The marble tomb was erected in Santa Maria sopra Minerva in Rome, the Mother Church of the Dominican Order. For this monument Antonio Raggi carved the figure of Charity, G. A. Mari that of Justice, and Ercole Ferrata the image of the cardinal as well as the two allegorical figures in the background. Bernini's drawing is a preliminary study. It establishes the essential form of the composition and its basic components. But in details it differs considerably from the tomb as executed. Raggi's *Charity*, for example, is almost unrelated, and though Mari's *Justice* follows Bernini's drawing quite closely, he adds a putto to support her fasces. In Ferrata's hands the cardinal's robes, so alive in the drawing, go limp.

Professor Wittkower has pointed out (*Bernini*, 1955, p. 27) that although the Pimentel monument is actually a rather shallow wall tomb, its composition gives the illusion of a free-standing tomb. This drawing, only recently discovered and not widely known, strongly suggests that Bernini originally designed the tomb to be actually free-standing: otherwise the allegorical figure in the back-

ground right, who turns completely away from the observer and is almost entirely hidden behind the architectural elements, would have little meaning. (Later sketches for this figure, now in profile and with her face visible, are in Leipzig.) The church of Santa Maria is so crowded with monuments that it is hard to imagine where a free-standing tomb could have been placed. The present structure rises against the wall of a relatively narrow passage. Besides its great intrinsic worth, the Morgan drawing materially enlarges our knowledge of Bernini's project and our ability to appreciate the original conception. [R.E.]

GIACINTO BRANDI
1623 Rome 1691

Brandi studied first under his brother-in-law G. B. Magni, and then became a pupil of Lanfranco, whose style he followed closely. Much of his work is dramatic, enlivened by abrupt contrasts of light and shade, bold movement, and staring figures. Brandi's ability to carry out large projects rapidly helped him to win many commissions, but also increased his tendency toward the careless and at times coarse execution that Pascoli had already noted early in the eighteenth century. But his success was recognized by his fellow-painters, who elected him head (principe) of the Academy of St. Luke in 1669. Brandi's best known work is the enormous *Fall of the Rebel Angels*, painted on the vault of San Carlo al Corso in Rome in 1674. Here his combination of *di sotto in su* for the rebel angels with an effect close to that of a *quadro riportato* for the Vision of Glory is understandably disturbing. His *St. Charles Borromeo* for the high altar of the same church is much more successful. Brandi's work can be found in many other Roman churches, including Sant' Andrea al Quirinale, San Rocco, Santa Margherita in Trastevere, San Silvestro in Capite, and the Church of Gesù e Maria al Corso, where toward the end of his life (1686-87) he painted the ceiling frescos and the high altar.

30. St. Cecilia with Musical Angels

St. Cecilia, born into a wealthy and aristocratic Roman family, met martyrdom in the third century. Legend says that while still alive she was so attuned to heaven she could hear the angels singing. At times they appeared before her. Cecilia played all instruments then known, but since none of these conveyed adequately the sound of celestial music, she invented the organ, which we see her playing in this painting. She sits in the midst of an angelic concert, while a cherub brings her a floral crown that symbolizes her virginity, and the palm that is a sign of her martyrdom.

Bob Jones University Collection, Greenville, S. C.

Canvas, 85 x 66¼ in.

Coll.: W. P. Wilstach, Philadelphia; Lawrence Stewart, 1956

Ref.: *Catalogue of the W. P. Wilstach Collection*, Philadelphia, 1922, p. 15, no. 35; *Bob Jones University Collection*, Greenville, 1962, p. 146.

Traditionally this painting has been attributed to Giacinto Brandi. That the work is Lanfrancesque no one can doubt. The pose of the floating cherub, drawn out on a low diagonal which the drapery intersects, is almost a hall-mark of his influence. But the

composition is too dynamic, the figure types too bulky for Brandi. St. Cecilia's broad rounded face with its full cheeks is one of Benaschi's most characteristic types. She appears as Faith in his frescos at San Carlo al Corso, and the blond cherub-urchin at the bottom of the same fresco is seen again in the lower right hand corner of the painting of St. Cecilia. The work should be assigned to Benaschi and belongs to his Roman phase. [R.E.]

GIOVANNI BATTISTA BENASCHI
1636 Turin—Naples 1688

Benaschi, who apparently had his earliest artistic training in Piedmont, came as a young man to Rome, where he studied under Pietro del Pò. He later abandoned his master's manner to turn to the style of Lanfranco, which by then had become somewhat *retardataire*. Benaschi's work in Rome, which is known only to a very few specialists, shows at its best in the altarpieces he painted in San Sebastiano al Palatino: rich, darkly colored canvases with bold and vigorous compositions. Other Roman work appears in the sacristy of the church of Santa Maria del Suffragio in Via Giulia, and on the vault of the right aisle of San Carlo al Corso. A recently discovered *St. Gregory in Glory* (Museo Civico, Rieti), a documented work, must belong to this early period. Later he moved to Naples where the volume of his work, almost entirely in fresco, indicates that he enjoyed considerable success, but in this last phase his colors grow duller and his compositions less vigorous. In Santa Maria degli Angeli, Naples, he painted the entire vault of the nave, the choir and the dome. His large fresco on the dome of Santi Apostoli, a *Vision of Paradise*, closely follows the prototype established by Lanfranco. In the same church Benaschi painted the frescos in the chapel of St. Michael. His work in San Niccolò al Molo is now destroyed, but other frescos by Benaschi can be found in the Gesù Nuova, the Church of the Gerolamini, and Santa Maria delle Grazie a Caponapoli, where he is buried. The confusion between the graphic work of Benaschi and Lanfranco has been admirably solved by Vitzthum and Bean (*Bollettino d'arte*, XLVI, 1961, pp. 106-22).

31. Two Young Men Blowing Trumpets

Janos Scholz Collection, New York, N. Y.

Black chalk on blue paper, 14 15/16 x 21 1/4 in. Verso: Figure of Christ

Ref.: Bean and Vitzthum in *Bollettino d'arte*, XLVI, 1961, p. 121; Janos Scholz Collection Exhibitions, Hamburg and Cologne, 1963.

So closely did Benaschi follow the manner of Lanfranco that even in the eighteenth century De Dominici reports (*Vita de' pittori*, III, 1742, p. 280) that drawings by Benaschi were sold as Lanfranco's. In the use of bold crossing diagonals the *Two Trumpeters* certainly recalls Lanfranco's compositions. But Benaschi's graphic work is more broadly conceived, with heavy undulant outlines and shading applied in decisive parallel strokes. Lanfranco's graphic style is more pictorial than Benaschi's; his line lighter, more nervous, and frequently broken; his shading less regular, and often built up with zig-zag strokes. [R.E.]

PIETRO BERRETTINI DA CORTONA
1596 Cortona—Rome 1669

Cortona began his career about 1609 as a student of Andrea Commodi in Florence. In 1613 he went to Rome and soon entered the shop of Baccio Ciarpi, a Tuscan artist working there. Cortona's reputation grew rapidly in the 1620s when he was one of the initiators of the neo-Venetian trend in Rome. Between 1633 and 1639 he created his most famous work, the ceiling fresco of the Gran Salone in the Barberini Palace, probably the greatest ceiling decoration of the Italian Baroque style. In 1637 Cortona went to Florence and began his frescos in the Sala della Stufa of the Pitti Palace. In the same year he made a short trip to Venice. The artist was in Florence for most of the period from 1640 to 1647, when he decorated ceilings in the Pitti Palace. In 1647 he returned to Rome. The most important paintings of his last two decades of activity were the ceiling frescos of the Chiesa Nuova (1647-65) and of the gallery of the Pamphili Palace (1651-54) in Rome.

Cortona was also one of the great architects of the seventeenth century. Among his buildings in Rome are the church of SS. Martina e Luca (1635-50), the façades of S. Maria della Pace (1656-57) and S. Maria in Via Lata (1658-62), and the dome of S. Carlo al Corso (began 1668).

32. The Oath of Semiramis

Queen Semiramis of Babylon vows to show no mercy to her rebellious subjects. (Compare no. 100.)

Denis Mahon, Esq., London.

Copper, 20⅛ x 27¾ in.

Coll.: Galerie Heim; acquired by the present owner in 1957.

Ref.: Briganti in Galerie Heim, *Tableaux des Maîtres Anciens*, Paris, 1956, p. 22; Mahon in *Italian Art and Britain*, London, 1960, p. 166; Briganti, *Pietro da Cortona*, Florence, 1962, pp. 63-64, 163-64; Emiliani in *L'Ideale classico del Seicento*, Bologna, 1962, pp. 129-30.

An early work by Cortona, this picture still shows connections to the style of some of the Tuscan artists working in Rome in the early seventeenth century. However, Cortona's boldness and immediacy in handling, and his special feeling for scenographic effects and rhetorical gestures are already very much in evidence. Characteristically, Cortona chose a highly melodramatic moment in the story. Briganti, suggesting a date of c. 1620-1624 for the painting, has pointed out its close relationship to Cortona's frescos in the Palazzo Mattei, Rome (1622-23).

A *pentimento* indicates that the messenger was originally farther to the left, which corresponds to Cortona's preparatory drawing in the Uffizi, Florence (no. 11771). Briganti considers another drawing by Cortona of the same subject (Uffizi, no. 11766) to be later. [D.P.]

33. St. Jerome in the Desert

The group of dancing figures in the middle distance is a reference to St. Jerome's words: "Often in the vast solitude of the desert I dreamed I was amidst the pleasures of Rome. While my companions were but scorpions and wild beasts, I imagined taking part in the dances of young ladies." (*Patrologiae, Epistola XXII ad Eustachium*, col. 398, 416)

The Detroit Institute of Arts, gift of Mr. and Mrs. E. Raymond Field, 1942.

Copper (irregular polygon), 17⅝ x 15¼ in.

Coll.: Medici, Florence; Le Brun, Paris; Sir Thomas Baring, Earl of Northbrook, 1919.

Ref.: *Galerie Le Brun*, Paris, 1764, I, 23; Fabbrini, *Pietro da Cortona*,

32.

Cortona, 1896, p. 273; Richardson in *D.I.A. Bull.*, XXII, 1942, 10; *D.I.A. Catalogue*, 1944, p. 31; Briganti, *Pietro da Cortona*, Florence, 1962, p. 217.

The original shape was oval, as is seen in the engraving for the *Galerie Le Brun*. The picture can be dated c. 1637, and was probably made while Cortona was working on the frescos of the Sala della Stufa in the Palazzo Pitti, Florence. A preparatory drawing is in the Louvre (no. 559). [D.P.]

34. *Hagar and Ishmael in the Wilderness*

Hagar, with her son Ishmael, driven from Abraham's house, was visited by an angel in the wilderness. "What aileth thee, Hagar? fear not; for God hath heard the voice of the lad where he is. Arise, lift up the lad, and hold him in thine hand; for I will make him a great nation." (*Genesis* XXI, 17-18)

Ringling Museum of Art, Sarasota, Florida.

Canvas, 45 x 58 13/16 in.

Coll.: Earl of Waldgrave, Prestage; Grosvenor-Westminister family, 1763-1925; Hibbard, 1926; Ware, 1926-1930; Vitale Bloch; John Ringling.

Ref.: Young, *Pictures at Grosvenor House*, London, 1821, p. 30;

Waagen, *Treasures of Art in Great Britain*, London, 1854, II, 170; Voss, *Malerei des Barock in Rom*, Berlin, 1924, p. 544; Suida, *Catalogue Ringling Museum*, Sarasota, 1949, p. 121; Briganti, *Pietro da Cortona*, Florence, 1962, pp. 219-20.

A sensuous, pathetic mood pervades the scene. The open design, the sumptuous color, the brilliant play of light, and the freedom of handling are characteristic of Cortona's mature style. The painting can be dated c. 1638. [D.P.]

35. *Half Length Female Figure*

Janos Scholz Collection, New York, N. Y.

Black and white chalks on brown paper, 26 x 25 5/16 in.
Coll.: Reichlen, Lausanne.
Ref.: A. Neumeyer and J. Scholz, *Drawings from Bologna, 1520-1800*, Mills College Art Gallery, Oakland, Calif., 1957, no. 27 (as A. Carracci).

This large drawing, done on five joined pieces of paper, served as a cartoon. Indentations along some of the contours indicate it was used to transfer the image to a surface prepared for painting. Though once assigned to Annibale Carracci, both Vitzthum and Pouncey

have related the drawing to Pietro da Cortona. In technique it is quite similar to a sketch in the Uffizi that served Cortona as a preparatory study for the figure on the right with back turned in his fresco *The Age of Silver* (Palazzo Pitti). In both drawings we find the same loose imprecise repetition of contours which tends to soften the plastic volumes. The figure's Junoesque proportions, her classicizing features and hair-do, the use of an arching scarf to frame her head and shoulders, all serve to remind us again how much Cortona's High Baroque style owes to the Hellenistic aspects of antique Roman art. [R.E.]

GIOVANNI FRANCESCO ROMANELLI
1610 (?) Viterbo 1662

For a brief period Romanelli was a pupil of Domenichino, before becoming first a student, then an assistant, and finally a follower of Pietro da Cortona. He never fully absorbed the High Baroque aspects of Cortona's style, however, but instead transformed it into something quieter and more classicizing. This gentle version of the Cortonesque appears at its best, full of charm and grace, in Romanelli's frescos of the life of Countess Matilda of Tuscany in the Vatican (1637-42). In the *Presentation of the Virgin*, now in Santa Maria degli Angeli (1638-42), where Romanelli combines figure types drawn directly from Cortona's early manner with cherubs taken out of Domenichino's *Last Communion of St. Jerome*, the fusion of these two styles is less complete.

When the Barberini fell into disgrace after the death of Urban VIII, and his special patron, Cardinal Franceso Barberini, fled to France, Romanelli joined him in Paris (1646-47). Returning to Paris for a second time (1655-57) he was showered with commissions. He left behind a sizable body of frescos in the Hotel Mazarin, and a still larger group in the Palais du Louvre, which served to bring to France a modified version of Cortona's style and left a strong imprint on the art of Le Sueur. [R.E.]

36. St. Thomas of Villanova Distributing Alms

Thomas of Villanova (1488-1555) was court preacher to Charles V and Archbishop of Valencia. He is particularly remembered for his prodigious kindness and generosity to the poor.

Mr. and Mrs. Milton J. Lewine, New York, N. Y.

Canvas, 26 x 19¼ in.
Ref.: Hazlitt Gallery, *Baroque and Rococo*, London, May, 1962

The painting is a preparatory study for the altarpiece for S. Agostino, Rome. (The illustration in Voss [*Die Malerei des Barock in Rom*, Berlin, 1924, p. 269] seems to be from an old copy; the original altarpiece, according to Jacob Hess, is in the convent [cf. Waterhouse, *Baroque Painting in Rome*, London, 1937, p. 89].) Waterhouse points out that St. Thomas, who was canonized in 1668, became popular around 1660, a fact that supports a very late date for the painting.

A number of important changes were made in the final composition, principally in the group at the left and in the placement of the architecture, which was reversed in the altarpiece. The changes lent greater animation to the composition and enhanced its dramatic effect. [D.P.]

37. Allegorical Figures

The figure to the right holding an olive branch is Peace. The cornucopia is symbolic of the abundance associated with her. The figure on the left leaning on books as she holds a baton in one hand and a sword (?) in the other has not been satisfactorily identified.

Robert and Bertina Suida Manning, New York, N. Y.

Watercolor, 4⅝ x 7⅞ in.
Coll.: Inscribed with same collection stamps as in no. 38 and with inv. no. 502.

38. Allegorical Figures

The figure on the left is Prudence, who gazes into a mirror to indicate that the prudent person has knowledge of self, by which he must regulate his actions. The eel-like sucking fish is another of her attributes (Ripa-Sangro, *Iconologia*, 1766, IV, 428). The figure who holds the mirror and sits beside the lamp of learning may be Wisdom, a natural associate of Prudence.

Robert and Bertina Suida Manning, New York, N. Y.

Watercolor, 4⅝ x 7⅞ in.
Coll.: Inscribed lower left with collection stamp of Charles-Philippe Marquis de Chennevières-Pointel (1820-99), Lugt 2072; and below to left, collection stamp of Flury-Hérard (c. 1860), Lugt 1015, and inventory number: "F. H. No. 503."

These works are studies for lunette frescos that Romanelli painted during his second trip to France (1655-57) in what was formerly the Queen's apartment in the Louvre and is now called the Salle des Antonins. The use of the watercolor medium is quite characteristic of Romanelli during his Parisian period. His transposition of Cortona's Baroque into a lower key with cooler colors and quieter rhythms blended easily into the classicizing current that dominated official French art during much of the century. [R.E.]

CIRO FERRI
1634 Rome 1689

Of all Cortona's many followers, Ferri is the one who most closely imitates his style, but Ferri's work is heavier, his colors less delicate, and his techniques less proficient than those of his master. His earliest works, done under Cortona's direction, are his lunette frescos at S. Prassede in Rome. In 1657 he became a member of the Academy of St. Luke (the painters' guild). By the following year he was sufficiently well established to receive the commission for the high altar of San Filippo Neri in Perugia. From 1659 to 1665 Ferri was in Florence where he had gone at the call of the Grand Duke Ferdinand II de' Medici to complete the fresco program in Palazzo Pitti that Cortona had left unfinished in 1647 when he returned to Rome. His work in the Sala d'Apollo closely follows Cortona's design, but Ferri alone is responsible for the ceiling frescos of the Sala di Saturno, where the ponderous bulk of the airborne figures makes their levitation seem all the more miraculous. During this period Ferri received a good number of commissions to paint altarpieces for churches not only in Florence but elsewhere in Tuscany. In the fall of 1665 he was in Bergamo, working on a fresco cycle in Santa Maria Maggiore and sending altarpieces to various towns in Lombardy. We know that he planned a trip to Venice, but in 1669, when word reached him of Cortona's death, he returned to Rome to carry out his master's unfinished work at St. Peter's. Among Ferri's last paintings are his high altarpieces for Sant'Ambrogio della Massima and Santa Maria della Morte, and his ceiling frescos in Villa Falconieri at Frascati. In 1681 and again in 1687 the Academy of St. Luke named him their head (principe) but both times he declined. At his death he was working on the domical fresco of Sant'Agnese in Piazza Navona, which his pupil Corbellini completed "non mezzanamente ma male" (Pascoli, I, 173).

39. Allegory for a Frontispiece

The figure to the right painting the portrait of what was to be the Pope is probably Fame. On her bosom is the sun, a symbol of truth, and below her a globe to suggest the extent of her dominion. Religion holds the portrait, while beside her are censor and crucifix. In his left hand a putto holds a bishop's mitre and a cardinal's hat, symbols of other ecclesiastical titles held by the Pope.

The Pierpont Morgan Library, New York, N. Y.

Brush and aqueous white and brown pigment over lead point indications, on brown prepared paper, 11 x 7$\frac{9}{16}$ in.

Ref.: F. B. Adams *et al.*, *Ninth Report to the Fellows of The Pierpont Morgan Library*, New York, 1959, p. 98

Ferri's drawing is the model for a frontispiece that was engraved by Gérard Audran, a French artist active in the 1660s in Rome, where he studied under Carlo Maratti. Miss Stampfle writes in the *Ninth Report*: "In the first state of the print (R. Dumesnil, *Le Peinture-graveur français*, IX, no. 65) the oval frame, which is left blank in our drawing, contains the portrait of Clement X; in the third state, the portrait of Clement X is replaced by that of his successor, Innocent XI. The third state of the print carries the inscription [in the large cartouche] at the bottom: 'EFFIGIES NOMINA ET COGNOMINA S.D.N. INNOCENTII P.P. XI ET RR. DD. S.R.E. CARDD. nunc uiuentum,' but we have not yet traced a publication incorporating a series of portraits of cardinals for which it would seem to have been planned." At the bottom of the print is the inscription: "Cirus Ferrus del. . . . g. Audran sculp." The volume of portraits of cardinals for which Ferri designed the frontispiece was published by Giovanni Giacomo de Rossi, whose name in Latinized form appears directly below the cartouche. Copies in Rome known to this writer are at the Hertziana and the Vaticana.

By 1670 Audran, who engraved Ferri's drawing, was back in France where a payment for his "Les Battailles d'Alexandre" is recorded in August of that year. Thus 1670 would seem to be a *terminus ante quem* for the drawing. Pope Clement IX died 9 December 1669, but his successor, Clement X, whose image appears in the first state of the engraving, was not elected until 29 April 1670, after an exceptionally long conclave. It would seem not unlikely that Ferri made his drawing, with the portrait left blank, during the interregnum of 1669-70. [R.E.]

40. Two Women

Janos Scholz Collection, New York, N. Y.

Black chalk on gray paper, 12⅛ x 8⅞ in.
Coll.: Piancastelli (Lugt 2078a) and Brandegee (Lugt 1860c).

The face types derive from Cortona and the style of drawing recalls his late manner but here the soft atmospheric surfaces are unrelieved, so that the effect is much less focused, more diffuse. While the drawing can easily be classified as by one of Cortona's followers, the attribution to Ferri (and not to any other member of his circle) still remains tentative. [R.E.]

ALESSANDRO ALGARDI
1595 Bologna—Rome 1654

Algardi spent several years at the academy of Ludovico Carracci, where he first learned drawing and painting, gradually becoming interested in sculpture. His first documented works—two stucco angels made in 1619 after his models for San Domenico in Bologna—show him already acquainted with contemporary Venetian sculpture. In 1622 he went to Mantua, where he was employed by Ferdinando Gonzaga to carve ivories and make models for casting in silver and bronze, and where he could study the frescos of Giulio Romano and the duke's collections of antiquities. In 1625 he settled at Rome after spending a few months in Venice.

During his first ten years in Rome he completed important restorations of ancient statues for Cardinal Ludovisi and other collectors, and was at first especially valued as a portraitist. His splendid busts of *Cardinal Laudivio Zacchia* (1626) and *Cardinal Garzia Mellini* (1629) reveal much of his personal style in their combination of Bolognese direct psychological penetration with a high degree of spiritual idealization. These qualities gained him appreciation among "classicist" artists and critics, like Poussin, Duquesnoy and Bellori. Celebrated also were his small sculptures in marble, of which the figure of *Sleep*, made about 1630 for Cardinal Borghese, is today the only extant example.

His first important commissions were the group of *St. Philip Neri and the Angel* in Santa Maria in Vallicella (1640), the monumental *Tomb of Pope Leo XI* in St. Peter's (1634-1652), and the group of the *Decapitation of St. Paul* for the church of St. Paul in Bologna (1634)—works that show the full scope of his talent and made him the most important sculptor of Rome next to Bernini.

The election of Pope Innocent X in 1644 and the continued protection of the Pamphili family, meant for Algardi the beginning of a new phase. By the Holy Year of 1650 he completed the two major works of these years: the memorial bronze statue of Innocent X for the Capitol, and the full size model of the great relief of the *Meeting of Attila and Pope Leo the Great* for St. Peter's. The Attila relief, completed in marble by 1653, shows a new integration of his Bolognese education and of his classical ideal with suggestions absorbed from Bernini and Pietro da Cortona, and a new interest in pictorial and dramatic expression.

His last works were the model for an altarpiece with the *Liberation of St. Agnes* and a group of figures for the apse of San Nicolà da Tolentino. Both were unfinished at his death and the group for San Nicolà was carried out by pupils, Ercole Ferrata, Domenico Guidi and Francesco Baratta.

41. *Pope Innocent X*

Giovanni Battista Pamphili (1574-1655), who aided the Venetians against the Turks and condemned Jansenism, was Pope Innocent X (1644-55), the subject of a famous portrait by Velazquez.

The Cleveland Museum of Art, Cleveland, Ohio, gift of Rosenberg & Stiebel, Inc., in honor of William Mathewson Milliken, Director 1930-58.

Bronze, H. 30¾ in.

Coll.: Baron Gustave de Rothschild, Paris; Palais Lambert, Brussels.

Ref.: H. Hawley in *Cleveland Mus. Bull.*, XLIX, 1962, 80-82; J. Pope-Hennessy, *Catalogue of Italian Sculpture in the Victoria and Albert Museum*, London, 1964, II, 625; A. Nava Cellini in *Paragone*, XV, 1964, 32.

Between 1645 and 1654 Algardi was responsible for several official portraits of Innocent X, the most famous of which is the grandiose bronze statue erected in 1650 in the Palazzo dei Conservatori. Of the portrait busts, we may recall three examples in the Galleria Doria-Pamphili—one marble, one bronze, and one bronze and porphyry—and a terracotta in the Giustiniani Odescalchi Collection at Bassano di Sutri. All portray the Pope in a pensive mood, with that searching and yet warm and human approach that is so characteristic of many of Algardi's portraits. According to the convincing analysis by A. Nava Cellini, the Pamphili marble is probably to be dated about 1646, the bronze bust about 1647-48, while the last two examples, which are more pictorial and freer in treatment, were probably made after the statue of 1650.

The Cleveland bust is closest to the Pamphili bronze; so close, indeed, that we suspect it was cast from the same mold, although possibly at a slightly later date. For other bronze busts of Innocent X, related to this group though sometimes with compositional variations, see R. Wittkower (*G. L. Bernini*, 1955, p. 211). [O.R.]

42. *Abraham Sacrificing Isaac*

Abraham, being tested by God, is ready to sacrifice his son Isaac, (*Genesis*, 22).

Seattle Art Museum, Seattle, Wash., Eugene Fuller Memorial Collection.

Terracotta, 31½ x 22¼ in.

Coll.: Chigi, Rome (?)

Ref.: *Art Quarterly*, XVIII, 1955, 305.

Algardi's terracottas, few of which have survived, show the development of his personality perhaps more directly and eloquently than other works. In this beautiful relief his technical and stylistic handling is clearly recognizable, in spite of the traditional character of the composition. His Abraham, nobly conceived as an ancient philosopher, recalls the classical stance and the broad movement of the togas in the figures of the *Three Saints Epifanio, Concordio e Papia*, in Santi Luca e Martina (about 1635-1641). The angel with the elegant sweep of his long limbs and the characteristic design of his thin swirling drapery recalls the musical angels of the *Ecstasy of Saint Mary Magdalen* in the same church (about 1635). Such controlled classicism, made warm and alive by the subtle handling of luminous planes and the melodious composing of all the elements of the picture, seems to distinguish Algardi's work in the thirties

and early forties when he was also working at the *Tomb of Pope Leo XI.*

In the life of Giuliano Finelli, Passeri mentions the models of a *Sacrifice of Abraham* made by Algardi for Cardinal Giulio Sacchetti, after Finelli's departure for Naples. According to the chronology of Finelli's life—recently re-established by A. Nava Cellini (in *Paragone*, XI, 1960, no. 131, p. 22), the lost model of Algardi was probably made shortly after the fall of 1638. It may be suggested here, for the first time, that the Seattle relief may well be Algardi's lost model, and that its date should be placed about 1638-1639. [O.R.]

43. *The Flagellation of Christ*

After Pilate had agreed to release Barabbas to the mob and let Jesus be crucified, he washed his hands and delivered Him to the soldiers to be scourged (*Matthew* 27, 24-26). Christ appears bound to a column similar to that which is venerated ...e true column in the church of Santa Prassede in Rome.

The University of Kansas Museum of Art, Lawrence.

Gilt bronze, H. 10½ in.
Ref.: *University Museum Handbook*, Lawrence, 1962, p. 67.

This group is one of several variants (Oxford; Florence; Gripsholm Castle, Sweden) of a gilt-bronze *Flagellation* (Kunsthistorisches Museum, Vienna), mentioned as Algardi's work in an inventory of 1750 (L. Planiscig, *Die Bronzeplastiken*, 1924, no. 295). The figure of Christ also may be compared with a silver statuette of *Christ at the Column* (Metropolitan Museum, New York) made for one of the Colonnas, possibly the Constable Filippo. On the other hand, the figures of the executioners are especially close to two slightly larger boxwood statuettes, formerly in the H. Harris collection (Sotheby sale, London, 24-25 October 1950, no. 113).

Whether the Kansas group was actually cast after a model by Algardi, or may be perhaps a variant which incorporates the changes of another master, it still seems to reflect the rhythmical, linear quality that must have characterized Algardi's original design. [O.R.]

GIROLAMO LUCENTI
(attributed)
1627 Rome 1698

44. *Pope Clement IX*

Giulio Rospigliosi (1600-69), who mediated the peace of Aix-la-Chapelle between Louis XIV and Spain, suppressed the Jesuit order, and temporarily closed the Jansenist controversy, was Pope Clement IX (1667-1669).

The Detroit Institute of Arts, gift of the Founders Society.

Bronze, H. 29¾ in.
Coll.: Baron Gustave de Rothschild.

This portrait is closely related to a bust in plaster that stands, together with three other papal portraits, in the church of Santa Maria in Montesanto in Rome. It is probably also related to a bronze bust in the Rosipigliosi-Pallavicini Collection, Rome, mentioned by F. Martinelli (*I Ritratti di Pontefici di G. L. Bernini*, Rome, 1956, p. 47, note 96).

The plaster casts are late replacements for a lost series of bronze busts originally placed in the church about 1679-80. They were mentioned by F. Titi (*Ammaestramento di Pittura, Scoltura*, Rome, 1686, p. 356) as the work of Girolamo Lucenti (1627-1698) who, in the case of a bust of Alexander VII, used a model by Bernini. Lucenti was a Roman sculptor and bronze founder, trained by Algardi and frequently employed in Bernini's studio for a number

of important commissions. He worked at the papal mint from 1668 to 1679 and it is quite likely that he may be the author of the Detroit bust, which seems to be reasonably dated within the same span of years. [O.R.]

ERCOLE FERRATA
1610 Pelsotto (Como)—Rome 1686

After spending seven years in Genoa in the shop of the sculptor Tommaso Orsolini, Ferrata went to Naples where he first found employment as an ornament carver. In 1637 he was received in the guild of sculptors and marble craftsmen. After 1641 his first independent sculptures in the Aquino chapel at Santa Maria la Nova, and his first portraits—recently identified by A. Nava Cellini—show that in Naples he was chiefly in contact with the Lombard Cosimo Fanzago and the Tuscan Francesco Finelli.

In 1647, after a brief stop at Aquila, he arrived at Rome, where Bernini immediately appreciated his technical skill and stylistic pliability and employed him for the marble decorations of the pilasters of St. Peter's. In 1654 he was entrusted with the main figure of the tomb of Cardinal Pimentel in Santa Maria sopra Minerva (see no. 29), one of his best. The same

qualities gave him an *entrée* into Algardi's studio. His participation in the Attila relief, finished in 1653, is not certain, but at Algardi's death in 1654 Ferrata inherited part of the contents of his studio, and had the main share in finishing the work for San Nicolà da Tolentino.

For twenty years the activity of Ferrata, now head of a large studio, was divided between his own commissions and his frequent work for Bernini who called upon him for the decoration of Santa Maria del Popolo, for the preparation of models for the Cathedra Petri (see no. 25), or for translating his design for the elephant carrying the obelisk on Piazza Santa Maria sopra Minerva.

In spite of his frequent association with Bernini, Ferrata found that his natural temperament drew him more towards an appreciation of classical sculpture and towards the work of Algardi, whom he tried to imitate especially as a portraitist. Throughout his life his works reflected the solid virtues, as well as the shortcomings of a deeply conservative nature. His Lombard origin and training transpired in his expert handling of marble, his soft, warm treatment of surface planes, the closed rhythm of his outlines, the peaceful mood of his best figures. Thanks to his technical proficiency he became the teacher of a whole generation of younger sculptors who flocked to Rome attracted by the genius of Bernini, but found they could get a solid apprenticeship in the studio of Ferrata.

45. *The Madonna and Child*

The University of Kansas Museum of Art, Lawrence.

Gilt bronze, H. 16 in.

Ref. *University Museum Handbook*, Lawrence, 1962, p. 67.

Filippo Baldinucci, in summing up his biography of Ferrata whom he had known, writes, "He did not have much imagination in composing; but as he knew that this was his weak spot, he tried to overcome it by having his assistants make all sorts of models for him, so as to clarify his own mind, and then, by taking away what he disliked or adding what he thought best, he arrived at his own solution." (*Notizie de' Professori*, 1773, XVIII, 170)

This *Madonna and Child* reflects a somewhat similar procedure, for its model is obviously based on two earlier Roman sculptures: the *Santa Susanna* by Duquesnoy (1629-1633) and a *Madonna and Child* by Algardi. From the first derive the classical stance of the figure, the design of the pleated robe and of the drapery closely wrapping the body; from the second—which is known through the bronze examples in Berlin and in the Galleria Nazionale at Urbino—is borrowed the gesture of the Virgin and the figure of the Child. Finally, the head of the Virgin repeats the type of a classical Niobid. Such a variety of borrowings, and the markedly classical tone of the whole, where the sculptor has tried to fuse together the purity of Duquesnoy's famous statue with the feeling of majesty of Algardi's Madonna, is a perfect example of the eclectic position assumed by Ferrata around 1660. This was the time of the Commissions for Sant'Agnese in Agone where similar observations may be made, and the same date may be suggested therefore for the Lawrence statuette.

Another example, or possibly this figure itself was once in the Giovene de Girasole Collection in Naples. [O.R.]

46. *Faith*

Faith is symbolized here, following the traditional iconography, as a woman holding a chalice with the Host of the Eucharist. The attribute and right forearm are missing, but appears in the marble version. To her left a putto is propping up a profile portrait medallion of the deceased Cardinal Lelio Falconieri.

The Toledo Museum of Art, Toledo, Ohio.

Terracotta, H. 14¾ in.

Ref.: *Museum News*, XL, Nov. 1961, 3; *Art Quarterly*, XXIV, 1961, 406; *Emporium*, CXXXIV, 1961, 233; H. Comstock, in *Connoisseur*, CXLIX, 1962, 133.

The marble figure of *Faith* by Ferrata at San Giovanni de' Fiorentini was among the most celebrated sculptures of the third quarter of the 17th century in Rome. Completed before 1674, when Titi mentions it in *Studio di Pittura*, it stands at the center of the large monument designed by Borromini for Cardinal Lelio Falconieri.

This sketch, close to the finished marble, reflects the most genuine side of Ferrata's personality: the broad, slow rhythm of the draperies and the quiet curves of the composition, as well as that feeling of fullness and dignity which seems to have been the most constant quality of his art. It is probably one of two models with this subject listed in 1686 as works by Ferrata in the inventory of his studio (V. Golzio in *Archivi*, II, 1935, 67, 73). A third model published by Brinckmann under the name of Ferrata and now in the Museo di Palazzo Venezia, Rome, is more likely to be, on the contrary, an alternative composition by Cafà, which is also mentioned in the same inventory. [O.R.]

46.

Charity in the Victoria and Albert Museum. The Child, on the other hand, is rather similar to the sporting putti made of stucco after Algardi's designs in the frieze of the main nave of Sant'Ignazio (1650).

Although an attribution to Algardi cannot be suggested at the moment, especially since none of his carvings in ivory has survived to offer us a valid comparison, we are probably not far from the truth in believing that we have here the work of an artist who was in contact with his studio, or perhaps with that of Ercole Ferrata, where many of Algardi's models remained to be used for guidance. Ferrata is known to have occasionally worked in wood, although the figures of saints he carved for the church of Pelsotto have nothing of the crisp, sparkling quality of this fine boxwood statuette. [O.R.]

ROMAN, MID-XVII CENTURY

47. *The Madonna and Child*

The Detroit Institute of Arts, gift of Robert H. Tannahill, 1949.

Boxwood, H. 11⅝ in.

Coll.: J. Brummer, New York (Sale, Parke-Bernet, 20-23 April 1949, no. 336)

The Algardesque source of this composition is evident when we compare this statuette with a relief of *The Rest on the Flight to Egypt* by Algardi. The original is now lost and is known only through a French, 17th century engraving by Chauveau, and through several variants in bronze, examples of which are in the Metropolitan Museum, the Victoria and Albert Museum and elsewhere. The figure of the Virgin, with her characteristic drapery swept up over the head is a rather faithful copy after this model, while the thin sensitive traits of her face are not unlike those of Algardi's bronze

ANDREA POZZO
1642 Trent—Vienna 1709

Erroneously known as "Padre", Andrea Pozzo was a lay brother who entered the Jesuit order in 1665. His early altarpieces at Sant'Ambrogio in Genoa are quite conventional paintings done under the influence of Rubens, but what first brought him fame was the amazing *trompe l'oeil* effect of his architectural perspectives which he painted in the form of a fictive dome at the crossing of the Chiesa della Missione at Mondovì (1676-77). His masterwork, *The Triumph of the Jesuit Missions* on the vault of the great nave of Sant'Ignazio in Rome (1691-94), is an architectural extravaganza. When viewed from a fixed point marked by an inset on the marble floor, it creates the illusion that the walls of the nave rise up to staggering heights before the eye passes on into the open sky filled with cloud-borne hosts. Though the work is a tour-de-force of mathematical perspective, critics have long pointed out that it looks backward to the perspective systems of the Early Renaissance. Seen in this light, it stands at complete variance with the most advanced currents of Roman High Baroque illusionism, as represented by Gaulli's fresco on the nave vault of the Gesù. In Pozzo's last major work, the *Triumph of Hercules* on the vault of the Great Hall of Palazzo Liechtenstein in Vienna (1704-08), he develops his architectural *quadratura* with less abundance but greater elegance.

48. *Study for a "Theatrum Sacrum"*

This drawing is a study for a more ambitious project that Pozzo designed to provide what was, in effect, a stage set for the religious ceremonies that the Jesuits carried out in their Mother Church, the Gesù in Rome, during Holy Week in the year 1685.

Donald Oenslager Collection, New York, N.Y.

Pen and bistre ink, with bistre and gray ink washes, on white paper, 16¼ x 6½ in.
Coll.: Mayr-Fájt; Scholz.
Ref.: A. H. Mayor and J. Scholz, *Baroque and Romantic Stage Design*, New York, 1950, p. 7; R. Parks *et al.*, *Piranesi*, Smith College Museum of Art, Northampton, 1959, no. 11; *Theatre Drawings from*

the Donald Oenslager Collection, Minneapolis Institute of Arts, 1963, no. 12; R. Wunder and A. H. Mayor, *Four Centuries of Theatre Design, Drawings from the Donald Oenslager Collection*, 1964, no. 18.

One cannot help but admire Pozzo for the boldness with which he elaborates and multiplies his architectural forms. For all that, in comparison with the revolutionary structures built by Borromini and Guarini, these imaginary edifices remain essentially conservative, little concerned with undulant surfaces and moulded space. The fully developed design, for which this drawing is a preliminary study, is reproduced in an engraving in Pozzo's *Perspective Pictorum et Architectorum*, Rome, 1693, pl. 71. (See also Mayor and Scholz, *Stage Design*, pl. 18.) [R.E.]

GIOVANNI BATTISTA GAULLI called Baciccio
1639 Genoa—Rome 1709

Though born in Genoa, Baciccio spent almost his entire adult life in Rome. He left his native city after the plague of 1657 or perhaps even earlier. The story, so often repeated, of his early apprenticeship to Luciano Borzone can have no foundation since Borzone died when Baciccio was no more than seven years old. Rather his earliest works show the influence of the new Genoese colorism developed, under the impact of Rubens and van Dyck, by such artists as Assereto and Valerio Castello. In Rome he became a protégé of Bernini. Bernini's sculpture left an indelible imprint on the young Baciccio, forming the basis for his treatment of drapery folds and his play of curvilinear line. Today we know him for his large public commissions such as the frescos on the pendentives of Sant'Agnese in Piazza Navona or his altarpieces in well-known Roman churches such as Sant'Andrea al Quirinale or Santa Maria in Campitelli. But his greatest fame comes from his fresco, *The Triumph of the Name of Jesus* (1676-79) on the great vault of the nave of the church of the Gesù, now fully recognized as a climactic moment in the history of illusionistic ceiling painting. From 1685 on Baciccio's style became increasingly classicizing. Critics of his day and our own agree that these late works are generally less successful. During his lifetime Baciccio won great fame for his portraits but few are known today. Instead we have come increasingly to appreciate his *bozzetti*, whose lively brush-work and rich hues mark him as the great colorist of the Roman High Baroque.

49. Adoration of the Lamb

The theme derives from the *Book of Revelation* dealing with the mystical visions of St. John. At the center of the painting, on a golden altar or throne, rests the Lamb of God through whose blood the sins of mankind are cleansed. Beneath Him is the book sealed with seven seals (representing the seven mystical revelations) and around him are seven torches. Below on cloud banks sit the twenty-four elders, raising their censers in praise of the Lamb, as well as many adoring figures with palms. Above is an arc of angels trumpeting His glory.

M. H. de Young Memorial Museum, San Francisco, Calif., gift of the M. H. de Young Endowment Fund, 1935.

Canvas, 25⅜ x 41¼ in.
Coll.: J. Gollober, San Francisco, 1935; M. Lucioni, Rome.
Ref.: Feinblatt in *Art Quarterly*, X, 1947, 253; Brugnoli in *Bollettino d'arte*, XXXIV, 1949, 235, 237; Heil, *M. H. de Young Museum, Selected Works*, 1950, pp. 28-29; Pecchiai, *Il Gesù di Roma*, 1952, p. 269; Seaver, *Flight: Fantasy, Faith, Fact*, Dayton, 1953, p. 15; Manning, *Genoese Masters*, Dayton, 1962, no. 35; Enggass, *Baciccio*, University Park, Pa., 1964, pp. 67, 157.

The painting is an oil sketch for Baciccio's fresco on the apsidal vault of the church of the Gesù in Rome. On 20 Nov. 1679 Ranuccio II Farnese, Duke of Parma, wrote to Gian Paolo Oliva, the Jesuit General, authorizing Oliva to commission Baciccio to begin work on the apsidal fresco of the Gesù, then as now the Mother Church of the Jesuit order. The de Young canvas, which is a very early study for that fresco, must have been painted shortly after this date. The fresco itself was unveiled on 30 July 1683. Another oil sketch, representing a later stage in Baciccio's development of the composition, is today in the Galleria dei Marmi of the Gesù, Rome.

This canvas is the most important example of Baciccio's work to be found within continental United States. In it he reveals his love of color and, still more, his delight in the possibilities of rapid open brush work. Here, before the final composition has crystalized, we can admire passages executed with a freedom unknown in his finished work, as with some of the lateral figures, pressing inward to the light of the Lamb, whose robes are built up out of riotous zig-zags of paint. [R.E.]

50. Rinaldo and Armida

This canvas takes its subject not from ancient mythology but

from late Renaissance Italian poetry: Torquato Tasso's *Gerusalemme liberata*, first published in 1581. Tasso's epic established a whole new iconography for Baroque artists, who were, however, less interested in the religious allegory than in the romantic details. Baciccio has chosen the moment when Rinaldo, the Christian Knight, meets Armida, his mortal enemy, who causes him to fall into a deep sleep. Gazing at him as he lies under her spell on the banks of the Orantes, Armida suddenly realizes that she has fallen in love with him. She orders her nymphs to bind him with light but unyielding chains of flowers, and carries him off in her chariot. (Canto XIV, stanza 68)

Robert and Bertina Suida Manning, New York, N. Y.

Canvas, 15 x 19¼ in.
Ref.: Enggass, *Baciccio*, University Park, Pa., 1964, pp. 28-29, 133-34.

This small but charming oil sketch is a study for a larger work, now lost. The nymph who kneels to weave the floral chain that will bind Rinaldo is a close variant of the maidservant kneeling before the Infant St. John in Baciccio's large altarpiece in Santa Maria in Campitelli in Rome, a documented work. Typical of Baciccio in his middle years when he was at work in the Gesù (1672-85) are the lively rhythms and bright gay colors that make use of *cangianti:* as, for example, in the robes that move from dark red to pale green or pale blue as they pass out of the shadows and into the light. [R.E.]

51. The Sacrifice of Isaac

See no. 42.

Atlanta Art Association, Atlanta, Ga. (The Kress Collection).

Canvas, 63½ x 51⅝ in.
Coll.: Alessandro Contini-Bonacossi, Florence.
Ref.: Ferguson, *Signs and Symbols in Christian Art*, New York, 1954,

50.

pl. V; Enggass in *Paragone*, VII (No. 73), 1956, 30-35; Suida, *Italian Paintings*, Atlanta Art Association Galleries, 1958, pp. 64-65; Manning, *Genoese Masters*, Dayton, 1962, no. 34; Enggass, *Baciccio*, University Park, Pa., 1964, p. 121.

The garments of Abraham and the angel both have elaborate drapery folds that generate the typically High Baroque rhythms that Gaulli developed in his frescos at the Gesù under the direct influence of Bernini's sculpture. The artist's tendency to translate sculpture into painting is particularly obvious in the edge of Abraham's tunic, which has a thickness, precision and angularity normally associated with carving in stone. A light drop in intensity of color and gesture (relative to Baciccio's work a decade earlier) suggests that the canvas should be dated about 1685-90, immediately after the Gesù complex. [R.E.]

52. *The Dream of St. Joseph*

"And when they were departed, behold, the angel of the Lord appeareth to Joseph in a dream, saying, Arise, and take the young child and his mother, and flee into Egypt . . . for Herod will seek the young child to destroy him." (*Matthew* 2, 13)

Robert and Bertina Suida Manning, New York, N. Y.

Pen and brush, brown ink heightened with white, on buff paper, 10¾ x 8 in. Monogram lower right: C. R.
Ref.: Manning, *Genoese Masters*, Dayton, 1962, no. 84.

Violent convolutions in the garment folds, reminiscent of Baciccio's great altarpiece at Fermo, place the drawing early in his middle phase, about 1675. Typical of Baciccio in this period are the contours drawn with thick rapid pen strokes. It is interesting to note how the artist began with the idea of an angel plunging downward along a sharp diagonal, then changed to one just alighting, whose windswept robes convey both the motion of flight and the emotion of the event. [R.E.]

53. *Allegory of the Liberal Arts (?)*

Mercury, appearing above with winged sandals and caduceus, became in later times the patron of learning. Famed as the discoverer of music, he was also known as the inventor of letters, numbers, mathematics and astronomy. In this drawing we see him pointing the way to allergorical figures whose attributes (globe, compass and triangle) all suggest learning (cf. Ripa's *Mathematica*).

Robert and Bertina Suida Manning, New York, N. Y.

Pen and brush, brown ink with gray wash on white paper, 11⅝ x 10¼ in.
Inscribed left on old mount: Pietro da Cortona.
Ref.: Manning, *Genoese Masters*, Dayton, 1962, no. 83.

Despite the old attribution to Cortona, Philip Pouncey assigned this drawing to Gaulli purely on the basis of style. His keen eye is confirmed by an engraving in the Farnesina in Rome for which it served as the model. The engraving bears the inscription: "Gio. Bat. Gaulli invento e delin. R. V. Audenaerde intag." Since Robert Van Audenaerd was born in 1663, Gaulli could not have made this drawing early in his career (unless—highly unlikely—the decision to engrave it was an afterthought), and the fully Baroque treatment of the figures would also exclude a late dating. The years between 1685 and 1690 seem the most appropriate. [R.E.]

CARLO MARATTI

1625 Camerino—Rome 1713

Maratti arrived in Rome while still very young, about 1636. Like most art students of the period, he copied the work of Raphael and the Carracci, but the greatest single influence on his style came through his long apprenticeship to Andrea Sacchi (1599-1661). His early work also shows the clear imprint of Correggio. By the 1670s Maratti was considered the leading painter in Rome.

Since Maratti was the leading pupil of Sacchi, and since Sacchi's distinctly conservative art contrasts sharply with the ebullient High Baroque for which Pietro da Cortona is noted (though both were protégés of the Barberini at the same time) it is natural that the critics should carry this opposition into the next generation, making Maratti the great proponent of classicism, in opposition to the Baroque of Baciccio. Like most generalizations, this is only partly true. But in Maratti's day the famous and highly influential art theorist, Giovanni Pietro Bellori, who had previously extolled Poussin, now championed Maratti as the new Raphael, the savior of the art of painting that had fallen into the gutter of the Baroque. Toward the end of the seventeenth century in Rome, most of the people who counted supported this view. In our own day, with Bernini and Baciccio back in fashion, Maratti is damned as a classicist and an enemy of the Baroque. The truth is that Maratti cannot easily be pigeon-holed. A highly talented artist who lived a long life, he painted in a number of different styles, sometimes classicizing, often not. The repeated comparison of his vault fresco in Palazzo Altieri (not one of his most successful works) to Baciccio's masterpiece on the vault of the Gesù, has not helped Maratti's reputation. But his powerful portraits are often as Baroque as Baciccio's and so close to them in style that at times only Maratti's cooler palette serves to distinguish the one from the other. Maratti's *Death of St. Francis Xavier* is less intense and less mystical than Baciccio's altarpiece of the same subject, but it is also

more abundant, more dynamic, more theatrical, and more grand. Before we condemn or praise Maratti for his classicism we should decide which Maratti we mean.

54. *The Martyrdom of St. Andrew*

Andrew, a simple fisherman but the first of those called to follow Christ, later won fame for his apostolate in eastern Europe. At Patros, in the Peloponnese, he miraculously cured Maximilla, wife of the Roman Proconsul Egeas. Nevertheless Egeas had him executed for preaching disobedience to the emperor. The cross before which the aged saint kneels is transverse, a shape today called St. Andrew's cross but not identified with the saint until the fifteenth century. The length of rope in the hands of one of the executioners refers to the legend that Egeas ordered the saint bound, not nailed, to the cross in order to prolong his suffering.

Bob Jones University Collection, Greenville, S. C., 1951.

Canvas, 47½ x 62 in.

Coll.: Cardinal Renato Imperialis; Phillips, Picton Castle, Eng.; D. Koetser, New York.

Ref: *Bob Jones University Catalogue*, 1954, pp. 80-81; Mezzetti, *Rivista dell' istit. naz. d'archeologia e storia dell'arte*, IV, 1955, 284, 325-26; *Bob Jones University Collection of Religious Paintings*, 1962, I, 158-59.

Dr. Mezzetti has identified this painting as the original from which J. Frey made the engraving inscribed: "Ex tabula Marattae observata in Aedibus Em.mi et Rev.mi Principis Josephi Renati S. R. E. Card. Imperialis. Nunc in Aedibus Honorabilis et ornatissimi D.ni Erasmi Philippi Angliae Baronetti". The painting belongs to Maratti's early phase, about 1665-70, when he was still under the influence of Andrea Sacchi, from whose painting of the same theme in the sacristy of St. Peter's in Rome Maratti took the central group of figures. Two of the warriors coming over the crest of the hill on the left are placed in such a way that the legs of the one in the foregound frame the head of the one behind—a motif derived ultimately from an engravlng of the School of Mantegna. Mezzetti considers three variants of this canvas to be school copies (Streit Collection, Hamburg; Earl of Wemyss, Gosford House; Louvre). [R.E.]

55. *Cleopatra*

So fabulous is the legend of Cleopatra that we are hard pressed to admit she existed in flesh and blood, the lover of a real Caesar and a real Marc Anthony. Cleopatra VII, last of the Ptolemaic rulers of Egypt, descendant of one of the generals in the army of Alexander the Great, is shown by Maratti at the moment when she is about to drop a pearl into a jar of wine. Tradition associates this motif with the sumptuous banquet (for two) which Cleopatra gave to welcome Marc Anthony.

Museum of Art, Rhode Island School of Design, Providence, R. I.

Canvas, 44 7/8 x 32½ in.

Ref.: A. Clark in *R.I. Sch. of Des. Bull.*, vol. 45, no. 4, 1959, p. 4; D. Miller, *Seventeenth and Eighteenth Century . . . Notre Dame*, Urbana, 1962, no. 26.

Bellori, in his life of Carlo Maratti, tells us that the artist painted for Francesco Montioni a series of six famous women, including a "Cleopatra with the pearl in her hand above a vase". Bellori thought the painting was done about 1695. If, however, the tradition is correct that Maratti used for his model his daughter Faustina, who was born in 1680 (and the resemblance between the Cleopatra in this painting and the portrait of Faustina in the Galleria Corsini seems to bear this out), then the painting should be dated about 1700, by reference to the age of the sitter. J. Frey made an engraving of the painting in 1720.

There are at least three versions. On the basis of quality the large canvas in the Museo di Palazzo Venezia in Rome has been considered the prime original (note, however, that it is almost full length while Bellori speaks of "mezze figure di donne"). Prof. Dwight Miller suggests that the version now at the University of Notre Dame—a half length figure almost identical in composition to the canvas here exhibited—is a studio copy. The Providence painting is smaller than the version in Rome. The face, more generalized, is now almost without reference to a specific model. Most of the elements have been simplified. But the modeling is firmer, the details crisper than in the canvas at Notre Dame. I would suggest that the Providence version is an autograph copy with studio assistance. [R.E.]

56. *Studies for an Angel of the Annunciation*

See Luke I, 28.

The Pierpont Morgan Library, New York, N. Y.

Pen and brown ink, 9 1/16 x 9 3/16 in.

Coll.: Charles Fairfax Murray.

Ref.: *Collection of Drawings formed by C. Fairfax Murray, Morgan Collection*, London, 1912, IV, no. 184; F. Dowley in *Art Quarterly*, XX, 1957, 168.

In this sketch it is neither pose nor gesture but the dynamics of line, bringing alive again the movements of the pen once held in Maratti's hand—the rush and swirl of its hectic passage—that

gives the drawing its wonderful sense of energy. Prof. Dowley points out that during these years, well before Gaulli could have been of any influence on him, Maratti emerges from his dependence on Sacchi to develop a new style, full of movement and vigor. The drawing is a study for the *Annunciation* which Maratti painted in two versions, one for the high altar of Sant'Antonio Abbate at Anagni (1659), the other for Vittoria della Rovere, wife of the Grand Duke Ferdinand II of Tuscany. [R.E.]

57. *Study for "Jael Slaying Sisera"*

Sisera was a general in the armies of Jabin, King of Canaan, who had oppressed the Israelites. When the soldiers of Israel destroyed his forces in battle, Sisera fled on foot to Jael who welcomed him into her tent and gave him milk to quench his thirst. As he slept

exhausted under the cover of her mantle, she came to him quietly with a hammer and drove a tent pin through his temple. Thus he died. (*Judges* 4, 1-21) The story is variously interpreted allegorically or symbolically as the victory of the Virgin over the devil, or as the Cardinal Virtue 'Strength', or as Youthful Victory, as was Judith.

The Metropolitan Museum of Art, New York, N.Y., Dick Fund, 1936.

Red chalk heightened with white on gray-blue paper, 8⅞ x 10¾ in.
Coll.: Henry Oppenheimer, London.
Ref.: *Oppenheimer Sale*, Christie's, London, 1936, no. 120; Wehle in *Met. Mus. of Art Bull.*, XXXII, Jan. 1937, 8.

The drawing is a preparatory study for the cartoons of the mosaics in the lunettes of the Cappella della Presentazione, St. Peter's, Rome. Maratti received his commission for the group (in which *Judith and Holofernes* was paired with *Jael and Sisera*) in 1677, but the mosaics were not finally in place until about 1686 (see Mezzetti, *Riv. dell'ist. naz. d'arc. e storia dell'arte*, IV, 1955, 344-45). Other drawings of Jael by Maratti can be found in the Kunstsammlungen der Stadt Düsseldorf (nos. 175-76) and the Kupferstichkabinett, Berlin (no. 171). The power of this drawing, and the eerie detachment of the lovely young girl in the act of killing her guest, should be an antidote for those who, repulsed by the endless Madonnas assigned to Maratti but executed by his followers, accuse Maratti of weakness and sentimentality. [R.E.]

GIUSEPPE PASSERI
1654 Rome 1714

Giuseppe first studied with his uncle, the painter, biographer and art critic Giovanni Battista Passeri, but soon left him to enter the studio of Carlo Maratti. Here he absorbed Maratti's manner and became one of his favorite pupils, but his mature style is more independent than that of most of Maratti's followers. Waterhouse notes Passeri's soft, fluid handling, his lack of rhetoric, and his technique of painting thinly over a dark ground (*Baroque Painting in Rome*, London, 1937, p. 84). Passeri spent his entire life in Rome. His principal paintings are to be found in her churches, including Santa Maria in Araceli, Santa Caterina a Magnanapoli, Santa Maria in Campitelli, and San Sebastiano fuori le mura. Toward the end of his life he painted two scenes of the life of St. Francis de Paul for San Giacomo degli Incurabili, and his *St. Peter Baptising in Prison* for the Baptistry of St. Peter's was done in 1714, the year he died.

58. *Christ between Moses and Elijah*

The scene shows the upper half of the Transfiguration, in which Christ appears miraculously on a cloud bank between Moses and Elijah. The horns on Moses' head, which derive from a mistranslation of the Hebrew term for "rays of light", and the curved tablet of the decalogue that he brought back from the mount, are his customary attributes. The lower section, not included in this drawing, would show the disciples Peter, James and John, to whom Christ thus revealed his divinity. The Transfiguration is often taken to foreshadow the imminent translation of Jesus to heaven, and to represent his fulfillment of both the Ancient Law and the predictions of the Old Testament prophets, symbolized respectively by Moses and Elijah.

Janos Scholz Collection, New York, N. Y.

Red chalk heightened with white on white paper, 6¾ x 10$\frac{3}{16}$ in.
Inscribed, upper left, in eighteenth century hand: "Gesù in mezzo di Moisé ed Elia Orig: di Gius: Passeri". Lower left: Scholz stamp (Lugt 2933b).
Ref.: J. Scholz, *The Life of Christ, Drawings from the Janos Scholz Collection*, University of Notre Dame Art Gallery, Notre Dame, 1964.

The soft handling of the volumes is characteristic of Passeri's style, but the highly classicizing composition depends in part on the rigidity of the iconographic tradition. Christ's glance and the placement of the whole group to the left suggest that the three disciples on the ground below must have been set over to the right, thus establishing a diagonal relationship between the two groups and lessening the overall symmetry. [R.E.]

MELCHIORRE CAFÀ
1635 Malta—Rome 1667/68

When very young Cafà went to Rome and entered the busy studio of Ercole Ferrata. Within his short career, abruptly ended following an accident in a foundry, Cafà was able to finish entirely only two monumental works: a statue of *Santa Rosa*, and the altarpiece of the *Ecstasy of Saint Catherine* in Santa Caterina de Siena, Magnanapoli. Both works show that, in spite of his association with Ferrata, Cafà's natural temperament drew him towards the exalted style of the late Bernini, whose spiritual heritage he understood better than any contemporary artist.

In Ferrata's studio Cafà received a solid technical and formal education. He soon distinguished himself for his great natural gifts and the brilliance of his imagination. He excelled in making clay and wax sketches, many of which remained in his master's studio long after his death. In 1660 he received through Ferrata his first important commission: the large marble relief of *St. Eustace among the Lions* for Sant'Agnese in Agone, and in 1661, through Baratta, the marble group of *St. Thomas of Villanova distributing Alms* for Sant'Agostino. Although he had time to carry along almost to completion only the *St. Thomas*, Cafà's surviving sketch-models for these commissions (Museo di Palazzo Venezia, Rome; La Valletta Museum, Malta) tell us much about the fluidity of his style, and the spontaneous rhythm of his strangely elongated, deeply expressive figures. His talent as a portraitist is apparent in a bust of Alexander VII whose large terracotta model is still at Ariccia and of which two bronze casts survive, one at the Metropolitan Museum, the other in the Cathedral of Siena.

59. *Pope Alexander VII*

Fabio Chigi (1599-1667), who issued a bull against the Jansenists, and patronized literature and architecture, commissioning Bernini's colonnade in the Piazza of St. Peter's, was Pope Alexander VII (1655-67).

The Metropolitan Museum of Art, New York, N. Y., Edith Perry Chapman Fund, 1957

Bronze, H. 39½ in. Signed and dated: Melchior.Cafa/Melitensis/ Fac.An.Dom./MDCLXVII
Coll.: Baron Gustave de Rothschild, Paris.
Ref.: R. Wittkower, *Art and Architecture in Italy*, Baltimore, 1958, p. 362; R. Wittkower in *Metropolitan Museum Bull.*, n.s. XVII, 1959, 197-204.

This superb portrait of the Chigi Pope, rightly called "the most Berninesque papal portrait of the second half of the seventeenth century" (Wittkower), is the most vivid witness to Cafà's exceptional gifts as a sculptor. One cannot but admire the warmth of this marvelous head, the generous movement of the short cape (*mozzetta*), truly pulsating with life, as well as the freshness of the bronze surface, probably chased and rasped by the artist himself.

The quality of this work is particularly evident when compared with two other busts of Alexander VII, also by Cafà, which are intimately related to it. One is the full size terracotta bust in the Chigi palace at Ariccia, near Rome. The other, an almost identical

bronze bust, with gilded orphreys, is now in the Cathedral at Siena. The first has been definitely identified as the full size model mentioned by Pascoli. As was eloquently shown by Wittkower, the first cast to emerge from the kiln must have been the Metropolitan Museum bronze. Because of a wide break running across the chest (visible now mainly from underneath), it obviously had to be laid aside. It was followed by a second casting which suffered no technical mishap and became the portrait now in Siena, accurately finished under the artist's supervision, but perhaps less vital and crisp than the first version now in the Metropolitan Museum. [O.R.]

60. The Baptism of Christ

Christ is shown here stepping down, in full humility, into the flowing waters of the Jordan, while John, in an act of deep reverence, pours water on Him. At left a small putto-angel is holding out a cloth, ready to wipe the Savior—a Baroque rendering of the traditional role played by standing grown up angels in Renaissance representations. (See *Matthew* 3,13-17.)

Seattle Art Museum, Seattle, Wash., Eugene Fuller Memorial Collection.

Bronze, 15 x 16½ in.

Coll.: Ravensworth Castle, Durham, England.

Ref.: S. E. Lee in *Art Quarterly*, XVIII, 1950, 260-61; Seattle Art Museum, *Handbook*, 1951, p. 123; A. Nava Cellini in *Paragone*, VII, 1956, 25.

Shortly before his death, Cafà devoted much time to the study of an important commission: the monumental marble group of the Baptism of Christ for the high altar of the church of San Giovanni at La Valletta (Malta). His biographers, Baldinucci and Pascoli, write that he left several models—large and small—for this composition. One of them is certainly the well-known terracotta group in the Vatican Museum, and another, of the figure of Christ alone, is now at the Museum of La Valletta. A number of bronze groups in various collections in Rome, Vienna, Pirano and in the Metropolitan Museum, probably cast shortly after Cafà's death, have been connected with the Vatican terracotta which they follow with considerable fidelity.

The Seattle bronze, attributed to Cafà on the same grounds, has undoubtedly a compositional affinity with the Vatican model. Yet there are a number of important changes in the gestures and the draperies of the figures that suggest that it may reflect an entirely different study by the artist for the same subject. While in the Vatican model (and in the bronzes derived from it) Cafà has poised the two figures of Christ and Saint John in a firm and well balanced composition, expressing the spiritual animation of the scene through the thrust of interlocking diagonal lines, the Seattle bronze is conceived as a succession of parallel waves that seem to rush from figure to figure, in a languid and vibrant motion which recalls Cafà's most Berninesque and influential creation, the relief of Saint Catherine at Magnanapoli. [O.R.]

PIERRE LEGROS THE YOUNGER
1666 Paris—Rome 1719

The son of the French sculptor Pierre Legros the Elder, he won the first prize at the Académie Royale, Paris, in 1686 and went to Rome in 1690 as a member of the French Academy there. After winning a competition for the decoration of the altar of St. Ignatius at the Gesù, he left the Academy and started a career on his own. The rest of his life was almost entirely spent in Rome, so that his work actually belongs to the mainstream of Roman Baroque sculpture. For the Jesuits, his first patrons, he completed a number of works: about 1698 the silver statue of *Saint Ignatius* and the group of *Religion overcoming Heresy* for the Gesù; in 1698-99 the marble altarpiece with the *Glorification of St. Luigi Gonzaga* for the church of Sant'Ignazio; and about 1704 the reclining statue of the *Blessed Stanislas Kostka* for the Novitiate at Sant' Andrea al Quirinale. All these works are fully expressive of the devotional and mystical spirit promoted by the order.

In 1703 Clement XI commissioned a series of twelve Apostles for the niches of the main nave of San Giovanni in Laterano from the best sculptors of the day, Legros among them. His huge statues of *St. Thomas* and *St. Bartholomew* were completed by 1711 and 1712, following models supplied by Carlo Maratti. Successful as they are in the dramatic role assigned to them in the nave of the basilica, these figures tell perhaps less about Legros' sensitive treatment of the surface of the marble, and mastery of light and shadow effects than the remarkable *Tomb of Cardinal Casanata*, in S. Giovanni, the statue of *St. Dominic* in St. Peter's, or the small marble version of *St. Bartholomew* recently acquired by the Metropolitan Museum.

61. St. Luigi Gonzaga in Glory

Born in 1568, the eldest son of Prince Ferrante Gonzaga, Luigi consecrated himself to a celibate life when still a boy and in 1585 entered the Jesuit Novitiate in Rome, against the wish of his father. He soon distinguished himself for his deep mysticism, spirit of penance and charity. In 1591, after having cared for the sick during an outbreak of the plague, he died at the age of twenty-three. His memory was immediately an object of veneration, and in 1605 Paul V declared him Blessed. In 1698 his bones were placed underneath a new altar in S. Ignazio, made at the expense of Prince Scipione Lancellotti. In 1726 he was canonized.

The Detroit Institute of Arts, gift of the Founders Society, 1942

Terracotta, 34 x 16 in.
Coll.: Curt Gläser, Berlin.
Ref.: Richardson in *D.I.A. Bull.*, XXII, 1942, 14-15.

This relief must probably be dated about 1698, when Legros obtained from the Jesuits in Rome one of his most successful commissions: the large marble altarpiece with the same subject in Sant'Ignazio. The finished marble which with its foamy lightness and elegance of treatment announced all the refinements of eighteenth century sculpture was immediately much admired by the *cognoscenti*. But even more expressive of Legros' personal style is this admirable *modello* with its feathery lightness of touch and the delicate vibration of its almost powdery surfaces.

When compared with the slightly earlier terracotta model for the group of *Religion overcoming Heresy* (1695), now in the Musée Fabre at Montepellier and one that shortly followed—the relief of *Clement XI and the Arts*, in the Accademia di San Luca—the Detroit *bozzetto* aptly illustrates the gradual development of the sculptor's style from a more sustained Baroque phase, towards an almost Rococo elegance and gracefulness. Sensitive, sophisticated and technically impeccable, the models and drawings of Legros appealed to contemporary collectors like Crozat. [O.R.]

II. *Siena and Urbino*

FRANCESCO VANNI
1563/65 Siena 1610

Vanni and his stepbrother (but artistic twin), Ventura Salimbene, were the only notable painters of the Sienese school around the turn of the century. Vanni received his first training from Angelo Salimbene, provincial local master, then continued a late Mannerist education in Rome under Giovanni de' Vecchi. But the effect of these experiences was superseded almost completely by the powerful sway which the art of the great Urbino painter, Federico Barocci, held over him by at least 1588 (date of Vanni's altarpiece in the Cathedral of Montalcino). This determined the essential physiognomy of Vanni's style. But working from the Barocci style, he discovered his own identity; his was a tender, fragile manner with a sinuous fluency of composition, a feminine delicacy of type, and a muted beauty of color in which one can sense echoes of Vanni's predecessor in Siena, Beccafumi. Vanni was quite prolific during his relatively short career. His paintings are found principally in churches in Siena and other towns in the region, but he was also well enough known to have received a commission for a large altarpiece for Saint Peter's in Rome, *The Fall of Simon Magus* (1603).

62. Study for the "Fall of Simon Magus"

Simon the Magician, a Samaritan sorcerer converted to Christianity, was rebuked by Peter for trying to buy the healing power of the disciples. (*Acts* 8, 9ff.) Various legends grew up about him. In imitation of the Ascension he flew above Rome, but in answer to Peter's prayers his supporting demons abandoned him and he fell to earth. Some say this killed him. Others say it only broke his legs and that he died by having himself buried alive in imitation of the Resurrection.

Museum of Art, Rhode Island School of Design, Providence, R. I.

Pen with brown ink and wash over black chalk on white paper; 3¾ x 7 in.
Coll.: Rumohr.
Ref.: Davidson, in *R. I. Sch. of Des. Bull.*, vol. 45, Dec. 1958, pp. 6-7.

This drawing is a study for the group of women in the lower right of Vanni's large *Fall of Simon Magus* (Cappella Clementina, Saint Peter's, Rome), dated 1603. Miss Davidson has noted the unusual number of studies for this ambitious painting which have survived, testifying to how carefully the artist prepared for his involved, multifigured composition. A drawing (Berlin Printroom), published by Voss (*Die Malerei der Spätrenaissance in Rom und Florence*, Berlin, 1920, II, 514), delineates the whole composition. It must be earlier than the drawing at Providence as the group of women seen in the former drawing are placed on the left rather than on the right as in the painting and in this drawing. [D.M.]

FEDERICO BAROCCI
called "Fiori da Urbino"
1526/28 Urbino 1612

Federico Barocci's (or Baroccio's) great-grandfather and his father, who had settled at Urbino, were Milanese sculptors. His first teachers were his father and the Venetian imitator of Michelangelo, Battista Franco, who came to Urbino in 1546 and again in 1551 to paint ceiling frescos in the Duomo. When still an adolescent, Federico went to Pesaro to study with his uncle, Bartolommeo Genga, court architect to Duke Guidobaldo II. Genga instructed the youth in architecture, geometry and perspective, and obtained for him entry in the ducal *guardaroba*, where Barocci was able to study the works of Titian and other painters. At the age of twenty, his father sent him to Rome to study Raphael. At the intervention of another uncle, who was the Majordomo of Cardinal Giulio della Rovere, the young man was granted the patronage of this powerful prelate whose portrait he also painted. Later he returned to Urbino. Attracted by Correggio's style, Barocci never became his slavish imitator—perhaps because he never went to Parma, therefore remaining free to develop his independent feeling for the use of color. In 1560 Barocci again went to Rome and did frescos with Federico Zuccaro, especially for the so-called Casino of Papa Pio IV. He left a vast oeuvre consisting of oils, pastels, drawings and engravings. Barocci settled permanently in Urbino and made but a few brief sojourns in other cities.

Barocci's scenes of Holy Families and Madonnas are invariably appealing because of their genre-like character. He invented a new technique of creating half-tones by "dotting"—a technique which influenced engravers of the next generation. His human types are attractive, yet never sugary; their lightness and grace in movement, Correggiesque to a point, must have appealed greatly to a later generation in the reaction against the "Maniera", an appeal which touched not only the Carracci, but even the Fleming Rubens when he came to Italy.

63. Aeneas' Flight from Troy

"Then come my dear father, rest upon my neck; I will support you on my shoulders, and such a toil shall not oppress me, whatever shall be the issue of our fortunes, we will both have one common peril, one safety." (Virgil's *Aeneid*; trans. Lonsdale and Lee.)

The Cleveland Museum of Art, L. E. Holden Fund.

Pen and brown ink, black chalk, brown and light yellow wash on a gray-green paper, 10⅞ x 16¹³⁄₁₆ in. Inscribed lower right with artist's name and "SS"; numbered lower left: 17.

Ref.: Richards in *Cleveland Mus. Bull.*, 1961, XLVIII, 63-65; H. Olsen, *Federico Barocci*, Copenhagen, 1962, p. 182.

Barocci painted two apparently identical versions of this subject, his only painting of non-religious content known (aside from his portraits). The earlier one, now lost, made for Rudolf II, was delivered to Prague in 1589. Fortunately, Barocci painted a replica, signed and dated 1598, for Monsignore Giuliano della Rovere (Borghese Gallery, Rome). Barocci's wonderfully theatrical composition made a strong impression on the Caracci. Agostino Carracci engraved it in 1595, evidently after the earlier version. Numerous drawings exist for this subject (Stockholm; Berlin; Windsor; Uffizi). The present one is the most complete and the best preserved. The small dog, running down the stairs at the lower left, is left out in the painting as are the plumes on Aeneas' helmet and the architectural detail of the circular decoration on the wall immediately behind the group of Aeneas and Anchises. [B.S.M.]

64. Head of the Virgin

Preparatory for the head of the Virgin who has fainted beneath the cross in the painting of the *Deposition*, Cappella di San Bernardino, Duomo of Perugia, executed by Barocci in the year 1569.

The Art Institute of Chicago, The Leonora Hall Gurley Memorial Collection.

Black and white chalk on paper, 11⅝ x 9⁷⁄₁₆ in.

63.

Coll.: E. Cheney, Badger Hall, Shropshire (Lugt 444).

Ref.: Sale, Sotheby's, London, April 1885; U. Middeldorf in *Art in America*, vol. 27, 1939, pp. 11-14; H. Tietze, *European Master Drawings*, New York, 1947, no. 47; H. Olsen in *Figura*, 6, 1955, p. 120, and *Federico Barocci*, Copenhagen, 1962, p. 153.

As was his custom, Barocci executed numerous drawings and a cartoon in preparation for the Deposition of 1569 (Duomo, Perugia). Many of the major Cabinets in Europe have studies by his hand for this work (Uffizi; Albertina; Oxford; Louvre; Frankfurt). Nearly all share the technique of charcoal heightened with white. This fine drawing, the only one known for the head of the Virgin, makes it clear how far Barocci in 1569 has come toward the expression of a kind of "ecstasy" usually associated with a later generation. In the painting itself this curious "breaking through" the limits of a basically Mannerist compositional scheme, with individual figures that breathe a kind of freedom that has come to be associated with the Baroque, creates a curious feeling of duality. Here Barocci reveals himself indeed as a precursor of a style to come. [B.S.M.]

III. *Bologna*

THE CARRACCI

Ludovico was the older cousin of the brothers Agostino and Annibale. He studied with Prospero Fontana and probably with Camillo Procaccini, and he is supposed to have traveled widely in Italy in his youth. Agostino was a student of Fontana, Bartolomeo Passarotti, and Domenico Tibaldi. According to tradition Ludovico taught Annibale. In the early 1580s the Carracci founded their shop, and they established an academy which eventually became one of the centers of intellectual life in Bologna. They collaborated on a number of fresco cycles in Bologna and possibly on some easel pictures.

The Carracci seem to have made a conscious effort to replace the contemporary Mannerist style in Bologna with pictorial forms that drew upon the naturalistic tradition of North Italy. By 1585 Annibale had been to Parma and had modified his style on the basis of his experience of Correggio. Annibale's work from 1588 to 1595 shows the impression that Venetian art made on him, undoubtedly during a trip to Venice in 1587/88. Agostino's first Venetian trip dates from 1582; he was in Venice again in 1588/89. In Ludovico's work Mannerist elements survived longer than in the art of his cousins and, in the last decade of Ludovico's life, these elements seem to have reasserted themselves. However, in the 1590s Ludovico was working in a painterly, proto-Baroque manner that anticipated and influenced the styles of Lanfranco and Guercino.

Agostino made his main contribution as a printmaker. He was active, from the beginning of his career, as a reproductive engraver. He perfected the engraving technique that had been developed by Marcantonio Raimondi and Cornelis Cort, and his style provided the basis for the later tradition of "academic" engraving. Agostino's painting style in general parallels Annibale's. He was fairly active as a painter in the 1590s and, between 1597 and 1599, he was in Rome, where he assisted Annibale on the fresco decoration of the Farnese Gallery. In 1600 he entered the service of Duke Ranuccio Farnese and frescoed a ceiling in the Palazzo del Giardino in Parma.

Annibale moved from Bologna to Rome in 1595. He was employed by Cardinal Odoardo Farnese to decorate the "Camerino" and the gallery of the Farnese Palace (c. 1595- c. 1597 and c. 1597- c. 1608 [?]). In Rome, under the influence of antique sculpture and the art of Raphael and Michelangelo, he created a grand, classical style that had great influence for the next two centuries. In 1605 Annibale became seriously ill and was virtually unable to work thereafter.

The Carracci founded the seventeenth century school of Bolognese painting, and their art was one of the main sources for both the "Baroque" and "Classical" trends of the next centuries. Among their students were Guido Reni, Albani, and Domenichino.

LUDOVICO CARRACCI

1555 Bologna 1619

65. The Assumption of the Virgin

It was typical of Ludovico to find unusual ways of presenting familiar religious subjects. Here, instead of a traditional sarcophagus-tomb, the Virgin's burial place is a grave. As Pinnell has shown, the details of the painting are didactic and symbolic; *e.g.* the tomb in the middleground at the left, an ancient Roman type, symbolizes the Pagan religions. Opposite, at the right, the tomb ornamented with the Mosaic Tablets of the Law represents the Jewish religion. In the background, seen amidst ruins of the pre-Christian era, is an obelisk, which has several associations appropriate to the theme and is an emblem of the triumph of Christ. Of the Apostles gathered around the empty tomb, St. Thomas, kneeling in the foreground, is identified by the girdle he wears and holds. According to Jacobus da Voragine's *Golden Legend*, Mary's girdle was dropped to Thomas in order to dispel his doubts about her miraculous assumption.

North Carolina Museum of Art, Raleigh, gift of Mrs. J. L. Dorminy (in memory of her husband)

Canvas, 96 ½ x 53 in.

Coll.: Marquis of Abercorn (mark on stretcher).

Ref.: Cochin, *Voyage d'Italie*, Paris, 1758, II, 157; Bodmer, *Ludovico Carracci*, Burg b.M., 1939, pp. 34-35, 127; *Mostra dei Carracci*, Bologna,

1956, p. 111; Pinnell in *N.C. Mus. of Art Bull.* I, 1957, 1-7; Emiliani in *Encyclopedia of World Art*, New York, III, 1960, 135.

Although there are still Mannerist elements in the composition and in the poses of the figures, the painting has a forceful, dramatic and pictorial directness that makes it a major early example of the reform of religious painting introduced by the Carracci in Bologna. In style the painting is closely connected to Ludovico's *Vision of St. Anthony* (Rijksmuseum, Amsterdam c. 1586) and to his *Conversion of St. Paul* (Pinacoteca Nazionale, Bologna, 1587-89), and it can be dated c. 1586/87.

Curiously, the picture is not mentioned by Malvasia. Cochin saw an *Assumption of the Virgin* attributed to Ludovico in the Palazzo Zambeccari in Bologna. In 1882 a studio replica or an old copy of the Raleigh picture came from the Zambeccari collection to the Bologna Pinacoteca. Bodmer, who didn't know the picture here exhibited, thought the Bologna painting authentic. [D.P.]

66. The Agony in the Garden

Peter and John slept while Christ, visited by an angel, prayed on the mount of Olives: "Father, if thou be willing, remove this cup from me: nevertheless not my will, but thine, be done." (*Luke* 22, 42) Judas and others approach to take Christ prisoner.

Denis Mahon, Esq., London.

Canvas, 39⅞ x 45 in.

Coll.: Robert Napier, West Shandon, until 1877; acquired by the present owner in 1960.

Ref.: Robinson, *Collection of Robert Napier*, London, 1865, p. 17; Nicolson in *Great Private Collections* (ed. D. Cooper), London, 1963, p. 120.

The visionary quality of the presentation and the romantic play of light relate the painting to Ludovico's *Vision of St. Anthony* of c. 1586 (Rijksmuseum, Amsterdam). However, the greater ease and

breadth in the movement and design of the forms suggest a somewhat later date, about 1588, just after no. 65.

In the Napier Collection the picture was ascribed to "A. Carracci." [D.P.]

67. *Study for an Allegory in Honor of the Duke of Mantua*

Over the arms of the Duke of Mantua stands a figure representing the prince clothed in armor, his arm around a palm tree. He is surrounded by the six chief deities of antiquity, each embracing a tree consecrated to him. On the left stand Apollo, Minerva, and Neptune; on the right are Jupiter, Venus and Hercules. In the right foreground is a river god and on the left a woman is seated with trophies designating the city of Mantua, seen briefly beyond her.

The Art Institute of Chicago, The Leonora Hall Gurley Memorial Collection.

Pen and brown ink, 5 11/16 x 7½ in.

Coll.: Jonathan Richardson, Jr.; William Esdaile (Lugt 2617); H. C. Jennings (Lugt 2771); W. E. Roscoe.

This is a preparatory drawing for a print by Olivieri Gatti bearing the designation "Lud Car Inu" and recorded (Bartsch, XIX, 18, no. 46) as *La Conclusion des Divinités*. It is a more finished version of a drawing in the Albertina, Vienna (no. 2090; Stix-Spitzmüller, VI, no. 77). The Vienna variant (Bodmer, *Ludovico Carracci*, 1939, fig. 134) is cited by Bodmer (*Old Master Drawings*, VIII, March 1934, 57) as a rapid notation of a first idea. The Chicago drawing is much closer to the finished composition; but in many ways it is as hasty as the Vienna drawing and should probably be thought of as an early version for the print.

By connecting the Vienna drawing with Ludovico's activity in the first decades of the seventeenth century and specifically with the frescos in the courtyard of the Monastery of S. Michele in Bosco, Bodmer infers a dating of about 1604-05. There is also a related drawing in the Ambrosiana, Milan (*Padre Resta*, no. 184). [F.C.]

AGOSTINO CARRACCI
1557 Bologna—Parma 1602

68. *Susanna and the Elders*

The elders approached Susanna at her bath, saying, "consent to us and lie with us. But if thou wilt not we will bear witness against thee, that a young man was with thee." (*Daniel* 13, 20-21 [Douay vers.]) The virtuous Susanna refused and the elders accused her of adultery, but Daniel questioned them and revealed the truth.

Ringling Museum of Art, Sarasota, Florida.

Canvas, 63 15/16 x 43 7/8 in.

Inscribed on the base of the plinth: *A. CAR BON. F.*

Coll.: Villa Aldobrandini; Buchanan; Sir George Holford, Dorchester House, until 1927; John Ringling.

Ref.: Waagen, *Treasures of Art in Great Britain*, London, 1854, II, 194; Benson, *Holford Collection*, London, 1927, p. 43; Suida, *Ringling Museum Catalogue*, Sarasota, 1949, p. 99; Calvesi in *Encyclopaedia of World Art*, III, New York, 1959, p. 142.

Benson listed the picture as Ludovico, Waagen as Annibale. The style excludes both of them as well as Antonio (Agostino's son), whose name would fit the inscription. Suida catalogued the painting as by Agostino, and the attribution has been accepted by Calvesi. Indeed, the style accords well with Agostino's works from around 1598 to 1600, such as the portrait of *Giovanna Guicciardini* (Berlin-Dahlem Museum) and the *Holy Family with St. Margaret* (Naples, Capodimonte Museum), although they seem to be of higher quality than the Sarasota picture.

Like Annibale's early Roman works (cf. no. 72) the *Susanna* combines "painterly" elements (especially in the treatment of the elders) and compact, monumental forms and structure. Here, however, the fusion seems more labored and less complete. [D.P.]

69. Seated Man Seen from the Back

Mr. and Mrs. Winslow Ames, Saunderstown, R. I.

Black chalk on grayish paper, 5 3/4 x 5 3/4 in.

Coll.: Walter Gernsheim

Ref.: Walter Gernsheim, *Exhibition of Drawings of the Bolognese School*, London, 1937, no. 5; *Old Master Drawings—Winslow Ames Coll.*, Ringling Museum, Sarasota, Dec. 1963.

This is a rather quick sketch for the crouching figure on the near side of the table in the *Last Supper* formerly at Casa Tanari, Bologna (Malvasia, *Felsina Pittrice*, Bologna, 1841, I, 355). Four versions of the painting are known today: one on deposit from the Prado at the San Telmo Museum, San Sebastián (H. Voss in *Zeitschrift für Kunstgeschichte*, II, 1933, 193-94); an identical copy in the depot of the Pinacoteca, Bologna (inv. 203, cited by Malvasia as retouched by Agostino and belonging to "Signori Casali"); a copy by Albani formerly in the Giustiniani Collection, later in the Royal Collection, Berlin (1826), and known through an engraving (L. Salerno in *Burlington Magazine*, CII, 1960, p. 95); a small variant by Agostino on copper for the ciborium of the high altar of the Certosa, Ferrara (*Mostra dei Carracci*, Bologna, 1958, no. 4, p. 156). Stephen E. Ostrow (doctoral dissertation on Agostino Carracci to be submitted to New York University) accepts the Prado painting as the original, dating it and our drawing on stylistic grounds around 1593-94. (We are indebted to Mr. Ostrow for bringing the drawing to our attention and for providing the substance of this note.) [F.C.]

ANNIBALE CARRACCI

1560 Bologna—Rome 1609

70. Crucifixion

A youth hands up the tablet with the inscription "Jesus of Nazareth, the King of the Jews," to be placed above Christ, crucified between the two thieves. (*Mark* 15, 25-28; *John* 19, 18-20)

Atlanta Art Association, Atlanta, Ga., Kress Collection.

Canvas, 47 3/4 x 40 3/8 in.

Coll.: Comte de Nocé, Paris; Ducs d'Orléans, 1724-98; J. Maitland, until 1831; Earl of Dunmore, 1857; F. Sabin; Samuel H. Kress.

Ref.: Dubois de Saint-Gelais, *Description Palais Royal*, Paris, 1727, p. 33; Mariette, *Description Palais Royal*, Paris, 1742, p. 33; Buchanan, *Memoirs of Painting*, London, 1824, p. 81; Waagen, *Treasures of Art in Great Britain*, IV, 1857, p. 456; Blunt in *Holbein and Other Masters*, London, 1950/51, p. 124, no. 305; Suida, *Italian Paintings from the Kress Collection*, Atlanta, 1958, pp. 37-38; Longhi in *Paragone*, XI, 1960, no. 125, p. 59.

Very Venetian in handling and in its forms, the picture derives its main elements from Tintoretto's *Crucifixion* in San Cassiano, Venice. However, the Venetian's composition has been revised so that it is more stable and coherent in structure. Unlike Tintoretto the artist here has represented this moment of the Crucifixion as a night scene, thus intensifying its lugubrious atmosphere. The youth, who hands up the superscription provides a genre element that strengthens the dramatic immediacy of the presentation. The group with the Virgin at the foot of the cross was possibly inspired by Veronese's related picture in the Louvre, Paris.

This writer knows the painting only from a photograph. However, in its manner as well as in its interpretation of Venetian sources it seems related to Annibale's work of the early 1590s. It may be compared to the *Crucifixion* of 1594 (Berlin-Dahlem Museum) where Annibale, partly on the basis of a print by Agostino (B. 1), made a similar revision of another Venetian painting, Veronese's *Crucifixion* in San Sebastiano, Venice.

The attribution to Annibale, which goes back at least to the early eighteenth century, recently has been questioned by Longhi, who proposed the name of Pedro Orrente (known as "the Spanish Bassano" [c. 1570-1645]).

The picture was engraved by Louis Desplaces when it was in the Orléans Collection. [D.P.]

71. The Penitent Magdalene in a Landscape

Denis Mahon, Esq., London.

Canvas, 26 7/16 x 33 in. (painted surface)

Coll.: Thomas Bodkin, acquired in Dublin c. 1924; acquired by the present owner in 1959.

Ref.: Sutton in *Country Life*, Jan. 7, 1960, p. 17; Mahon in *Italian Art and Britain*, London, 1960, pp. 161-62; Nicolson in *Burlington Magazine*, CII, 1960, 79; Sutton in *Arte Figurativa*, VIII, 1960, 28; Longhi, in *Paragone*, XI, no. 125, 1960, p. 61, no. 401.

The original attribution was made by Bodkin, supported by Borenius, and has been accepted by all writers except Roberto Longhi who believes the painting to date from the later seventeenth century. (Mr. Mahon writes, and requests the compiler to record that Professor Longhi knows the painting only from a photograph.) It is related to an etching (vertical format) by Annibale, dated 1591 (B. 16), for which there is a preparatory drawing in the Louvre (cf. Bacou in Cabinet des Dessins [Louvre], *Dessins des Carrache*, Paris, 1961, pp. 26-27, no. 26). Mr. Mahon has argued that the only period in Annibale's career into which the painting could fit is

around 1586/87, after his trip to Parma but before Venetian influence became paramount in his work. However, this date is not excluded by the style of the Louvre drawing. Mahon thinks the painting and drawing were created about the same time, and the latter then used for the etching. [D.P.]

72. *The Coronation of the Virgin*

Denis Mahon, Esq., London.

Canvas 46½ x 56 in.

Inscribed lower left concealed by frame: *244 D CARCCI* (del Carracci).

Coll.: Aldobrandini family, from at least 1611; Pamphili family; Borghese Palace; Alexander Day, from c. 1799 to 1833; Samuel Rogers, until 1856; 5th Duke of Newcastle and heirs, at Clumber House, until 1937; acquired by the present owner in 1939.

Ref.: (Bellori) *Nota delli Musei*, Rome, 1664, p. 7; Bellori, *Vite de' pittori*, Rome, 1672, p. 84; Malvasia, *Felsina Pittrice*, Bologna, 1678, I, 501; Félibien, *Entretiens*, Paris, 1679, III, 285; (Roisecco, ed.) *Roma antica e moderna*, Rome, 1745, II, 540; Vasi, *Itinéraire de Rome*, Rome, 1797, I, 313; Buchanan, *Memoirs of Painting*, London, 1824, II, 9, 135; Jameson, *Private Galleries of Art*, London, 1844, pp. 389, 392; *Art Treasures Exhibition*, Manchester, 1857, no. 335; Mahon, *Studies in Seicento Art*, London, 1947, pp. 40-41; Briganti, "The Mahon Collection," *Connoisseur*, CXXXII, 1953, 5, 16; Mahon in *Artists in 17th century Rome*, London, 1955, pp. 26-28; Cavalli in *Mostra dei Carracci*, Bologna, 1956, pp. 214-15; Mahon in *Gazette des Beaux-Arts*, XLIX, 1957, 284; Jaffé in *Burlington Magazine*, CII, 1960, pp. 27-28; Mahon in *Italian Art and Britain*, London, 1960, pp. 160-61; P. della Pergola, "Inventari Aldobrandini (1611; 1626)," *Arte antica e moderna*, 1960, pp. 426, 427 (no. 14), 432, 442; *ibid.* (1682), 1963, pp. 77 (no. 361), 86; (Holland) *The Carracci*, Newcastle-upon-Tyne, 1961, no. 203; Nicolson in *Great Private Collections* (ed. D. Cooper), London, 1963, p. 120.

The inscription refers to the 1626 inventory of Cardinal Ippolito Aldobrandini. The painting is also listed in the 1611 and 1682

Aldobrandini inventories. It was engraved by J. J. Frey in 1741.
This important work dates from c. 1596/97, shortly after Annibale moved from Bologna to Rome. It is possible that the commission came from Pope Clement VIII Aldobrandini or a member of his family. Jaffé published a large preparatory drawing (Dijon Museum) which is very "painterly" and "North Italian" in style. The painting, with its "classical" balance, its greater emphasis on *disegno*, and its more monumental forms, shows the immediate impression made on Annibale by the art of Rome. Jaffé suggested that the drawing may have been made in Bologna just before Annibale's departure. This is supported by a painting by Pietro Faccini (*Madonna and Child with Saints*, Mirandola [Modena], Museo Civico; cf. *Arte in Emilia* [ed. Quintavalle], Parma, 1961, pp. 100-101, fig. 85) where certain elements seem to derive from Annibale's drawing, which Faccini could have known only in Bologna. [D.P.]

73. *Landscape with Jacob's Dream*

The story of Jacob's vision of a ladder rising to heaven with God standing above it blessing his progeny is told in *Genesis* 28, 10-17.

The Metropolitan Museum of Art, New York, N. Y., Hewitt Fund, 1917.

Pen and brown ink, brown wash, 16$\frac{3}{16}$ x 10$\frac{5}{16}$ in. Inscribed below to right: "Di mano di Anniballe Carracci"; and on old mount: "Jacob a sleep, ye ladder with angels at a great distance."
Coll.: Sir Peter Lely; Earls of Pembroke; Pembroke Sale, London, Sotheby's, 5-10 June 1917, no. 376.
Ref.: Strong, *Drawings from the Pembroke Collection*, London, 1900, no. 44; Tomory, *The Ellesmere Collection of Old Master Drawings*, Leicester, 1954, p. 26; Mahon, *Mostra dei Carracci, Disegni*, Bologna, 1956 and 1963, pp. 162-63, no. 241.

Tomory has associated this drawing with a sheet in the Ellesmere Collection bearing the date 1595 (no. 64, now on deposit at the Leicester Museums and Art Gallery; Mahon, *Carracci Disegni*, 1963, no. 241, figs. 113, 114). By this association Tomory has identified the subject of the Ellesmere drawing as Jacob dreaming. However, Mahon has not wholeheartedly accepted the connection between these two sheets. The present work must derive from Annibale's Bolognese period and a date in the mid-1590s seems most probable. [F.C.]

74. *Portrait of a Man*

Seiferheld and Company, New York, N. Y.

Red and black chalks on two pieces of paper joined near the top of the head, 15¼ x 11 in.
Inscribed on verso: "Ritratto di Annibale Carracci".
Coll.: R. Udney (Lugt 2247); William Esdaile (Lugt 2167); Sir J. C. Robinson (Lugt 1433).

A study from life for the *Lute Player* in the Dresden Museum (*Die Staatliche Gemäldegalerie zu Dresden, Die romanischen Länder*, 1929, pp. 150-51, no. 308). Documents in Dresden which came from the Duke of Modena with the painting list the sitter as "Mascheroni". Malvasia (1678, I, 502) described the sitter as "Il sonatore Mascheroni, intimo amico di Annibale". However, in the late nineteenth century the sitter came to be known as Giovanni Gabrielli, "Il Sivello", humorist and friend of Annibale. (For a note on the identity of the sitter see Mahon, *Studies*, pp. 266-67, note 50.) There are variants in the Albertina, Vienna (inv. 2506, Cat. B., 109), and the Uffizi, Florence (inv. 12405), showing the sitter turned slightly to the left; and in the Louvre, Paris (inv. 7625, Jabach Coll.). There is another pen and ink drawing of the sitter by Annibale at Windsor (Mahon [*Carracci Disegni*, Bologna, 1963, no. 102] dates it around 1593-94). [F.C.]

75. *Head of an Elderly Man*

Rudolf and Margot Wittkower, New York, N. Y.

Red chalk, 11¾ x 8⅝ in. Old inscription in ink in the lower right corner: A. C. F.

Ref.: Denis Mahon, *Mostra dei Carracci, Disegni.* Bologna, 1956, p. 148, no. 216.

The drawing shows Annibale's characteristic red chalk manner of the late Bolognese period (c. 1590). Denis Mahon's date, second half of the 1590's, would appear to be too late. The similarity of this head with the old man, traditionally called Annibale's father, in the family group portrait of the Brera, Milan (also c. 1590, see *Mostra dei Carracci*, Bologna, 1956, p. 183, no. 64) is striking. [R.W.]

76. *Flying Cupid*

Janos Scholz Collection, New York, N. Y.

Black chalk, with some pen and brown ink, 11⅝ x 7¼ in. Same subject on verso.

Ref.: Neumeyer and Scholz, *Drawings from Bologna*, Oakland, 1957, no. 20.

These two studies are similar in style to those for the Farnese frescos (Wittkower, *Carracci Drawings at Windsor Castle*, nos. 306, 307). [F.C.]

Domenico Zampieri, called *DOMENICHINO*
1581 Bologna—Naples 1641

Domenichino spent a short time in the shop of Calvaert in Bologna before transferring, along with Reni and Albani, to the Carracci Academy around 1595. In 1602 or 1603 he arrived in Rome, and his style was mainly formed under Annibale Carracci

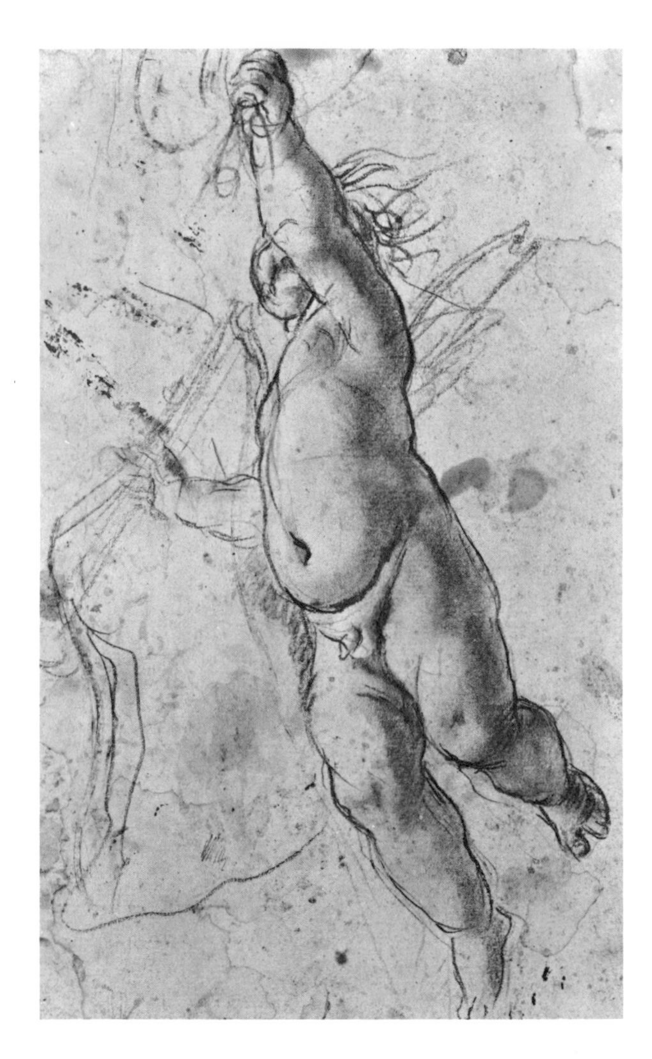

there. His famous frescos at Grottaferrata were painted in 1608-10, and he established his reputation in Rome by 1614, when he completed the St. Cecilia fresco cycle in S. Luigi dei Francesi. In 1617 he returned to Bologna, where he stayed until 1621, when Pope Gregory XV Ludovisi called him to Rome. Domenichino's major work of the 1620s was the fresco decoration of the apse and pendentives of S. Andrea della Valle, Rome (1622-1627). In 1631 he went to Naples to decorate the Cappella del Tesoro in the Cathedral. He visited Rome in 1634/35 and then returned to Naples.

Domenichino was the most faithful follower of the late Roman style of Annibale Carracci, and his work was greatly admired by such artists as Poussin, Sacchi, and Maratti. Domenichino also made a major contribution to the development of the "ideal" landscape style.

77. *St. Jerome with Angels*

Denis Mahon, Esq., London.

Copper, 19⅜ x 14¾ in.
Coll.: M. Paillot; Ducs d'Orleans; Henry Hope, until 1816; George

Watson Taylor, until 1823; Mrs. Whyte; Capt. Arthur Finch Dawson, until 1928; acquired by the present owner in 1952.

Ref.: Bellori, *Vite dei pittori*, Rome, 1672, p. 295; Félibien, *Entretiens*, Paris, 1685, IV, 167; Dubois de Saint-Gelais, *Description . . . Palais Royal*, Paris, 1727, p. 123; Briganti, "The Mahon Collection," *Connoisseur*, CXXXII, 1953, 5-6, 16; Mahon in *Artists in 17th Century Rome*, London, 1955, pp. 40-41; Mahon in *Italian Art and Britain*, London, 1960, pp. 155-56; Cavalli in *L'Ideale classico del Seicento*, Bologna, 1962, pp. 96-98.

A date of 1608-10 for the painting (contemporary with the artist's frescos at Grottaferrata) is generally accepted. At that time Domenichino was perfecting a refined, even exquisitely sober version of the ideal, or classical, style of Annibale Carracci's late work. An interesting *pentimento* reveals that the artist changed his first idea of the position of the angel's leg. The final pose, as noted by Briganti, is based on one in Annibale's *St. Gregory in Prayer* (destroyed; formerly Bridgewater House). The relation of this picture to other versions by Domenichino and Albani is discussed by Cavalli. The painting was engraved by Pietro del Pò, by Berseneff when it was in the Orleans Collection, and by Devilliers. [D.P.]

78. Landscape with a Fortified Building

Denis Mahon, Esq., London

Canvas, 44 x 76 in.

Coll.: Etienne Texier d'Hautefeuille, before 1703; Ducs d'Orleans; Duke of Bridgewater; Marquess of Stafford; Lord Francis Egerton, Earl of Ellesmere, and heirs, until 1946; acquired by the present owner in 1946.

Ref.: Dubois de Saint-Gelais, *Description . . . Palais Royal*, Paris, 1727, p. 125; Ottley and Tomkins, *Stafford Gallery*, London, 1818, Class II, no. 54; Jameson, *Private Galleries of Art*, London, 1844, p. 105; Waagen, *Treasures of Art in Great Britain*, London, 1854, II, 35-36, 490; Briganti, "The Mahon Collection," *Connoisseur*, CXXXII, 1953, 6-7, 16; Mahon in *Artists in 17th Century Rome*, London, 1955, pp. 41-43; Salerno in *Il Seicento Europeo*, Rome, 1956, p. 119; Mahon in *Italian Art and Britain*, London, 1960, pp. 158-159; Röthlisberger, *Claude Lorrain*, New Haven, 1961, pp. 306ff.; Cavalli in *L'Ideale classico del Seicento*, Bologna, 1962, pp. 122-24; Jaffé in *Burlington Magazine*, CIV, 1962, 417; Nicolson in *Great Private Collections* (ed. D. Cooper), London, 1963, p. 120.

This painting, rigorously structured, yet seemingly relaxed in its charming, pastoral mood, is one of the major monuments of the "ideal" landscape style of the early seventeenth century. It points to both the "heroic" landscapes of Poussin and the "idyllic" landscapes of Claude. In the nineteenth century, it was much admired by Constable who said, "The grandeur of the composition and the urbanity of the tone which pervades it, places this picture in the highest class of landscape." (Quoted in Leslie, *Memoirs of the Life of Constable*, London, 1843, pp. 132ff.)

The painting is closely related to Annibale Carracci's *Landscape with the Flight into Egypt* (Doria-Pamphili Gallery, Rome), and Mahon has suggested that Domenichino painted it in 1634/35, when he had returned to Rome from Naples and could have re-studied Annibale's picture. This dating is confirmed by the style of three related drawings, two at Windsor (Pope-Hennessy, *Domenichino Drawings*, London, 1948, pp. 27, 44, nos. 207, 208), and one, identified by Mahon, in the Louvre (no. 7333). Jaffé has pointed out that there are figures in the middle distance to the right which apparently represent the Holy Family on the flight into Egypt.

The picture was engraved by Michel (in the Orléans Collection), by Devilliers, and C. Heath. [D.P.]

79. *Head of a Young Woman, Seen Twice*

Janos Scholz Collection, New York, N.Y.

Red and white chalk on blue paper, 9½ x 12¼ in.
Inscribed lower left: "Domo Zampieri"
Coll.: Piancastelli (Lugt 2078a); Brandegee (Lugt 1860c).

The attribution to Domenichino is based on similar drawings at Windsor Castle (Pope-Hennessy, *Domenichino Drawings*, 1948, pls. 31 and 61). [F.C.]

GUIDO RENI
1575 Bologna 1642

Reni studied with Denis Calvaert, a Flemish Mannerist working in Bologna, before he entered the Carracci shop about 1595. He went to Rome about 1600 and stayed there, with interruptions, until 1613/14. From around 1604 to 1607 he experimented with a Caravaggesque manner. Reni painted his famous *Aurora* (Casino Rospigliosi) in 1613/14. About 1614 he made Bologna his permanent home and became the leading painter in that city. A major change in his art occurred around 1630 as he shifted from a dark, "golden" manner to a style characterized by a light "silvery" tonality. In general, Reni was able to preserve and use elegent *maniera* formulae, going back through his teacher Calvaert to Parmigianino, in the context of a glowing, melodramatic "ideal" style that was wholly attuned to the taste of the seventeenth century.

80. *St. Cecilia*

Collection of Walter P. Chrysler, Jr.

Canvas, 37¾ x 30 in.

Coll.: Cardinal Paolo Emilio Sfrondato, Rome; Borghese family, until 1821; Prince Lucien Bonaparte, 1824; Queen of Etruria; Duke of Lucca, 1840; Lansdowne Collection, Bowood, 1854-1952; David Koetser.

Ref.: Scanelli, *Microcosmo della pittura*, Cesena, 1657, p. 354; Bellori (ed. Piacentini), *Vite di Reni*, Rome, 1942, p. 12; Sandrart, *Academia Picturae*, Nuremberg, 1683, p. 185; Buchanan, *Memoirs of Painting*, London, 1824, II, 289; Waagen, *Treasures of Art in Great Britain*, London, 1854, II, 152; Campori, *Raccolta di cataloghi*, Modena, 1870, p. 205; Kurz in *Jahrbuch Kunsthist. Sammlungen*, Vienna, XI, 1937, 213; Gnudi and Cavalli, *Guido Reni*, Florence, 1955, p. 55; R. Manning, *Bolognese Baroque Painters*, New York, Finch College Museum, 1962, no. 6.

The painting, thought to be by Domenichino when it was in the Lansdowne Collection, was correctly attributed to Reni by Kurz. It must have been painted for Cardinal Sfrondato relatively soon after Reni arrived in Rome about 1600. The sentimental idealization of the figure is derived from Raphael's *St. Cecilia* in Bologna (Pinacoteca Nazionale). The solidity of the forms and the general strength of definition may already reflect Reni's initial impression of Caravaggio's style. [D.P.]

81. The Meeting of David and Abigail

(Reproduced in color as frontispiece)

David was provoked by Nabal and he set out against him with a band of armed men. However, Nabal's wife, Abigail, appeased David by riding to meet him at the foot of a hill with lavish gifts of food and wine. The dramatic situation, as well as David's armor and the two soldiers behind him, indicate that the subject is this first meeting of David and Abigail. However, the gifts are not in evidence, and certain elements, like the wreath of flowers in Abigail's hair and the architecture at the left, suggest that Reni combined elements from two moments in the story. After the death of Nabal, Abigail was sent for by David, who wanted her as his wife. "And Abigail hasted, and arose, and rode upon an ass, with five damsels of hers that went after her; and she went after the messengers of David and became his wife. (*I Samuel* 25, 42)

Collection of Walter P. Chrysler, Jr.

Canvas, 61½ x 64½ in.

Coll.: Duc de Noailles; Ducs d'Orléans, until 1800; Edward Cox, 1807; Lord Feversham, Duncombe Park, Helmsley, York; David Koetser, 1950.

Ref.: Malvasia, *Felsina Pittrice*, Bologna, 1678, II, 91; Dubois de Saint Gelais, *Description . . . Palais Royal*, Paris, 1727, pp. 194-95; Oretti, *Notizie*, (c. 1760/80), IV, 259-260 (Ms. B. 126, Bibl. Com., Bologna); *Galerie du Palais Royal*, Orleans, 1786, I, opp. p. 108; *Edward Cox Sale*, London, 1807, pp. 28-29; Buchanan, *Memoirs of Painting*, London, 1824, I, 95; Waagen, *Treasures of Art in Great Britain*, London, 1854, II, 495; Campori, *Raccolta di catologhi*, Modena, 1870, p. 162; Sweetser, *Guido Reni*, Boston, 1878, p. 157; Gnudi and Cavalli, *Guido Reni*, Florence, 1955, pp. 81-82; B. S. Manning in *Chrysler Collection Paintings*, Portland (Ore.), 1956, p. 29; R. Manning, *Bolognese Baroque Painters*, New York, Finch College Museum, 1962, no. 7.

This resounding orchestration of brilliant colors and melodious compositional rhythms has been dated c. 1630 by Gnudi and Cavalli. This writer would suggest a date in the early 1620s.

An "Abigail" by Reni (*Uno Bigiam* [sic] *con sette figure*) was listed in an inventory of the Savelli Collection in Rome, when that collection was for sale in 1650 (cf. Campori). This was possibly another version of the "*storia di Abigaille che co' doni va a placer Davidde, copiosa di figure grandi al naturale*" recorded by Malvasia in the collection of Agostino Franzone in Genoa. Apparently Oretti knew the same picture in the Franzone Collection around the middle of the eighteenth century. The exhibited painting appears to be autograph and it was almost certainly the picture originally in the Orleans Collection (cf. O. Kurz, cited by B. Suida Manning), where it was recorded in 1727 as coming from the Duc de Noailles (1650-1708). Thus, it is surely not from the Franzone Collection as has been suggested recently (1956, 1962). Nor is there any evidence that it is the painting that had been in the Savelli Collection. Another version (Budapest Museum) was in the Praun Collection, Nuremberg in the eighteenth century, when it was engraved by Preissler (cf. Pigler, *Barockthemen*, Budapest, 1956, I, 140-41). A version in the Toulouse Museum is probably a copy of the present picture (listed as a copy in the *Inventaire général des richesses d'art de la France, Provence*, VIII, 1908,

no. 372). In 1786, when it was in the Orléans Collection, the painting was engraved by Patas. [D.P.]

82. *Salome with the Head of John the Baptist*

As a reward for her dance, Salome, obeying her mother Herodias, asked Herod for the head of John the Baptist. "And his head was brought in a charger, and given to the damsel." (*Matthew* 14, 11.)

The Art Institute of Chicago, Frank H. and Louis B. Woods Purchase Fund, 1960

Canvas, 97¾ x 68½ in.

Coll.: Colonna, Rome; Earl of Darnley, Cobham Hall; Wildenstein

Ref.: Assarino, *Pitture di Guido Reni*, Bologna, 1639; Malvasia, *Felsina Pittrice*, Bologna, 1678, II, 90; Titi, *Descrizione delle pitture*, Rome, 1763, p. 483; Lalande, *Voyage en Italie*, Paris, 1769, III, 577; Chiusole, *Itinerario d'Italia*, Rome, 1782, p. 263; *Catalogo Casa Colonna in Roma*, Rome, 1783, p. 29, no. 174; Ramdohr, *Mahlerei in Rom*, Leipzing, 1787, II, 79; Waagen, *Treasures of Art in Great Britain*, London, 1854, III, 21; Zeri in *Paragone*, XI, 1960, no. 121, pp. 50-60; Clark in Chicago Art Institute *Quarterly*, LIV, no. 2, 1960, pp. 3-7; Chicago Art Institute, *Catalogue of Paintings*, 1961, p. 394.

This is apparently the picture seen by Assarino in Guido's studio in 1638/39. Presumably, since it is partly unfinished (note especially the legs of Salome and the page, the ground, and the woman holding the curtain), it was still in the shop when the artist died. It was probably bought then by Cardinal Girolamo Colonna, Archbishop of Bologna from 1632 to 1645. The painting remained in the Colonna Collection (where it was recorded by Malvasia mistakenly as "Judith with the Head of Holophernes") until about 1797.

This *Salome* is one of the masterpieces of Guido's late period, when the artist's paintings became almost vaporous in their lightness and freedom of handling. Here the drama is expressed by an exquisitely colored arrangement of idealized figures in dance-like poses. The draperies and the gestures of the figures create confluent patterns of movement, accompanied by the play of light acid green, translucent rose and gold, and pearl whites against a slate gray background.

The painting was engraved by J.J. Frey in 1745. The related picture in the Ringling Museum, Sarasota, which seems to be not by Reni himself, was believed by Suida to be the Colonna *Salome* (cf. Gnudi and Cavalli, *Guido Reni*, Florence, 1955, pp. 88-89). [D.P.]

83. *Head of a Sibyl*

Denis Mahon, Esq., London.

Canvas, 29⅛ x 22⅞ in.

Coll.: George Nassau, 3rd Earl Cowper, and heirs (no. 17, 1779 inventory of the 3rd Earl's Florentine villa; later at Panshanger, Hertford) until 1953, when it was acquired by the present owner.

Ref.: Waagen, *Treasures of Art in Great Britain*, London, 1854, III, 15; *Mostra di Guido Reni*, Bologna, 1954, p. 113; Gnudi and Cavalli, *Guido Reni*, Florence, 1955, pp. 91-92; Mahon in *Italian Art and Britain*, London, 1960, p. 146.

The painting dates from the last years of Reni's life. The image, with its sequence of sweeping curves and its transparent pearl-gray tonalities, represents the final product in the evolution of an artistic ideal whose beginnings are here illustrated by the *St. Cecilia* (no. 80). [D.P.]

84. *Diana*

This large cartoon, possibly prepared for an unknown fresco, is one of a pair representing Apollo and his sister, the children of Leto. Diana holds the spear and bow designating her as Goddess of the Hunt.

Fogg Art Museum, Harvard University, Cambridge, Mass., gift of Denman W. Ross.

Black chalk heightened with white and touches of red on gray paper mounted on canvas, 50 x 22¾ in.
Ref.: R. A. Parker in *International Studio*, XCV, 1930, 38; A. Mongan and P. J. Sachs, *Drawings in the Fogg Museum of Art*, Cambridge, 1940, no. 291; J. Watrous, *The Craft of Old Master Drawings*, Madison, Wisc., 1957, p. 132.

Mongan and Sachs relate the drawing and its companion to the *Aurora* in the Casino Rospigliosi, inferring a date of about 1613. This is a reasonable dating on stylistic grounds. The figures recall in particular the victorious *Narses* and *Heraclius* in the Chapel of Paul V, S. Maria Maggiore, Rome, for which Guido's final payment was received in 1612 (Gnudi, *Reni*, 1955, p. 65). [F.C.]

85. *Study of Hands and Forearms of a Man*

Janos Scholz Collection, New York, N. Y.

Black, red, and white chalks, on light brown paper, 6¼ x 8¼ in.
Coll.: Wawra; Friedrich, Archduke of Austria (Lugt, no. 960); Albertina, Vienna.
Ref.: Janos Scholz exhibitions: Oakland, Calif., 1957; Columbia,

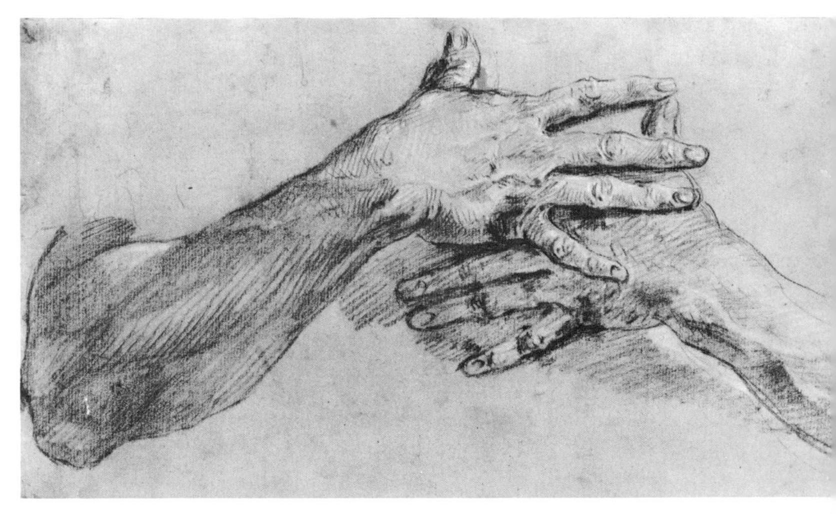

S.C., 1961; Hamburg, Germany, 1963; Cologne, Germany, 1963-64.

The drawing shows one idea for the hands of San Carlo Borromeo holding a crucifix in the *Pietà dei Mendicanti* in the Bologna Pinacoteca (Gnudi, *Reni*, 1955, 72). Although the position of the hands is different in the painting, this would seem to be a study from the studio model, viewed straight on, for San Carlo Borromeo. The first payments for the altarpiece were made in 1614. No doubt the drawing should be placed early in the preparatory stages, ca. 1614. [F.C.]

86. *Torso of Christ on the Cross*

The Pierpont Morgan Library, New York, N.Y.

Black and white chalks on gray paper, 14½ x 9¹¹⁄₁₆ in.

Coll.: Comte Moriz von Fries; Marquis de Lagoy (Lugt 1710); Thomas Dimsdale (?); Sir Thomas Lawrence (Lugt 2445).

Ref.: *Eleventh Report to the Fellows of the Pierpont Morgan Library*, New York, 1961, pp. 82-83.

The drawing is treated with Guido's typical feathery touch in repeated, short chalk hatchings which appear to float on the surface and only with effort attach themselves to anatomical parts. It is a study of Christ's torso for *La Crocifissione dei Capuccini* (Bologna, Pinacoteca). This picture, Reni's first of the theme, is dated by Cavalli around 1616, just after the *Pietà dei Mendicanti* and just before the *Assumption* (S. Ambrogio, Genoa). [F.C.]

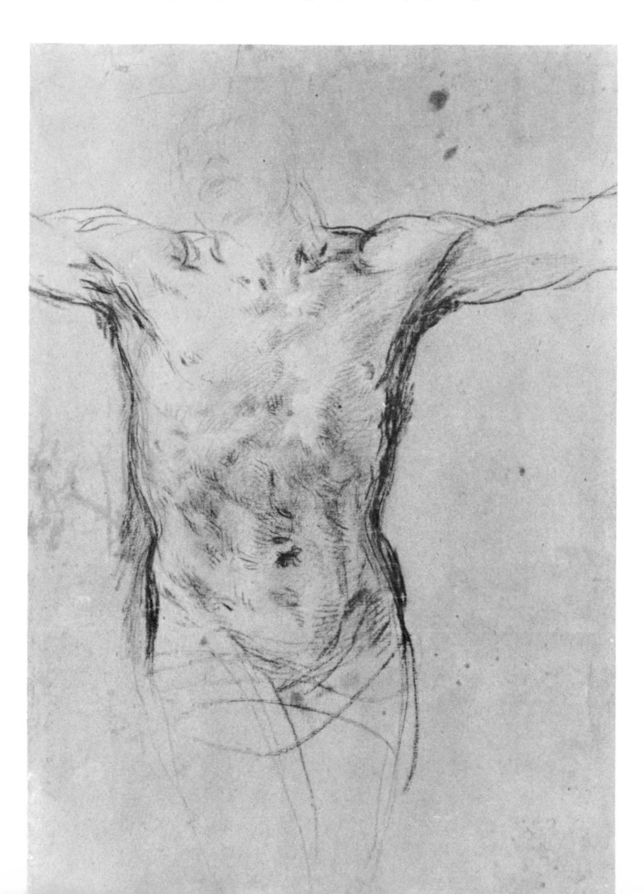

FRANCESCO ALBANI

1578 Bologna 1660

Albani transferred from his first teacher, Calvaert, to the Carracci shop around 1595. About 1600 he went to Rome and, by 1604, became Annibale Carracci's chief assistant. After Annibale's death Albani was quite successful in Rome, but in 1617/18 he moved to Bologna, where he stayed, with a few interruptions, for the rest of his life.

Albani's style, partly influenced by Guido Reni, seems a kind of sweetened version of the classicism of Annibale Carracci. It was taken up and developed by his pupil, Andrea Sacchi. Albani painted frescos and altarpieces as well as relatively small landscapes with religious or mythological subjects. The latter, which he and his school often repeated in different versions, are certainly his most appealing works. Frequently, in their poetic effects of light and atmosphere, they seem to anticipate the paintings of Claude Lorrain. [D.P.]

87. *Rest on the Flight into Egypt*

See no. 161.

Robert and Bertina Suida Manning Collection, New York, N.Y.

Canvas, 22⅜ x 18¼ in.

Coll.: Marquis of Stafford

Ref.: Ottley, *Engravings of Marquis of Stafford's Collection*, London, 1818, II, no. 57, p. 61 (Drawn by W. M. Craig, Engraved by G. Corbould).

Giovanni Andrea Donducci, called *MASTELLETTA*
1575 Bologna 1655

Although Mastelletta worked in Bologna in proximity with the Carracci and their direct pupils, he remained by force of personal vision, a secessionist from their movement. His sources—assimilated into one of the most personal and eccentric styles of the century ("spirito guizzante, fumoso, brilliante" as Malvasia characterizes him)—are sensed rather in the landscape phantasy of his Emilian predecessor, Niccolo dell'Abbate, and in the fervent style of the great Venetian Tintoretto. The influence of Jacopo Bassano is also felt from time to time. Mastelletta's pictorial imagination still reverberates with late-Mannerist tone although there is an essential awareness of vital elements in his 17th century Emilian cultural milieu, which makes his work much more complex and suggestive than that of a simple-minded *retardataire*. His extraordinary *Death of Saint Francis* (San Francesco, Castelmaggiore), for instance, curiously anticipates the diaphanous-soft, mellifluous style of a Cignani or a Dal Sole, working in Bologna toward the end of the century.

Mastelletta's life was fairly uneventful. There was a sojourn in Rome sometime early in the second decade of the century and—if Malvasia is correct—some contact with the work of the Roman landscape painter, Agostino Tassi. He returned to Bologna in 1613, executing thereafter a number of important commissions for altarpieces in churches of Bologna and environs and painting strangely spectral interpretations of biblical stories in landscape settings. It is for these that he is best known today. Toward the end of his life he became increasingly neurotic in his behaviour and his biographer Malvasia notes finally of him that he died in misery and neglect.

88. Landscape with Balaam and the Angel

The soothsayer, Balaam, was asked by Balak, King of Moab, to drive the Israelites, encamped on the plain of Moab, from his land. He was warned by God but yielded to Balak's entreaties. On the road he encountered an angel, sword in hand and was made conscious of his error. (Numbers 22, 5-35)

Mr. and Mrs. Paul H. Ganz, New York, N. Y.

Canvas, 28½ x 38 in.

Ref.: R. Manning, *Bolognese Baroque Painters*, New York, Finch College Museum, 1962, no. 5.

The event, according to the Biblical account, took place in a narrow walled passageway between vineyards. Mastelletta places it rather on a prominence over-looking a majestic expanse of mountains rising from a valley which swings off to the left. The delicate filigree of spires and turrets of a city on a distant slope, irradiated as if by an inner light, rises like a sorcerer's dream. The meeting of Balaam and Jehovah's Angel is enveloped by a sense of the grandeur and mystery of this somber, enchanted world of nature which the artist—stimulated by the landscape fantasies of his predecessor, Niccolo dell'Abbate—has conjured for us. [D.M.]

GIACOMO CAVEDONE
1577 Sassuolo—Bologna 1660

Giacomo Cavedone, native of Sassuolo (Province of Modena), was sent to Bologna as a boy by interested citizens of his native city, to be trained as painter under the Carracci in Bologna. The essential character of his manner was formed in this environment and especially under the inspiration of Ludovico Carracci. More than any other direct pupil of the Carracci, he exploited the monumentalizing tendency of Ludovico's style and in a series of imposing altarpieces for Bolognese churches—notably the "Virgin and Child with Saints Alò and Petronio (Pinacoteca of Bologna) —he emerged as one of the most significant personalities of the Carracci movement. His resonant mode of color and the nobility of his compositions also testify to the crucial impact which Titian made during Cavedone's Venetian sojourn. Cavedone was also in Rome for a period of probably less than a year (1610) and is said to have assisted Reni on decorations in the Palazzo Quirinale. He returned to Bologna and did important work during the teens but by the early twenties an impoverishment of his manner is noted. Malvasia speaks of a fall from scaffolding in S. Salvatore and notes also that the death of a son in 1630 was so traumatic that the artist painted little after this. Although he lived on until 1660, Cavedone ceased to be active for approximately the last twenty-five years of his life.

89. A Seated Bishop Saint

Fogg Art Museum, Harvard University, Cambridge, Mass., Bequest of Charles A. Loeser.

Charcoal heightened with white on brown paper, 11¼ x 15¼ in. Inscribed on verso: S. Salvatore—Bologna Giacomo Cavedone—cartella sopre uno dei 4 (?) archi.

Coll.: Unidentified collections, Lugt 2501 and Lugt 2781.

Ref.: Mongan and Sachs, *Drawings in the Fogg Museum of Art*, Cambridge, Mass., 1946, I, cat. no. 242; I. Moskawitz (ed.), *Great Drawings of All Time*, New York, 1962, pl. 276; W. Ames, *Italian Drawings from the 15th to the 19th Century*, New York, 1963, pl. 84, p. 116, and comment p. 121.

Cavedone, as Malvasia noted (*Felsina Pittrice*, Bologna, 1844, 2nd ed. II, 145), painted the four Church Fathers in fresco over chapels in the Bolognese church of San Salvatore ("... li quattro Dottori di Santa Chiesa in certi ornati di stucchi a fresco sopra le cappelle ..."). The connection of the drawing in the Fogg Museum to one of these figures was first suggested by A. Mongan and P. Sachs (1946, I, 126). They also noted a drawing at Windsor Castle (no. 5284; O. Kurz, *Bolognese Drawings at Windsor Castle*, London, 1955, cat. no. 91), which they regard as a more detailed study of the head.

The four figures of the Fathers of the Church were painted in oval spaces on the external surfaces of arches of four chapels in San Salvatore. Cavedone's *Miracle of the Supper* for this church can be securely dated 1621 and as Renato Roli notes (*Paragone* no. 77, May, 1956, p. 46 and note 31), the fall from the scaffold while painting the aforementioned *Four Fathers of the Church*, may have taken place in 1624. [D.M.]

CARLO BONONI
1569 Ferrara 1632

Bononi's style developed in the artistic matrix of the 16th century Ferrarese tradition which extended from Dosso Dossi through the generation of his older contemporaries Bastianino and Scarsellino and his teacher Bastarolo. But he did not become capsulated in his local culture, rich and viable though it was. Of considerable significance to him was the ferment of ideas produced by the Carracci reform in Bologna. Specifically one senses in Bononi's work clearest reflections of the somber, romantic vision of Ludovico Carracci. Also trips of study to Parma, Venice and Rome (where he worked for over two years), broadened his cultural horizon. The exuberance of color and scenographic richness of such large paintings as the *Marriage at Cana* (Pinacoteca, Ferrara), clearly reveal the impact of Veronese's art. Bononi's activity was largely restricted to the Emilian centers of Ferrara, Bologna, Modena and Reggio Emilia. His most ambitious undertaking was the decoration for Santa Maria in Vado, Ferrara.

90. The Adoration of the Shepherds

Luke 2, 15-16.

Mr. Frederick Mont, New York, N.Y.

Canvas, 9 7/16 x 9 1/16 in.
Coll.: Herman Voss, Munich
Ref.: *Italienische Malerei des 17 und 18 Jahrhunderts*, Wiesbaden, 1935; *Pittura del Seicento Emiliano*, Bologna, 1959, no. 133; R. Manning, *Bolognese Baroque Painters*, New York, Finch College, 1962, no. 4.

The question arises whether this little painting, close to Bononi's *Adoration of the Shepherds* (Church of SS. Pietro e Prospero, Reggio Emilia), is a preliminary study or a second and perhaps later version. The latter is most likely the case. The more expressive role given the architecture with the reflective play of light over walls—and the poignant mood of reverie in the landscape vista which the artist now permits us to see (a landscape kindred in spirit to that of Guercino), heightens the poetic suggestiveness and sonority of this work over that of the larger counterpart. [D.M.]

PIETRO TACCA
1577 Carrara—near Florence 1640

Tacca was trained in Florence in the studio of Giovanni Bologna whom he succeeded in 1609 as official court sculptor. A gifted modeller and a skillful bronze founder, he was able to finish the works which Giovanni Bologna left incomplete at his death: the equestrian monument of the Granduke *Ferdinand I* for Florence, and that of *Henry IV* of France for Paris. These were followed by the equestrian monument of *Philip III* of Spain which still conformed to his master's design, but was entirely executed by him (1614-16). Working mainly for the granduke, Tacca produced a number of celebrated works: four crouching slaves around the monument of *Ferdinand I* at Leghorn, two grotesque fountains on Piazza dell'Annunziata, and the bronze *Fontana del Porcellino*, after the antique, on the Piazza del Mercato Nuovo, Florence. In these works he developed a personal style in which the decorative preoccupations of Florentine Mannerism are allied with a novel interest in direct studies from nature. The last is especially apparent in the "curvetting" horses which were to assure much of his fame: the equestrian statuette of the Duke of Savoy, *Carl Emanuel*, executed in 1619 (Löwenburg, Cassel), and the equestrian monument of *Philip IV* of Spain in Madrid, completed by Tacca just before his death in 1640.

91. Equestrian Statue of Philip IV

In 1621 Philip IV (1605-1665) succeeded his father, Philip III, as King of Spain. He was a fine horseman, a keen hunter and a convinced lover of the arts and letters. He was the patron of Velásquez who portrayed him several times. The king is shown here wearing the stiff collar (*golilla*) which was introduced into Spain about 1623. His traits, though recognizable, are somewhat generalized, for, as pointed out by Valentiner, at the time this model was prepared, Tacca had not yet received the painted portraits of the king which he was to follow in his final version of the monument.

The Detroit Institute of Arts, City appropriation, 1929.

Bronze, H. 15¾ in.

Coll.: Marchese Spinola, Genoa; William Newall, Croxley Green, England; Eugene Bureau, Antwerp (?)

Ref.: Bode, *Italian Bronze Statuettes of the Renaissance*, London, 1912, III, 3; W. Newall Sale, London, Christie's, 27 June 1922, no. 66; Heil in *D.I.A. Bull.*, XI, 1930, 46-47; Valentiner in *D.I.A. Bull.*, XV, 1935, 34-38; Albright Art Gallery, *Master Bronzes*, Buffalo, 1937, no. 144; Thieme-Becker, *Allgemeines Lexikon der Bildenden Künstler*, XXXII, 1938, 390.

This fine bronze statuette was identified by Valentiner as a first study for the equestrian monument of *Philip IV of Spain*, now standing on the Plaza de Oriente, Madrid. Although the actual monument, finished by Tacca in 1640, shows the king riding on a horse in rearing position, with his hoofs lifted so high up that he seems to be curvetting, this was not the original design of the sculptor. Shortly after receiving the commission, in 1635, Tacca had prepared a wax model showing the king sitting on a walking horse (*di passeggio*). Its design deliberately followed that of his monument of *Philip III* of some twenty years earlier. This first model, rejected by the king who expressly wished to be represented on a rearing horse,

has not survived. Its aspect, however, is probably faithfully preserved in the Detroit bronze which, as suggested by Valentiner, must have been executed during the first half of 1635.

From a stylistic point-of-view, it may be noted that, while the elegant linear quality of this statuette still owes much to Florentine Mannerism and especially to Giovanni Bologna, Tacca's own personality comes out in its naturalistic detail and the warm and broad treatment of its surface. [O.R.]

92. Rearing Horse

Seattle Art Museum, Seattle, Wash., Donald E. Frederick Memorial Collection

Bronze, H. 8¾ in.

Coll.: Phillipon, Paris; A. C. de Frey, New York

Ref.: Lee in *Art Quarterly*, XIII, 1950, 260; *Art Museum Handbook*, Seattle, 1951, 123; Fine Arts Gallery, *The Horse in Art*, San Diego, 1963, no. 63.

The theme of the rearing horse seems to have been popular in the workshop of Giovanni Bologna, since Baldinucci, writing about 1680, mentions "il Cavallino, che sta in su due piedi" among the bronzes still being cast after Giovanni Bologna's models. (*Notizie de' Professori*, Florence 1770, VII, 126). Bologna's original seems to be lost, but a number of bronze statuettes carrying one or the other princely rider, or alone, are found in various European collections and may be derived from it. These bronzes are sometimes attributed to Francesco Susini (d. 1646) who, in Baldinucci's words "made many models of small horses, and some times used those of his uncle (Antonio Susini) and of Giovanni Bologna" (*Notizie*, 1772, XII, 204). The theme was especially popular with Pietro Tacca, who made studies of rearing horses after nature when he was working in 1619 on the model for the bronze statuette of the Duke of Savoy, Carl Emanuel. (C. Justi, *Miscellaneen aus drei Jahrhunderten Spanischen Kunstlebens*, Berlin, 1908, p. 263.) The Seattle horse with its flying mane, its excited look, the structure of its head and nostrils, seems to be reminiscent of the type of horse preferred by Tacca. It is, in all likelihood, to be related to his work, or his studio, and probably must be dated around the middle of the seventeenth century. [O.R.]

BARTOLOMEO SCHEDONI
1578 Modena—Parma 1615

According to Malvasia (1672) and l'Orlandi (1704) Schedoni had his early training under Annibale Carracci. In 1599 he received a commission to do an altar-piece *Adoration of the Magi* for the convent of S. Eufemia and from 1602 to 1606 he worked for the Duke of Modena in his Palazzo. In 1607 he executed *The Madonna del Rosario* for the *Parrochiale di Formigine*. His frescos for the *Sala del Consiglio* in the *Palazzo Comunale* in Modena (1606-1607) are rather manneristic and show their dependence on Niccolo dell'Abate. During the last five years of his life in Parma a complete change took place in his style with Correggio as the principal source of his inspiration. This great change is particularly evident in such works as the *Three Marys at the Sepulchre* (1614) and the *Deposition* (both Galleria Nazionale, Parma). This late manner, with its strong chiaroscuro, so greatly impressed Lanfranco during his return to Parma (1610-1612) that it played a major role in the development of his High Baroque style.

93. Rest on the Flight into Egypt

When Herod, the King, heard that a child had been born who would become King of the Jews, he was angry, and sought to find the child in order that it might be destroyed. But an angel appeared to Joseph, the husband of Mary, and warned him to take the Infant Christ and flee into Egypt to escape from Herod.

In this composition Schedoni depicts the Holy Family resting by the side of the road during the long journey into Egypt.

(See no. 161.)

Mr. and Mrs. Paul H. Ganz, New York, N. Y.

Panel, 12 x 15½ in.

Coll.: Anon., New York; Victor Spark, New York; Frederick Mont, New York.

Ref.: C. P. Landon, *Annales du Musée et l'Ecole des Beaux-Arts*, 2d coll., pt. anc., III, Paris, 1813, 67, and pl. 33 (version engraved by M. Soyer); *Gemaldegalerie zu Dresden*, Berlin, 1929, no. 167 (version on panel: 16⅜ x 20½ in.); *Duke Anton Ulrich Museum*, Brunswick, 1932, no. 494 (version on panel: 17¾ x 25⅜ in.).

Smaller than both the Dresden and Brunswick versions, this charming little painting with its very dramatic chiaroscuro is certainly a late work by Schedoni around 1610 to 1615 when he was strongly influenced by Correggio. The Christ Child recalls particularly the types represented by Correggio in the *Madonna of St. George* (Dresden) and in the *Madonna of St. Jerome* (Parma). Schedoni has used the identical pose of the Child in the *Madonna and Child in Glory with Saints John the Baptist, Jerome, Francis of Assisi, and Lawrence* (Museo Nazionale, Naples; no. 376), and also in a small interior composition showing the Madonna and Child with the young St. John the Baptist seated before a crib (Ferdinado Rizzi Collection, Sestri Levante). The present composition can also be related to a drawing by Schedoni, *Holy Family Fed by Angels* (Uffizi, Florence [9134 Sant.]); the Madonna is in almost the same pose and the St. Joseph is also portrayed in a profile position to her right. [R.L.M.]

94. Franciscan Monk

Janos Scholz Collection, New York, N. Y.

Black and white chalks on gray paper, 17 x 11¼ in. Inscribed upper right: "Studio del S. della pala Antecedente"

Coll.: Düb (Lugt 2197a).

Ref.: Janos Scholz Collection exhibitions: Oakland, California 1956; Hamburg, Germany, 1963; Cologne, Germany, 1963-64.

Similar to a drawing of a standing boy at Chatsworth (A. Strong, *Drawings in the Chatsworth Collection*, London, 1902, pl. 51), as pointed out in the Cologne catalogue by W. Stubbs; he dates it about 1613/15. Previously Popham and Gilbert assigned it to Bordone. [B.S.M.]

GIOVANNI LANFRANCO
1582 Parma—Rome 1647

In the intermingling poles and antipodes of seventeenth century Italian art, Lanfranco was the arch-opponent and even the enemy of Domenichino. As a native of Parma and a pupil of Agostino Carracci, Lanfranco adopted the palette and the compositional types of Correggio, and also like his Emilian forerunner developed a nervous, energetic, and painterly style. Even in early work around 1605 for the Camera degli Eremiti, Palazzo Farnese, he seems quite unaffected by the grave, Roman manner of Annibale Carracci. A renewed experience of Correggio in Parma between 1610 and 1612, perhaps interpreted through the late style of Bartolommeo Schedoni, assisted him to become the champion of the High Baroque. Upon returning to Rome Lanfranco soon outdistanced Domenichino with the supreme achievement of his career, the dome of S. Andrea della Valle (1625-28). Here he introduced in Rome the illusionism of Correggio on its grand scale and marked a departure from his more reserved manner of the previous decade. The second half of Lanfranco's career was spent in Naples (1633-46) where he completed four major fresco cycles. The intensity of his dynamic High Baroque manner was to influence definitively the course of later Neapolitan painting. Preti, Giordano, and Solimena were especially impressed by his vivid style.

95. Head of Christ

Janos Scholz Collection, New York, N.Y.

Black and white chalks on gray paper, 12¼ x 13½ in.
Coll.: Piancastelli (Lugt 2078a); Brandegee (Lugt 1860c).
Ref.: Janos Scholz Collection exhibitions: Oakland, Cal., 1957; Hagerstown, Md., 1960; Staten Island, N. Y., 1961; Columbia, S.C., 1961; Notre Dame, Ind., 1964.

Preparatory drawing for the face of Christ in the *Paradiso* (Parma Gallery). (See L. Testi, *Parma*, Bergamo, 1920, p. 20.) [F.C.]

96. The Martyrdom of St. Matthew

The exact manner of St. Matthew's death is uncertain. According to legend he suffered martyrdom in North Africa either by sword or spear or stabbing.

The Metropolitan Museum of Art, New York, N. Y., gift of Walter Lowry, 1956.

Pen and brown ink, brown wash, 6⅞ x 6 in.
Ref.: Vitzthum in *Burlington Magazine*, CII, 1960, 75; J. Bean and W. Vitzthum in *Bolletino d'Arte*, XLVI, 1961, 110.

This drawing is a fine example of how Lanfranco, working on a small scale, sketched out entire sections briskly with pen and then indicated the deployment of light and shadow with brush and wash. Its vividness and excitement give an excellent idea of the brilliance of an all-too-little-known draughtsman. The sheet prepares for the right half of the lunette over the west door of the Church of the Holy Apostles (Naples). The frescos of the choir, crossing, and nave of SS. Apostoli, one of Lanfranco's chief undertakings in Naples, were painted between 1638 and 1644 (Passeri, ed. Hess, p. 156 note 3). Wittkower (1958) gives the date of the entire decoration as 1638-46. There are other studies in the Uffizi, Florence (inv. 12689), at Capodimonte, Naples (no. 352) and at Windsor (Blunt-Cooke, *Roman Drawings at Windsor Castle*, 1960, no. 194). [F.C.]

97. *An Angel*

University of Louisville Art Collection, Louisville, Ky., Morris B. Belknap, Jr., Bequest Fund, 1955

Brush, black chalk, heightened with white on gray paper, 15¾ x 12 in.

Ref.: Newark Museum, *Old Master Drawings*, March, 1960, no. 28.

Until Lanfranco's drawing style is more thoroughly understood, it seems reasonable tentatively to assign this drawing of very high quality to his immediate circle. [F.C.]

Giovanni Francesco Barbieri called *IL GUERCINO*

1591 Cento—Bologna 1666

The main influences on the young Guercino were the works of Ludovico Carracci and the Ferrarese painter Scarsellino. In 1617 Guercino went to Bologna. He made trips to Venice and Mantua before going to Rome in 1621 where, for the Papal family, the Ludovisi, he painted his great ceiling fresco, the *Aurora* (Casino Ludovisi). In 1623 he returned to Cento. In 1642, when Guido Reni died, Guercino moved to Bologna.

Guercino's early style represents one of the strongest and most brilliant statements of the Baroque trend in Italian art. However, his experience of the Roman grand tradition, led him to modify the painterly exuberance of his style. Later, in the Emilia, he rapidly developed a restrained, classical style that was much influenced by Guido Reni.

98. *The Mystic Marriage of St. Catherine*

St. Catherine, native of Alexandria and a Christian virgin martyr, according to legend was beheaded about 307 after failure of an attempt to torture her on a spiked wheel. The popular devotional subject known as "The Mystic Marriage of St. Catherine" is an allergory of the spiritual union between Christ and the redeemed soul.

Denis Mahon, Esq., London.

Canvas, 34⅝ x 27½ in.

Coll.: Cavalier Piombino da Cento; (probably) Sir Paul Methuen, Corsham Court, Wiltshire, before 1757; Henry Gilbert, Devizes, before 1846; acquired by the present owner in 1958.

Ref.: Malvasia, *Felsina Pittrice*, Bologna, 1678, II, 364; Baruffaldi, *Vite de' pittori Ferraresi*, Ferrara, 1844, II, 443; Sullivan, *Observations Made During a Tour*, London, 1780, p. 90; Britton, *Corsham House*, London, 1806, p. 41; Waagen, *Works of Art in England*, 1838, III, 102; Mahon in *Italian Art and Britain*, London, 1960, pp. 139-40; Nicolson in *Burlington Magazine*, CII, 1960, 79; Nicolson, in *Great Private Collections* (ed. D. Cooper), London, 1963, p. 119.

This sensuous, yet solemn, painting is undoubtedly the one mentioned by Malvasia as made for the Cavalier Piombino in 1620. The bold, painterly handling and the dramatic play of light reveal the artist's debt to Ludovico Carracci, especially to such a picture as

Ludovico's altarpiece of 1591 in the Cento Museum. Works like this proved a source of inspiration for Giuseppe Maria Crespi.

A preliminary drawing is preserved in the Ashmolean Museum, Oxford (Parker, *Catalogue*, II, 1956, no. 856). A copy was formerly in a private collection in Prague, and another (with vertical strips added to both sides) is in the Museum at Valenciennes. [D.P.]

99. Salome Visiting St. John the Baptist in Prison

Denis Mahon, Esq., London.

Canvas, 31⅞ x 38⅜ in. (painted surface)

On the stretcher, the remains of a red wax seal with a coat of arms, probably Italian eighteenth century.

Coll.: Lord Radstock; Marquis of Lansdowne, Bowood, until 1930; acquired by the present owner in 1964.

Ref.: Jameson, *Private Galleries of Art*, London, 1844, p. 303; Hazlitt, *Criticisms on Art*, London, 1844, II, Appendix, p. xxi; *Art Union*, IX, 1847, 330; Ambrose, *Catalogue of Paintings Marquis of Lansdowne*, London, 1897, p. 40; Zucchini, *Catalogo Collezioni communali d'arte*, Bologna, 1938, pp. 121-123, fig. 25.

Mrs. Jameson, who saw the painting at Bowood, thought it represented "some famous brigand of that time [*i.e.*, early seventeenth century] visited by his wife in his dungeon." Zucchini, discussing a copy, suggested "Joseph in Prison Visited by Potiphar's Wife," but this is much less likely than the present identification, for which Professor Panofsky is responsible. He has kindly informed us that there is evidence the tradition that Salome was in love with the Baptist, familiar in the nineteenth century, was known at least since the twelfth century. This and other paintings of the sixteenth and seventeenth centuries that can be related to the tradition will be discussed by Professor Panofsky in a study he is now preparing.

Mr. Mahon suggests a date of c. 1622-24 (written communication). In addition to the copy discussed by Zucchini, two others have appeared on the art market in recent years. [D.P.]

100. Semiramis

Semiramis, Queen of Babylon, was at her toilet when told of the revolt of her subjects, which she successfully put down. (*Valerii Maximi Factorum et Dictorum Memorabilium*, IX, 3, ext. 4.)

Museum of Fine Arts, Boston, Mass.

Canvas, 44¼ x 60¾ in.

Coll.: Daniele Ricci, Bologna; Gerrit Reynst, Amsterdam; Dutch States General; Charles II, 1660; Duke of Grafton, Euston Hall; Sir Thomas Banner; Dukes of Grafton, 1746-1948.

Ref.: Malvasia, *Felsina Pittrice*, Bologna, 1678, II, 366; Mahon in *Art Bulletin*, XXXI, 1949, 217-23; Mahon in *Burlington Magazine*, XCII, 1950, 16; Oberlin College, *Italian Paintings of the 17th Century*, 1952, p. 51.

According to Malvasia the picture was made for Ricci in 1624, just after Guercino returned from Rome to Cento. The violence of movement and the intensity of color still seem thoroughly Baroque, and the rather plebian type of the Queen relates the painting to the artist's early works. However, the important modifications that Guercino's style underwent during his short stay in Rome are here revealed in a new clarity of presentation and in an emphasis on the arrangement of the forms on the picture plane.

Guercino painted two other versions (Dresden Gallery; and [formerly] Northbrook Collection) later in his career (Mahon, 1949). The Boston painting was engraved by J. Falck when in the Gerrit Reynst Collection. [D.P.]

101. St. Jerome

Mr. and Mrs. Paul H. Ganz, New York, N.Y.

Canvas, 27½ x 24½ in.

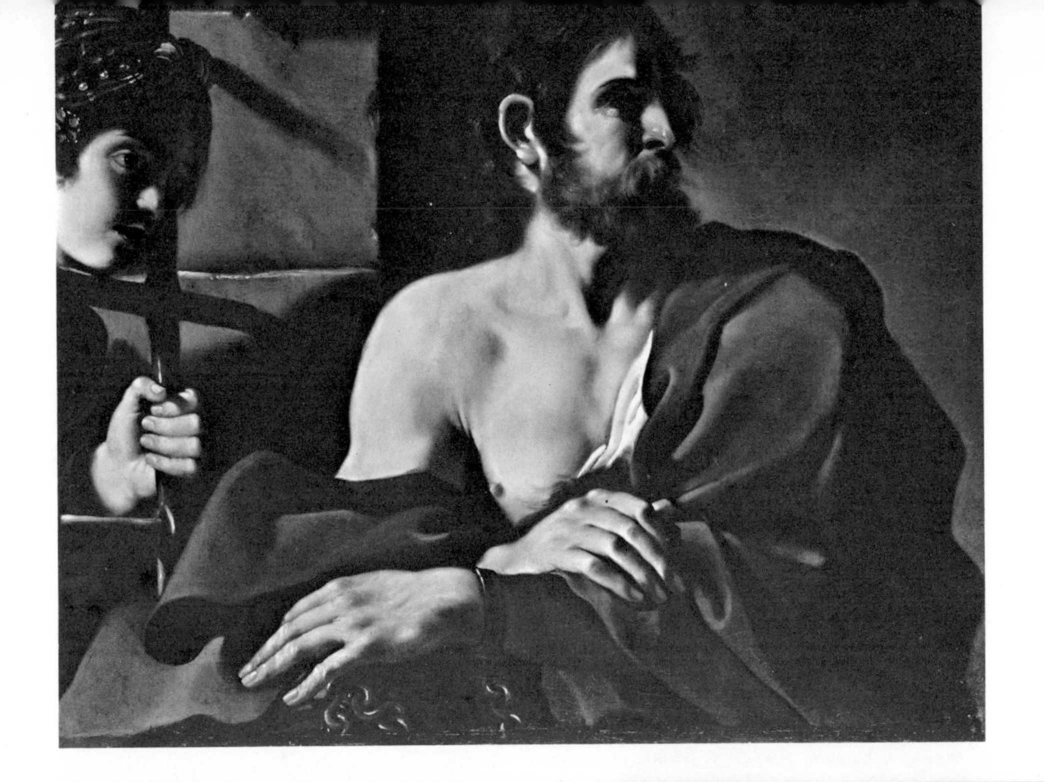

Ref.: R. Manning, *Bolognese Baroque Painters*, New York, Finch College Museum, 1962, no. 17

The dignified features and the quiet pose of St. Jerome, the relatively diffused lighting, and the delicacy of handling are characteristic of Guercino's later style. Denis Mahon has suggested a date in the late 1640s or early 1650s when Guercino is known to have painted several half-length St. Jeromes (letter 3-I—65). [D.P.]

102. Esther before Ahasuerus

"And the king loved Esther above all the women, and she obtained grace and favour in his sight more than all the virgins; so that he set the royal crown upon her head, and made her queen instead of Vashti." (*Esther* 2, 17).

The University of Michigan Museum of Art, Ann Arbor.

Canvas, 62½ x 84¾ in.

Coll.: Cardinal Magalotti; Cardinal Onofrio Barberini; Pope Urban VIII; Camuccini (until 1856); Duke of Northumberland.

Ref.: Malvasia, *Felsina Pittrice*, Bologna, 1841, II, 264, 291, 319; Waagen, *Galleries and Cabinets in Great Britain*, London, 1856, IV, 465, 470; Brit. Institution, 1857, no. 45; Newcastle, 1887, no. 824; *Art Journal*, XXIII, 1963-64, 148; *Art Quarterly*, XXVII, 1963, 99, 109.

This painting which we are fortunate to have in America and which has been viewable only in the last few weeks is listed by Malvasia as a work commissioned by Cardinal Onofrio Barberini in 1639 as a gift to his brother Urban VIII. Malvasia also asserts that the picture received wide acclaim among painters when it was exhibited in Bologna. With a measure still of Guercino's middle period, it already suggests what Guercino's late style was to be like. The composition is now classical with subdued emotional responses, subdued while retaining the marvellous softness of his earlier works. Exhibiting the great lucidity of his late style, the work no longer has the intensity of Guercino's earlier productions. [F.C.]

103. Venus in a Chariot and Cupid

The Cleveland Museum of Art, Dudley P. Allen Fund, 1925

Pen and bistre ink, bistre wash and red chalk, 10 x 15 in.
Coll.: P. & D. Colnaghi and Co., London
Ref.: Albright Art Gallery, Buffalo, N.Y., 1935, cat. no. 38; Smith College Museum of Art, Northampton, Mass., 1948, cat. no. 45; *Seventy Master Drawings*, Fogg Museum of Art, 1948, cat. no. 45; *Fiftieth Anniversary Exhibition*, Worcester Art Museum, 1948, cat. no. 45; *Magazine of Art*, XLIII, Feb. 1950, 78; H. Tietze, *European Master Drawings in the United States*, New York, 1947, no. 57, p. 114; A. Mongan, *One Hundred Master Drawings*, Cambridge, Mass., 1949, pp. 72-73; M. Marangoni, *Guercino*, Milan, 1959, p. 11; T. Lurie, *Art Quarterly*, XXVI, 1963, 217-33.

Miss Lurie has demonstrated clearly that this beautiful drawing, rather than being related to the celebrated *Aurora* (Casino Ludovisi, Rome, 1621), actually predates it in style by several years and belongs to the period of the artist's youthful enterprises in Cento. Miss Lurie notes the relationship of the drawing (brought to her attention by Mr. Denis Mahon) to two ceiling frescos of Apollo and Diana in chariots, which Guercino, with assistants, executed in the Casa Pannini, Cento (1615-17). The tiny figure of a seated female doodled at the bottom of the sheet corresponds, as she notes, to that of the aforementioned Diana—further evidence of some connection of the Cleveland drawing with this commission. One can only speculate on the nature of this. The subject of Venus does appear on a wall in the Casa Pannini, as Mr. Mahon has pointed out (by letter), and perhaps a Venus in her chariot was originally considered for the vault of one of its rooms. Be that as it may the suggestion that the Cleveland drawing represented a kind of first formulation of the Aurora composition, which was to come some five years later, is not convincing for the simple reason that the artist could not possibly have anticipated the proffering of such a commission. [D.M.]

104. Hercules Slaying the Lernean Hydra

One of the twelve labors of Hercules. The nine-headed monster of Lernea dwelled in a swamp near the well of Amymone. Each time a head was knocked away, two others immediately grew in its place. With the help of his servant, Iolaus, Hercules was able to burn off the nine heads, burying the middle and immortal one under a rock.

Mr. and Mrs. David E. Rust, Washington, D.C.

Brown pen and wash, $10\frac{11}{16}$ x $7\frac{5}{8}$ in. Marks lower right, one illeg., other *HD* (Henri Delacroix ?); lower left, *Guerchin* (?).
Ref.: Malvasia, *Felsina Pittrice*, Bologna, 1678, II, Pt. IV, 159 and 363 (as 1618); *Notizie della vita, del Barbieri*, Bologna, 1808, p. 11; *Pitture della citta di Bologna*, Bologna, 1792, p. 20.

This drawing has been identified by Denis Mahon as a preparatory sheet for Guercino's early fresco on the façade of Palazzo Tanari, Bologna, 1618. The fresco, mentioned by Malvasia, is no longer extant. [F.C.]

105. Mars and Cupid

Allen Memorial Art Museum, Oberlin College, Oberlin, Ohio, R.T. Miller Fund, 1958

Pen and ink, $10\frac{1}{16}$ x $7\frac{3}{16}$ in.
Coll.: Benedetto and Cesare Gennari, Bologna; Carlo Gennari (1763); Francesco Forni, Bologna (until 1780); Edward Bouverie.
Ref.: *Art Quarterly*, XXI, 1958, 431, 440; *Allen Mem. Mus. Bull.*, XVI, 1958-59, 28, 87, 231; XVIII, 1960, 4-19; *College Art Journal*, XVIII, 1959, 251, 253; *Amer. Univ. Coll.*, Kenwood, London, 1962, no. 36.

This brilliant display of calligraphic bravura reveals another register of Guercino's drawing style. Here at times the line takes on an improvisatory freedom from its form-defining function and becomes purely expressive of itself. Redisciplined, it now feels freely, sensitively toward the contour or groups itself closely to define a plane. One has the sense of the instantaneous, deftly captured. [D.M.]

106. Domestic Conflict

Worcester Art Museum, Worcester, Mass.

Ink and bistre on white paper; 11$\frac{5}{16}$ x 10$\frac{5}{16}$ in. Signed "Guercino" in pencil lower left.

Coll.: Sir Peter Lely (Lugt 2092), L. D. Lempereur (Lugt 1740), Lionel Lucas (Lugt 1733a), Claude Lucas

Ref.: *Sale;* Christie's, London, Dec. 9, 1949, no. 75; *Six Centuries of Drawings*, State University, Iowa City, 1951, no. 65; *Worcester Art Museum Annual*, VI, 1958, 25; *Catalogue of Drawings by European Masters*, Worcester Art Museum, 1958, p. 53, no. 93.

This curious scene may relate to some literary theme or, as Horst Vey has conjectured, may illustrate a subject from the contemporary theater. The artist's handling now is abrupt, with angry, graceless strokes of the pen, and an almost reckless boldness in the way the washes have been laid in. [D.M.]

107. A Man Sitting at a Table Reading

Fogg Art Museum, Cambridge, Mass., bequest of Charles A. Loeser, 1932.

Pen and wash, 9 x 8¼ in.

Ref.: A. Mongan and P. Sachs, *Drawings in the Fogg Museum of Art*, Cambridge, Mass., 1946, no. 263.

This is a delightfully informal notation by Guercino of a subject from everyday life which caught his fancy. It is executed with a swift and spontaneous line which, rather than searching out the actual contour, defines the gesture of the figure with life-enhancing vibrancy. Washes are laid in broadly, economically and with adroitness in structuring the form at the same time generating a lively pictorial drama. [D.M.]

108. Beggar Holding a Broken Jug

Janos Scholz Collection, New York, N.Y.

Black oil and white chalks on brown paper, 14$\frac{3}{16}$ x 10$\frac{3}{16}$ in.

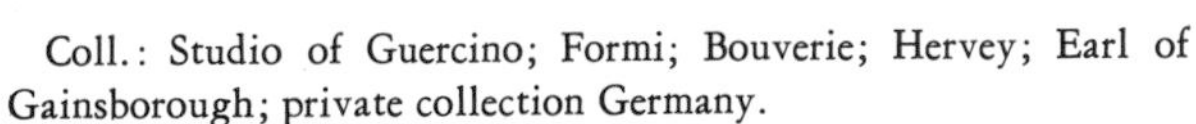

Coll.: Studio of Guercino; Formi; Bouverie; Hervey; Earl of Gainsborough; private collection Germany.

Ref.: A. G. B. Russell, *The Drawings by Guercino*, London, 1923, p. 16; Janos Scholz Collection exhibitions: Columbia Museum of Art 1961; Hamburg, Germany, 1963; Cologne, Germany, 1964; Yale University Art Gallery, 1964; Mills College Art Gallery, Oakland, Calif., 1957.

For comment, see no. 109.

109. Man with Arms Spread Wide

Robert and Bertina Suida Manning, New York, N.Y.

Pen and brush, brown ink, 7⅝ x 7 in.

Coll.: Dan Fellows Platt, Englewood, N. J. (Lugt Suppl. 750a); Princeton Art Museum, Princeton, N. J.; Dr. H. S. Schaeffer, New York, N.Y.

A strain of rusticity runs through Guercino's work, reminding one that he lived the greater part of his life in Cento, a small market town in the heart of the fertile agricultural plain of Emilia. From his earliest years he produced delicious bucolic scenes such as those for the Casa Pannini (now in the Pinacoteca of Cento), and his drawings often record subjects taken from the local scene—from the daily experience of the artist in his provincial home. In the present

sheets, he draws his tattered subject from life with an earthy vigor but not without undertones of sympathy. [D.M.]

110. The Prodigal Son

The prodigal son who wasted his inheritance but who was, nevertheless, reinstated in his father's good graces, is related in the Book of *St. Luke*, 15, 11-32.

Mr. and Mrs. Paul H. Ganz, New York, N.Y.

Red chalk on white paper.
Coll.: P. & D. Colnaghi & Co., London.

From a photograph Denis Mahon identified this as an autograph work in Guercino's late style. (letter of Dec. 24, 1964). [F.C.]

111. Pope Gregory the Great

Pope Gregory I (c. 540-604), one of the Four Doctors of the Church and commentator on the Book of Job, was an important link between the early Latin Church and its medieval inheritors. In the painting for which this is a study, Gregory is shown interceding for souls in Purgatory by recommending them to the Virgin and the Holy Trinity.

Mr. and Mrs. Lawrence A. Fleischman, Detroit, Mich.

Pen, ink, and wash on cream-colored paper, 7⅞ x 6⅜ in.
Coll.: Guercino's nephews, Benedetto and Cesare Gennari, 1719 (Lugt suppl. 2858c); W. Bateson, London (mark in black, lower right W.B.; Lugt suppl. 2604a); D. F. Platt, New York (mark in gray, verso; Lugt suppl. 750a); H. S. Schaeffer, New York, 1964

This study for *St. Gregory Rescuing Souls from Purgatory* (S. Paolo, Bologna) is an important, well-documented, late work. It shows a substantial use of deep, heavy wash to develop shadow, a vibrant repeated use of horizontals in the areas of medium shading, and the broadest economy in the outlying sections. The sketch demonstrates how Guercino retained the richness of his earlier style and utilized it for a heightened, expressive intensity in his last years. [F.C.]

LIONELLO SPADA
1576 Bologna—Parma 1622

Spada received his training in the Carracci Academy in Bologna and subsequently worked with the highly reputed *quadraturista*, Girolamo Curti called *Dentone*, probably in the capacity of *figurista*. Later he became one of the prominent figures in the Carracci circle, collaborating in group enterprises in which they were involved, such as the decorations of the Oratorio San Colombano (c. 1600) or those in the cloister of San Michele in Bosco (1604-5). There is reason to doubt that his perigrinations in lower Italy and as far south as Malta occurred early enough for him to have had direct contact with Caravaggio (there is evidence of his presence in Emilia during the years 1607-8), but the fact remains that traces of his work can be found in La Valletta in Malta, suggesting that he retraced the tortured wanderings of Caravaggio during his last years. The influence of the latter, while certainly not crucial, is responsible for the tone of realism in a style basically Carraccesque. Spada returned to his native Bologna by at least 1614 where by 1616 (Wittkower, 1958) he painted his huge *St. Domenico Burns the Books in the Presence of Heretics*, in San Domenico. There and in other Emilian centers he executed commissions for churches and ended his career in Parma, attached to the court of Ranuncio Farnese.

112. David with the Head of Goliath

Robert and Bertina Suida Manning, New York, N.Y.

Pen and brown washes, 10 x 6 in.

Inscribed on lower right of sheet: "Leon Spada le tableau est dans la galarie du Marquis Cospi. Malvasia a Bol 107"

Coll.: D. B. (Lugt 729); handwritten monogram in the center of the reverse; P. & D. Colnaghi, London.

The inscription on the lower right corner refers to a passage in Malvasia's biography of Spada (*Felsina Pittrice*, Bologna, 1844, 2nd ed. II, 76) where two paintings of David with the Head of Goliath are noted. But Malvasia's description ". . . colla spada in una mano, coll'altra *impugnavano il teschio* dell'orgoglioso Golia . . ." would seem to exclude a relationship of the drawing in question to either of these paintings. Nor does the drawing seem to relate to the painting by Spada in the *Gemäldegalerie* at Dresden which is described as a "David Giving the Head of Goliath to a Soldier"

In pose and relationship of David to the giant Goliath's head placed beside him on a kind of pedestal, Spada clearly formulated a variation of Guido Reni's conception of the subject (versions at Sarasota and the Louvre of 1604/5). Remembering Malvasia's anecdote about Guido's remark to Spada that he was born to fresco painting and should restrict himself to this medium—which so offended the young artist that he "giuro voler un giorno superar l'emulo ancorche tanto più di lui avvantaggiato di valore e di grido . . ."—one is led to conjecture that in handling the Guido invention in his own way he may have been measuring himself against his more precocious compatriot. It is noteworthy though that in contrast to the Caravaggesque overtones of Guido's two paintings, Spada's taste in the figure is Carraccesque. [D.M.]

Guido Canlassi, called
CAGNACCI
1601 Castel Sant' Arcangelo di Romagna—Vienna 1681

Cagnacci's early paintings, found in churches of Rimini and nearby Castel Sant' Arcangelo, reveal a subtle, probing artistic intelligence, working in the frame of a fundamentally Caravaggesque culture. Whether one feels it necessary to postulate a Roman sojourn to explain this contact, or is content as explanation with the proximity in the Marches of works left by Orazio Gentileschi and Giovan Francesco Guerrieri da Fossomboni, the fact of the influence of Caravaggesque ideas on Cagnacci early in his career is indisputable. It would seem that after this phase—certainly by 1644, the date of two large paintings for the tribune of the Cappella Madonna di Fuoco in the Cathedral of Forli (now Pinacoteca, Forli)—Cagnacci's imagination was fired by the ethereal beauties of Guido Reni's later work in Bologna. Indeed, it is very likely that he spent some time in Reni's studio. But the Reni influence was assimilated and translated into purely personal terms. Cagnacci developed into one of the most rarefied, perversely intriguing artists of the century as was demonstrated by his languorous dying Cleopatras, Lucretias or Penitent Magdalens in the important exhibition, "Maestri della Pittura del Seicento Emiliano", held in Bologna in 1959. They are steeped in a kind of morbid eroticism, curiously ambivalent and disquieting. The hedonistic spirit of Cagnacci's art was peculiarly congenial to the sophisticated, precious, and courtly tastes of the time. After a period of activity in Venice in the early fifties, we find the artist by 1658 in Vienna, appointed court painter to Leopold I.

113. David with the Head of Goliath

Collection of the Columbia Museum of Art, Columbia, S. C.
Samuel H. Kress Collection, 1955

Canvas, 50⅝ x 38 in.

Coll.: Colonna, Rome (?); De Faucigny, Paris (?).

Ref.: *Catalogo Casa Colonna*, Rome, 1782, p. 22, no. 128; Decamps, *Comte De Faucigny Sale*, Paris, April 11-13, 1878, p. 11; *Maestri della Pittura del Seicento Emiliano*, Bologna, 1959, p. 169; D. Miller in *Burlington Magazine*, CI, 1959, 211; R. Manning, *Baroque Painters of Bologna*, New York, Finch College, 1962, no. 18; *Art of the Renaissance from the Kress Collection*, Columbia, S. C., 1962, p. 110-11.

Formerly attributed to Bernardo Strozzi, William Suida first tentatively identified this painting as a work by Guido Cagnacci. The attribution was supported by the discovery of a print by

Domenico Cunego (1727-1803), after this painting, when it was in the Colonna Collection, which identified it as by Cagnacci. Exactly the same model and pose were used again in *David with the Head of Goliath* formerly in the Tamburi collection in Bologna. In this picture, however, the youth wears a fashionable striped satin costume with slashed sleeves. This picture was exhibited as a work by Lorenzo Pasinelli in the aforementioned Bolognese exhibition, *Maestri della Pittura del Seicento Emiliano* (cat. no. 79); the present writer saw fit to challenge the attribution, calling attention on the one hand to characteristics atypical of Pasinelli and on the other noting the Cunego print and furthermore the close relationship of the painting (taste for costume, peculiarities of facial type) to Cagnacci's *Women who Beats Two Fighting Dogs* in the Prince Vitaliano Borromeo collection of Milan (see Miller, 1959, p. 211). Since then, the problem has been complicated by the recent appearance on the Italian Art market of a *Triumph of David* in which the same figure of David appears as in the Bolognese picture but now loosely executed and with elements of style more reminiscent of Pasinelli than Cagnacci (see *Finearte Vendita Pubblica . . . d'Opera d'Arte Antica*, Milan, May 15-16, 1962, cat. no. 54). Be that as it may, the present work is clearly by Cagnacci; it belongs to the artist's full maturity. Given our present knowledge of his chronology, it is not possible to date it more precisely than sometime during the 1640-55 period. [D.M.]

GIOVANNI ANDREA SIRANI
1610 Bologna 1670

Sirani first studied with Cavedone, then around 1630 entered the studio of Guido Reni where he remained as assistant until the latter's death in 1642 and completed his unfinished paintings. As a student he amazed his friends with imitations of the drawing styles of well-known masters. Unfortunately this mimic ability delimited his own artistic identity. In Reni's studio he fell completely under the domination of the master and was never able to establish an autonomous style. Before the day of more discerning connoisseurship it was common for his pictures to be mistaken for those of Reni. Sirani's most ambitious painting was a large *Supper of the Pharisee* (San Girolamo, Bologna), 1652. Six years later his celebrated daughter Elisabetta painted a companion piece, *The Baptism of Christ*. [D.M.]

114. Apollo Accompanied by Amor

Collection of Walter P. Chrysler, Jr.

Canvas, 53½ x 43 in.

Ref.: Manning in *Bolognese Baroque Painters*, Finch College, New York, 1962, no. 19.

Once considered to be a late Guercino, recently this painting was attributed to Sirani by Bertina Suida Manning. *A Sibyl* (Kunsthist. Mus., Vienna) formerly given to Guido Reni, has been recognized by Denis Mahon as a work of Giovanni Andrea Sirani, and a comparison of these two paintings indicates that both are by the same hand. The Amor in this painting is similar to one in Reni's *Fortuna* (Pinacoteca, Vatican) except their positions are reversed. [R.L.M.]

DOMENICO MARIA CANUTI
1626 Bologna 1684

Canuti's artistic curriculum was unusually varied and included short terms of study with a number of prominent Bolognese masters (Bertusio, Reni, Guercino, Albani, G. A. Sirani) as well as Lanfranco in Rome. The even wider range of important influences included Mattia Preti and Pietro da Cortona. He emerged as a painter of striking originality with a special gift for fresco decoration on a grand scale. His most impressive work in this sphere is a vast *Hercules in Olympia* (*Salone* vault, Palazzo Pepoli, Bologna, 1669-70). In Rome, whence Canuti was called in 1672, he was engaged for a series of important decorative enterprises—notably the frescos in the nave and tribune of SS. Domenico e Sisto (1674-75). He returned to his native city by 1677 and spent the remaining years of his life working on the extensive cycle of frescos in the library and church of the Monastery of San Michele in Bosco. Canuti's style, vehement, dynamic, stood as the Baroque opposition in the later Bolognese tradition to the calm, meditated classicism of Carlo Cignani. In Canuti's studio several of the most vigorous talents of the succeeding generation, Dal Sole, Burrini, Crespi, received an important part of their training.

115. Jupiter Astride his Eagle

Pen and brown ink wash heightened with white, 9½ x 13½ in. Inscribed lower left: Domenico Maria Canuti Scólare del Guido; and above right of center: fresco del Palazzo Colonna.

The Pierpont Morgan Library, New York, N.Y.

Coll.: Alliance des Arts (Lugt 61)

Ref.: *Thirteenth Report to the Fellows of the Pierpont Morgan Library*, New York, 1964, p. 100.

This drawing is a preparatory study for the decoration of 1675 in the Palazzo Altieri, Rome (see E. Feinblatt, *Art Quarterly*, vol. 15, 1952, pp. 51 ff.). The Jupiter in the drawing differs from the definitive figure only in variations in the gestures of the arms. The drawing is wonderfully vigorous in execution; the masterful grasp of contour and the plastic vitality of the figure recall the virile, learned manner of Annibale Carracci in his studies of the male nude form. But there is a nervous intensity to the touch, an animation of surface which lends a quite individual nuance of style to Canuti's drawings. The dynamic articulation of the figure in space demonstrates clearly why Canuti was so praised by his contemporaries for his skill in handling the foreshortened figure. [D.M.]

116. Self-Portrait

Janos Scholz Collection, New York, N. Y.

Colored chalk on buff paper, 19¼ x 13 13/16 in.

Coll.: Geiger.

Ref.: Neumeyer-Scholz, *Drawings from Bologna*, Mills College Museum, Oakland, 1957, no. 11; Planiscig-Voss, *Drawings from the Geiger Collection*, Zurich, n.d., I. pl. 62; Grosso-Pettorelli, *Disegni di Palazzo Bianco Genoa*, Milan, 1910, pl. 21, for a later copy; Janos Scholz Collection exhibitions: Staten Island, N. Y., 1961; Columbia, S. C., 1961; Hamburg, Ger., 1963; Cologne, Ger., 1963-64.

Formerly attributed to Terbrugghen, this drawing was cited by Janos Scholz as identical with the drawing reproduced in the first volume of the Geiger collection although the measurements as recorded differ. He also identified it as a self-portrait by Canuti on the basis of its relation to the engraving included in Malvasia's *Felsina Pittrice*, III, 1769, 110. Dwight Miller writes of this drawing, "The candid, easy informality of the characterization which Canuti has given this portrait reminds one that Bolognese artists always tended to keep more closely in tune with everyday life (see no. 75) with the charm and poetic suggestiveness of the local scene than did their more urbane counterparts in Rome. Such a work as this reveals at once Canuti's kindredship in spirit to the portrait manner of the Carracci, with its special sensibility for the grain of actuality —for its ability to convey a sense of the unpretentious natural dignity of the sitter." [F.C.]

FLAMINIO TORRE

1621 Bologna—Modena 1661

Torre is said, by his biographer Malvasia, to have begun his training in Bologna under Giacomo Cavedone, subsequently entering the studio of the much more successful Guido Reni. However his relationship with Guido quickly soured and he resumed his studies under Simone Cantarini, a master of exceptional gifts, who as a pupil of Guido also had difficulties with the master and was driven forth from his studio. The few paintings by Torre known today reveal him as a thoughtful, sensitive artist but too much under Cantarini's shadow to emerge as a figure of major significance or to confirm Malvasia's high evaluation of his artistic stature ("gran virtuoso"). Aside from his own work as painter and print-maker, Malvasia especially praises his ability to make copies of paintings by the great masters (*Felsina Pittrice*, 1842, II, 383). Torre was called to the Este court in Modena and worked there as court painter to Duke Alfonso the last years of his relatively short career.

117. The Virgin Appearing to St. Jerome

The Metropolitan Museum of Art, New York, N. Y., Rogers Fund, 1960.

Red chalk on beige paper, 15 11/16 x 5 9/16 in.

Coll.: Charles Gasc (Lugt 542); Sir Robert Ludwig Mond (Lugt 2813a).

Ref.: Borenius-Wittkower, *Collection of Drawings by the Old Masters Formed by Sir Robert Mond*, London, 1937, no. 257, pl. 46; Kurz, *Bolognese Drawings of the XVII and XVIII Centuries at Windsor Castle*, London, 1955, pp. 139-40, fig. 104; *Maestri Della Pittura del Seicento Emiliano*, Bologna, 1959, p. 133.

This drawing corresponds closely to the left half of one by Torre in the Albertina, Vienna (S.B. 543; Kurz, fig. 105), and relates as well to another at Windsor Castle (Kurz, no. 543). Kurz has noted their relationship to a painting by Torre in the Galleria Estense (Pallucchini, *I Dipinti della Galleria Estense*, Rome, 1945, no. 330, fig. 112). The general lines of the composition and major figure motifs are close to those seen in the drawings but now Saint Niccolo da Tolentino replaces the standing figure of Saint Jerome and other less important alterations are made. It would seem that all these items were made in preparation for a major altarpiece, and indeed a painting of this description, considered Torre's masterpiece, was until the 19th century in the church of Santa Maria della Carità, Bologna. ("[Cappella] Fontana Bombelli, il gran quadro con la Beata Vergine sollevata in alto col Figlio, sotto li Santi Gio. Battista, Girolamo, Carlo e Nicola da Tolentino . . ." *Le Pitture di Bologna*, Bologna, 1766, p. 157). The manner of feeling toward the form by swift, summary strokes—the particular phrasing and pressure of the lines in Torre's drawing here exhibited are reminiscent of one of the drawing modes of his master Cantarini. [D.M.]

GIUSEPPE MARIA CRESPI
1665 Bologna 1747

Among the weightiest statements in the Bolognese artistic tradition, was the work of Giuseppe Maria Crespi. Indeed, of the painters of Bologna of Crespi's time—painters active during the later decades of the 17th and earlier decades of the 18th centuries—only he has gained widespread interest of modern scholars. That strong spirit of independence which gave him the will to cut through the conventions of a persuasive artistic culture to record direct responses to the daily life and the local scene of Bologna with a pungent honesty and sardonic humor, has for modern sensibilities, given him a commanding stature in his school. This is not to say that Crespi did not deeply identify himself with the rich artistic evolution of Bologna—did not feel a sense of reverence for his predecessors; it is to say only that these sentiments never inhibited the energy and integrity of his personal vision as artist. Crespi studied both with Canuti and Cignani; he was certainly more temperamentally responsive to the vehemence of the former than the refinement and culture of the latter. Sojourns of study to the Marches (Baroccio), Parma (Correggio) and above all to Venice widen his horizons. The experience in Venice especially enriched his resources in color and in this he had common aims with Burrini and the older painter Pasinelli, exponents of what can be called a neo-Venetian strain in Bolognese painting of the late *Seicento*. After a quite successful undertaking in fresco decoration (Palazzo Pepoli, Bologna, 1691) Crespi abandoned this facet of painting, devoting himself to oil painting. His career was quite successful; his pictures went into the best collections not only of Italian patrons but were sought by foreign princes, among them the Electors of the Palatinate, of Saxony, of Bavaria. He was an especial favorite of Ferdinand, Grand Duke of Tuscany.

118. Continence of Scipio

(Reproduced in color on page 22)

Collection of Walter P. Chrysler, Jr.

Canvas, 86 7/8 x 66 in.

Coll.: Count Antonio Colato, Bologna; Bertolini, San Remo, 1953; N. M. Acquavella Galleries, New York.

Ref.: Zanotti, *Storia dell'Accademia Clementina*, Bologna, 1739, II, 63; Crespi, *Vite de'Pittori Bolognesi*, Rome, 1769, p. 216; B. S. Manning, *Paintings from the Collection of W. P. Chrysler, Jr.*, Portland, Oreg., 1956, no. 44.

Crespi's *Continence of Scipio* was mentioned by both his biographers, Giampietro Zanotti and Luigi Crespi as having been painted for Count Antonio di Colato. Zanotti noted that its pendant was *Brutus Kissing the Ground*. Neither biographer offers any specific clue as to the date of the painting. It certainly belongs to the fully mature phase of Crespi's career; it is closest to two superb paintings in the Palazzo Venezia, *David and Abigail* and *Finding of Moses*, which, according to Zanotti, were ordered by Cardinal Tomasso Ruffo, Papal Legate to Bologna. Ruffo's term of office in Bologna was 1721-27 which would bracket the execution of these paintings (*Mostra Celebrativa di Giuseppe Maria Crespi*, Bologna, 1948, nos. 38-39). The *Continence of Scipio* could have been painted c. 1730 as it is mentioned by both Zanotti and Crespi after the two paintings in the Palazzo Venezia.

Crespi's controlled power as a colorist is never seen to better advantage than in this darkly splendid painting where richly modulated whites, reds, blues, greens and golds, glow forth with a deep refulgence from their somber ambient. Plastic density and depth of color interact to give it an extraordinary weight. The narrative is curiously inflected by the enigma of eyes obscured in shadows, forms emerging from or sinking into darkness. [D.M.]

DONATO CRETI
1671 Cremona—Bologna 1749

The Bolognese painter Donato Creti was an exact contemporary of Giuseppe Maria Crespi; relative to the orientation of his style, he was Crespi's antipode. Indeed, the art of these two painters reveals the diversity of possibilities inherent to the Bolognese tradition—the central line of which stemmed from the Carracci and their direct pupils. Creti, with his intense formal idealism, his crystalline color and extraordinary purity of line, was the last important exponent of Bolognese classicism; Crespi's style, on the other hand, elaborated from the pictorial aims and resources of that darkly romantic vein in Bolognese painting which had its origins in the art of Ludovico Carracci. Creti was a pupil of Lorenzo Pasinelli and it was this subtle master who inspired the most delicate nuances of his manner. Also an important enrichment of his imagination as painter came from his study of the beautiful paintings and drawings of Pasinelli's master, Simone Cantarini. The cool intellectuality of Reni's art also provided a strong impulse for the orientation of Creti's style. The most genial aspect of his work consists of his easel paintings of mythological subjects and pastoral idylls. Here the singular intensity and perfection of his handling is seen to best advantage. He had great distinction too as draughtsman; the corpus of his drawings is large, the style quite individual.

119. Musical Group

(Reproduced in color on page 6)

Collection of Walter P. Chrysler, Jr.

Canvas, 77½ x 57½ in.

Coll.: Viscount Palmerston, Broadlands, Hants; H. Crevat, London, 1951; David M. Koetser, New York City, 1954.

Ref.: Palmerston, *Inventory of Pictures at Broadlands* (MS, 1773); Manning in *Paintings Collection Chrysler*, Portland, Ore., 1956, no. 45; R. Roli in *Arte Antica e Moderna*, 1959, p. 328.

This brilliant *Musical Group* poses several perplexing questions. It clearly relates to the later seventeenth century Bolognese school; reverberations of Lorenzo Pasinelli's manner are sensed, though the painting is not his. The chief candidates for its authorship are two of Pasinelli's best pupils, Domenico Maria Muratori (1662-1749) and Donato Creti (1671-1749). Muratori's *Death of Cleopatra* (Museum, Rhode Island School of Design, Providence) shows notable analogies of style: a similarity in the painting of the drapery not too generic not to be quite significant in the likeness of facial type and manner of composing the figures close to the foreground with a plinth and base of column behind. The painting, if Muratori's, would belong to his Bolognese period rather than the later years in Rome where his mature career unfolded. However, the attribution of the painting to Creti, first proposed by Bertina Manning, seems, all things considered, more convincing. It would certainly fall early in Creti's development—the mode of composition does not reoccur in his mature style and the handling is more relaxed—somewhat less adroit and intense than in the mature paintings. The work fits comfortably, however, with the earliest identified products of Creti's hand—the *Holy Family* (Davia-Bargellini Gallery, Bologna), two drawings dated July 1695 (Uffizi; Roli, figs. 146b,c,d). There are other indications of Creti's authorship. For instance a variant of the lute player on the left is similarly placed in Creti's superb *Dance of the Nymphs* (Palazzo Venezia, Rome), but now executed with the glacial elegance of Creti's mature style. The *Musical Group* is by far the most impressive work from this early phase of Creti's development; its brilliance is not unexpected, however, for this singularly gifted artist's precocity was stressed by his biographer, Giampietro Zanotti. [D.M.]

GIUSEPPE CHIARI
1654 Rome 1727

Giuseppe Chiari was one of the most talented among the many pupils of the *caposcuolo* of Roman painting during the latter decades of the century, Carlo Maratti. Chiari gained the special admiration of his master by the skill he displayed in finishing decorations in the

Cappella Marcacioni, Church of S.M. del Suffraggio, begun by Nicolo Berrettoni but left incomplete at his death in 1682. Chiari's subsequent career in Rome was quite successful; in addition to his production in paintings, he worked extensively as fresco decorator. His urbane, sophisticated manner was highly considered by a clientele which included not only Roman patrons of the Church and aristocracy, but princely collectors in France, the German countries and England. Chiari was president of the Accademia di San Luca of Rome from 1723-26. He is one of the many fine and worthy artists of the later 17th century whose career still awaits close study by modern historians.

120. Rest on the Flight into Egypt

Bob Jones University Collection, Greenville, S. C.

Canvas, 18¾ x 24¾ in.

Coll.: J. Weitzner (1955).

Ref.: *College Collections*, Michigan State University, East Lansing, 1959, no. 20, p. 9; *Bob Jones Collection*, Greenville, 1962, no. 91.

The identification of this lovely painting—formerly attributed to Maratti—was proposed by Federico Zeri (letter 1955). This opinion was subsequently endorsed by Denis Mahon. The types and the coloring, with its predominant red-blue theme, are Marattesque to a high degree. But subtle inflections from Maratti's style—a special suavity of touch, subtlety of tonal modulation and other less definable qualities, indicate the refined hand of the master's gifted pupil. [D.M.]

MARCANTONIO FRANCESCHINI
1648 Bologna 1729

Franceschini, though he has not yet been granted his proper place of importance by modern critics, was considered in his own time a leading personality among Northern Italian painters active during the later 17th century. He was taken under the wing of the highly reputed Carlo Cignani and after assisting this master in Bologna for over a decade—especially in his numerous commissions for fresco decorations—Franceschini established his own studio and embarked upon a strenuous and quite profitable career. His special ability and reliability as frescoist, brought him some of the most important commissions for decorations of the period (Corpus Domini, Bologna; Cathedral, Piacenza; Palazzo Ducale, Modena and Genoa etc.). However, concurrently with this sphere of activity, he produced an extraordinary number of altarpieces and easel paintings—biblical histories, mythologies and pastoral idylls (the latter perhaps the most appealing part of his work to modern taste). Though he never left the confines of Italy, he received commissions for nearly two decades (1691-1709) from one of the most important patrons of the period, Prince Johann Adam of Liechtenstein, who resided in Vienna. He was also a favorite painter of Pope Clement XI who called him to Rome in 1711 to provide cartoons for decorations in mosaic for one of the monumental chapels in Saint Peter's. Franceschini's style carried on into the early decades of the 18th century the classicism which had evolved in the Bolognese tradition out of the Roman work of Annibale Carracci, the art of Domenichino, Guido Reni, Francesco Albani and the later Guercino.

121. Bacchus and Ariadne

The story of Ariadne and Bacchus, is told by Pausanius, Philostratus, Catullus and other ancient writers. Ariadne, daughter of King Minos, fell in love with Theseus, gave him the sword which he used to kill the minotaur, accompanied him on his voyage back to Athens but was abandoned by him on the Island of Naxos. In her grief she appealed to the Gods; Venus took pity and granted her an immortal husband, Bacchus. The scene here depicts the first encounter of Bacchus with the distraught Ariadne on Naxos.

Dr. and Mrs. Michael W. Freeman, Detroit, Mich.

Canvas, 31¾ x 26½ in.

According to Franceschini's account book (MS. B4067, Biblioteca

Comunale, Bologna), he did the subject of Bacchus encountering the abandoned Ariadne on at least six occasions during his career. The present picture clearly belongs to his later maturity when the cool placidity of his manner and refinement of execution were at their highest. Therefore it could be either one commissioned in June of 1717 by Girolamo Durazzo, patrician collector of Genoa or one commissioned "da un certo Inglese" in March of 1726. An earlier version is found in the Galleria Davia-Bargellini, (Bologna). More contemporary is "Bacchus and Adriadne" (commissioned Oct. 1716) for the ceiling of the *Sala del Pranzo*, Palazzo Reale (Turin). Older accounts of the collection of pictures in the Palazzo Reale (Genoa) mention a "Bacchus and Adriadne" by Franceschini in the throne-room, but this picture is no longer found there. [D.M.]

122. The Death of Saint Catherine dei Vigri

Among the many talents of Saint Catherine were those for music and painting. The story is told that as she lay dying she asked the sisters of her order to bring her a viol and she played propped up in her bed as solace during her last days.

The Cooper Union Museum, New York, N. Y.

Pen and gray-brown wash squared for transfer, 8¼ x 10 15/16 in. Ref.: D. Miller, in *Art Bulletin*, XLIII, 1961, 133; R. Wunder, *Extravagant Drawings of the Eighteenth Century*, New York, 1962, no. 37.

This squared preparatory drawing was made for the cycle of fresco decorations in Corpus Domini, the church of the convent founded in Bologna in 1456 by Saint Catherine. The ensemble was carried out with the assistance of Luigi Quaini and the *quadraturista* Enrico Haffner during 1690-96. Another drawing related to this series of decorations is also at Cooper Union. The cartoon for the present subject is preserved in the Opera del Duomo at Orvieto.

Characteristic of Franceschini's refined taste and stylistic proclivities as classicist, is the restraint with which he handles the washes. Though warm in their coloristic effect, they are carefully controlled so that distinctness of contour is never threatened. Structure and planar alinement rather than pictorial movement is defined; an effect of calmness predominates. The dulcet pathos which suffuses the scene is apropos to the subject and an eloquent and genuinely felt manifestation of the pathetecism characteristic of much of Catholic art of the post Counter-Reformation period. [D.M.]

IV. *Florence*

JACOPO CHIMENTI
called Jacopo da Empoli
c. 1554 Florence 1640

Chimenti's only master, Maso da San Friano (known mainly for his pictures in the Studiolo of Francesco I) left little trace on his style; much more important was the painter's assiduous study of the work of his Florentine antecedents of the earlier Cinquecento—especially Andrea del Sarto and Pontormo. Chimenti's subsequent development evolved almost wholly under influences of his local artistic tradition, although there are reflections from time to time of his awareness of Caravaggio's revolutionary artistic vision. Recently attention has focused on Chimenti's contribution to the development of the still-life genre in Italian painting (*La Natura Morta italiana*, Naples, 1964, pp. 76 ff.).

123. St. James the Great

The patron saint of Spain, St. James the Great was one of the twelve Apostles and brother of St. John. He is also reputed to have been closely related to Christ and especially intimate since he was present at the Ascension and Transfiguration. It is for such a scene that this drawing may have been prepared.

Private Collection, Detroit.

Black and white chalk on prepared paper, 11 x 9¼ in.

The exhibition of drawings by Jacopo da Empoli from the *Gabinetto dei Disegni* of the Uffizi (*Mostra di Disegni*, Florence, 1962) has given clear definition to the various possibilities in the drawing style of this important Florentine artist. The particular tremulous intensity which the line takes, characterizing the head of the monk in this sanguine study, the oblique angle of vision, the muted treatment of the eyes (an echo of the artist's earlier involvement with the art of Pontormo), are unmistakable for this artist and are encountered again in a number of drawings in the Uffizi exhibition (nos. 29, 61). [D.M.]

124. *Man in a Cloak*

Janos Scholz Collection, New York, N.Y.

Red chalk on white paper, 17⅜ x 7⅝ in.

Ref.: Janos Scholz Collection exhibitions: Oakland, 1961; Hamburg, Germany, 1963; Cologne, Germany, 1963-64.

Ludovico Cardi, called **IL CIGOLI**
1559 Castelvecchio (Tuscany)—1613 Rome

Ludovico Cigoli, native of Castelvecchio, came to Florence at the age of thirteen, studied painting with Alessandro Allori and Santo di Tito and architecture under Bernardo Buontalenti who was architect to the Medici court. By the last decade of the century Cigoli had become the key figure in Florentine painting in the movement of reform against the rather sterile condition of the late Mannerist style. In this regard his position was parallel to that of Annibale Carracci in Bologna; similarly he found a way out of the late Mannerist *cul de sac* through his understanding study of the viable elements of style—the supple organicism of form and sensuous beauty of color of the work principally of Correggio, Titian and Barocci. Cigoli served the Medici court in Florence not only as painter but also as architect and designer of pageantry for court festivities. He sojourned intermittently in Rome from 1604 until the end of his career and was engaged for several among the most important decorative enterprises of that period there—notably the decorations of the Chapel of Paul V in Santa Maria Maggiore in 1613.

125. A Kneeling Male Figure

Fogg Art Museum, Harvard University, Cambridge, Mass., bequest of Charles A. Loeser, 1932.

Brush drawing heightened with white on green-gray prepared paper, 15⅜ x 11¼ in.
Coll.: Peter Lely (Lugt 2092).
Ref.: A. Mongan and P. Sachs, *Drawings in the Fogg Museum of Art*, Cambridge, Mass., 1946, no. 245.

This is a characteristic brush drawing by Cigoli, executed with exceptional freshness—*alla prima*—without the preliminary underdrawing in pencil, conventional for the period. The style with its painterly realization of form, shadows and half-tones washed in broadly and sluggish, fatty white highlights set off strongly against the green-gray of the paper—is quite personal, easily recognized and demonstrates the kind of technical and stylistic innovations which projected the art of Cigoli out of the orthodoxy of its period, toward the new spirit of the Baroque style. The drawing may be a study, as Mongan and Sachs have suggested, for a kneeling figure in the lower left of Cigoli's *Entrance of Christ into Jerusulem* (Santa Croce, Florence), although the figure in the painting looks up at the passing Christ. [D.M.]

CRISTOFANO ALLORI
1577 Florence 1621

Cristofano, son of the important late-Mannerist painter, Alessandro Allori, first studied with his father. But attracted by the new developments in Florentine painting, spearheaded by Cigoli and Pagani, he entered the studio of the latter. Cristofano developed a warm, vibrant manner particularly attractive for its characteristic velvety richness of coloring. He gained a considerable reputation not only through his numerous altarpieces in Florentine churches but as portraitist. Moreover, a sketch-book with a series of landscape drawings, highly praised by his biographer Baldinucci, suggests the artist's talent for this subject (the landscape paintings which Baldinucci mentions have not been identified). Cristofano died in 1621, still relatively early in his career. Today he is remembered chiefly for one painting, the hauntingly beautiful *Judith with the Head of Holofernes* in the Pitti Gallery, Florence.

126. Constancy

Robert and Bertina Suida Manning, New York, N. Y.

Panel, 24⅝ x 28¾ in.

Coll.: Private collection, Rome (inventory no. on verso 2122).

This figure, originally identified as a personification of Justice, is rather Constancy. Cesare Ripa (*Nuovo Iconologia*, Venice, 1669, p. 124) describes Constancy as "A lady, her right arm embracing a column and in her left hand an unsheathed sword held above a large brazier with fire, showing herself thus willing to burn her hand and arm." Ripa goes on to explain the significance of this action: "Constancy has a firm disposition and does not yield to bodily pain nor is overcome by sadness, fatigue or any other travail. The raised hand indicates constancy in virtuousness." The features resemble those of Judith in Cristofano's best known painting *Judith with the head of Holofernes* in the Pitti Gallery and one wonders whether the lady who posed for Judith, the painter's *innamorata*, "La Mazzafirra," did not also serve here. [D.M.]

MATTEO ROSSELLI

1579 Florence 1650

Rosselli was a pupil of Gregorio Pagani (1558-1605), who spearheaded the reform movement in Florentine painting. Early in his career Rosselli spent six months in Rome assisting the Florentine painter, Domenico Cresti, called "Il Passignano". There, according to Baldinucci, he studied Raphael and Polidoro da Caravaggio. By the second decade of the century, Rosselli had established himself as one of the leading painters in Florence. His sober and correct manner was highly considered by his contemporaries, and he had a very active career in the production of altar-pieces, easel paintings, and frescos. His studio must have been a lively congenial place, judging from the number of important Florentine painters who trained there: Giovanni da San Giovanni, Furini, Jacopo Vignali, Lorenzo Lippi, Baldassare Franceschini, etc.

127. The Triumph of David

Canvas, 79 x 91⅜ in.

Bob Jones University Collection, Greenville, S. C., 1960.

Coll.: Conti (?); Dr. Isaac Lea; Elizabeth Lea, Philadelphia.

Ref.: C. del Bravo; *Paragone*, 135, March 1961, p. 32; *Bob Jones Collection*, Greenville, S. C., 1962, I, 120-21.

This handsome painting was given to Matteo Rosselli by Hermann Voss (Bob Jones Univ. *Cat.*, 1962, I, 121.). Later it was published by Carlo del Bravo as a work by Rosselli's gifted pupil, Jacopo Vignali; Mina Gregori (letter) concurs in this attribution. Del Bravo, sensing the proximity of the painting to Rosselli's manner, argues that it falls early in the career of the pupil (1615-20). The present writer prefers the attribution to Vignali. [D.M.]

Francesco Motelatici, called *CECCO BRAVO*

1607 Florence—Innsbruck 1661

Although well reputed in his own time, Cecco Bravo has been rescued only recently from oblivion through the articles of G. Ewald and the monograph by Anna Masetti (*Cecco Bravo Pittore Toscano del Seicento*, Venice, 1962). Now that proper definition has been given to this intriguing, highly personal master of the Florentine 17th century, a number of his paintings previously attributed to better-known masters—especially his compatriot, Francesco Furini, and the Venetian Sebastiano Mazzoni—have been correctly identified. The artist was born in Florence in 1607 and his art formed under the primary influences of painters belonging to what Lanzi refers to as "the second generation of innovators in Florence" —Bilivert, Cristofano Allori, Matteo Roselli etc. It is likely, as Dottoressa Masetti has noted, that he was the pupil of Roselli. But it is also important to note the clear reverberations in his work of great Florentine masters of the earlier *Cinquecento*—especially Andrea del Sarto and Pontormo. The influence of Correggio and the important Venetians of the *Cinquecento* upon his development is fundamental. Cecco Bravo's gift as frescoist is seen in a number of decorations in Florence, notably in one of the most important decorative undertakings of the Florentine 17th century, the *Sala degli Argenti* in the Palazzo Pitti.

127

128. *Angelica and Ruggiero*

The story of the love of Angelica and Ruggiero is told in Ariosto's *Orlando Furioso;* the subject of our painting is described in verses CXV of Canto X.

Samuel H. Kress Foundation, New York, N. Y.

Canvas, 12¾ x 17½ in.
Coll.: Dan Fellows Platt, Englewood, N. J.
Ref.: *Paintings and Sculpture from Kress Collection*, Washington, 1949, p. 131; N. Ivanoff in *Memorie di Storia dell' Arte*, Venice, 1959, II, 222; G. Ewald in *Burlington Magazine*, CII, 351 and note 35; Masetti, *Cecco Bravo*, Venice, 1962, no. 19.

This painting, formerly attributed to Francesco Furini and more recently to Sebastiano Mazzoni (by M. Murano and N. Ivanoff), was published as a work by Cecco Bravo in 1960 by G. Ewald and in 1962 by Dottoressa Anna Masetti in her monograph on the artist. Cecco's idiosyncratic manner—the peculiar urgency with which his figures gesture or move, their features muted by a delicate *sfumato*, the agitated impasto tracings of his brush—are all so personal to him as to be easily recognizable now that his style has been sufficiently defined. *Angelica and Ruggiero* belongs to the very last years of the artist's activity—to the most *recherché* exoticisms of his style. It has been brought into relationship with the equestrian portrait of Granduke Ferdinand Charles of the Tirols, upon which Cecco collaborated with the portraitist Justus Sustermans around 1660 (Ewald, p. 351 and Masetti p. 91). Masetti has noted two paintings with scenes from Ariosto's *Orlando Furioso* in the Merenda collection at Forlì, one of which she believes to be a replica of the Kress picture. [D.M.]

BALDASSAR FRANCESCHINI
1611 Volterrano (Tuscany)—Florence 1668

Baldassar Franceschini, called *Il Volterrano* after his native city, first came to Florence as a youth of sixteen and in 1630 entered the studio of the prominent

Florentine master of the period, Matteo Rosselli. Later he came especially to admire the work of Giovanni da San Giovanni and spent five months as the latter's assistant for the decorations in the Sala degli Argento of the Palazzo Pitti. Also an important experience for the artist was his study of Correggio's fresco decorations in Parma on the occasion of two trips to artistic centers in Northern Italy. Volterrano developed especially an ability as fresco decorator; his many works in this medium are found chiefly in Florence and Volterra. Noteworthy among these are the *Coronation of the Virgin* in the immense cupola of the SS. Annunziata in Florence and the extensive cycle of decorations treating episodes from the life of Cosimo de'Medici I, in the loggia of the Villa Petraia. Unusual for a decorator in the grand manner is the vein of popular realism which runs through his work and is best known in the spirited *The Practical Joke of the Priest Arlotto* (Pitti Palace, Florence).

129. Allegory

Museum of Art and Archaeology, The University of Missouri, Columbia, Mo., 1964

Reed pen over red chalk on cream paper, 6½ x 9¼ in.
Coll.: Lucien Goldschmidt, New York

Volterrano's drawing manner was among the most individual of the century. Typical of his eccentric mode of draughtsmanship is this *Allegory* where the basic compositional sketch in sanguine has been reinforced by vigorous strokes of a reed pen, creating an entangled web of lines through which the forms are indistinctly discerned. More than anything else the artist seemed interested in defining the dominant themes of compositional movement. His brusque, unmeditated linear notations are caught up in the over-riding rhythmic impetus of the gesture of drawing itself. The subject is obscure. A winged figure reclines before a tomb. Another winged figure, rather agitated, seems to have just discovered the first. Above the tomb are seated two skeletons; to the right are vestiges of antiquity and a landscape vista beyond. No painting could be connected to this drawing. [D.M.]

STEFANO DELLA BELLA
1610 Florence 1664

Della Bella, gifted and prolific print-maker (De Vesme lists 1052 prints), had one of the most interesting and diversified artistic careers of the 17th century. His first training was as a gold-smith. This was followed by brief periods of study with a succession of Florentine painters (Orazio Vanni, his son Giovanni Battista, Cesare Dandini), but his native inclination led him to concentrate on the technique of etching. The great French engraver Callot was at this time working in Florence and the young Della Bella's

study of Callot's prints was decisive for the formation of his taste and the development of his technical resources. Of some importance, too, in Della Bella's formation was the work of the engraver Remigio Cantagallina, active in Florence 1603-35. Della Bella was taken under the protection of Archduke Lorenzo de'Medici and worked throughout his career for successive grand dukes of Tuscany. He executed commemorative prints of important court functions—marriage ceremonies, obsequies, receptions, fêtes and public amusements sponsored by the ducal family. Della Bella's sojourn in Rome in 1633, which provided him with an important repertory of Roman scenery, was sponsored by Duke Lorenzo. In 1639 he was attracted to Paris, probably because of the flourishing state of Parisian print publishers; almost at once he was employed by Cardinal Richelieu to etch the sieges of Rochelle and Castelet by the armies of Louis XIII, and for the rest of his ten year stay he produced superb prints of court functions—ballets and theatrical spectacles, important episodes in the military campaigns of the French, views of the city of Paris. Mention should be made of his trip to Amsterdam in 1647 which very likely brought him into direct contact with Rembrandt. Della Bella returned to his native city in 1650 and for the rest of his career worked for the Medici court. His practical interest in art pedagogy, which resulted in several etched drawing manuals, was put to use by Ferdinand II, who appointed him drawing master to his young son Cosimo de'Medici.

130. Wolf Hunt

Robert and Bertina Suida Manning, New York, N. Y.

Pen and brush, brown ink with gray wash, 7⅝ x 10⅜ in.
Coll.: Giuseppe Vallardi (Lugt 1223); P. & D. Colnaghi, London.

This sparkling pen sketch executed with characteristic virtuosity, is especially attractive for its quality of sunny luminosity. The warm *sfumato*-like modelling of horse and rider is set off directly against a largely untouched field of paper. The snap of this tonal contrast enhances the suggestiveness of the paper itself as space,

light and atmosphere. Della Bella's peculiarly vibrant calligraphy intensifies the sense of action. [D.M.]

131. Head of an Actor

Janos Scholz Collection, New York, N. Y.

Sanguine on white paper, 5⅞ x 4¾ in.
Coll.: Simon Meller, Budapest.

The attribution of this drawing to Stefano della Bella is credited to Mlle. Roselin Bacou of the Cabinet des Dessins of the Louvre. She notes a similar drawing by Della Bella in that collection. Its picturesqueness, in common with many of Della Bella's prints and drawings, anticipates the capricious fancy of the Rococo. [D.M.]

ERCOLE BAZZICALUVA
c. 1600 Pisa—(?)

Bazzicaluva, engraver and etcher, was born in Pisa around 1600, but was largely active in Florence. He was a pupil of Giulio Parigi and was strongly influenced by Callot, who earlier had worked with Parigi in Florence. From his relatively small graphic production and the various positions he held as court functionary and custodian, it would seem that he only sporadically made prints.

132. *Italian Soldiers and a Blind Beggar*

The Detroit Institute of Arts, gift John S. Newberry, Jr., 1946

Pen drawing, 5⅛ x 7¾ in.

This drawing, as Janos Scholz has noted (letter) belongs to the *milieu* of Giulio Parigi, Ramigio Cantagallina, and the early work of Stefano della Bella (to whom it was previously attributed). The debt to Callot (who worked in Florence from 1611 until 1621) is substantial. The penmanship is derived from Callot engravings as is also the taste in figure type and costume. Indecisions of perspective and a certain lack of authority of line in the figures suggests a younger Florentine artist. Stefano della Bella might have done such a drawing during his formative years but his line is always more taut, his figures have a more piquant elegance. A more likely candidate is Ercole Bazzicaluva, whose several drawings in the Albertina, Vienna, seem close in style (see Stix and Fröhlich-Bum, *Zeichnungen der Toskanischen Umbrischen und Romischen Schulen*, Vienna, 1932, nos. 827-30). [D.M.]

MASSIMILIANO SOLDANI BENZI
1656 Montevarchi (Florence) 1740

In 1675 Soldani went to Florence to study at the drawing classes held at the Granducal Galleria. Chosen by Cosimo III to be trained as a medallist, he was sent to Rome to study modelling under Ercole Ferrata, drawing under Ciro Ferri, and the medallic technique under Pietro Travani. After a short visit to Paris, he returned to Florence in 1682 to be put in charge of the Granducal mint, a post held until 1722.

Besides working as the official medalist of the Granduke and producing over fifty cast medals that rank among the best of their time, Soldani was asked to make drawings and models for gold and silver reliquaries and ostensories, and many bronze reliefs and groups, not only for members of the Medici family, but also for German princes and English noblemen. For Prince Liechtenstein of Vienna he made three allegorical reliefs (1694-97); for the Palatine Elector, the reliefs (1708-11) of the *Four Seasons* (Bayerisches Nationalmuseum, Munich). Both series show Soldani's characteristic compositional clarity and typical Florentine sharpness of outline, as well as his refined technical accomplishment as a sculptor in bronze. To the teaching of Ciro Ferri and Ferrata, he added motives derived from the masters of the Roman Baroque—Bernini, Algardi, Pietro da Cortona and Gaulli—assimilated in a personal way and directed towards original decorative effects.

Among his small statuettes and groups in bronze, best known are a *Lamentation of Christ* of which the Walters Art Gallery and the Seattle Art Museum have variants, and *Venus and Adonis*, also in Baltimore. His bronze decorations for the main altar at Santa Maria di Carignano in Genoa (1699), and the two impressive wall tombs of the Great Masters of the Order of Malta—*Marcantonio Zondadari* and *Manoel de Vilhena* (1722-29), San Giovanni, La Valletta (Malta), were Soldani's most ambitious undertakings, the climax of an artistic career which made of him, next to Giovanni Battista Foggini, the best representative of Florentine late Baroque art.

133. Venus and Adonis

In the Soldani group, Adonis, the handsome youth beloved by Venus, is dying on a rocky ledge, wounded at hunt by a wild boar. The goddess holds his head in her lap. A sorrowing putto uncovers the wound on the thigh of Adonis, from whose blood a red anemone grows on the ground. (See Ovid's *Metamorphoses*, X, 708-28.)

Walters Art Gallery, Baltimore, Md.

Bronze, H. (incl. ebony base with bronze mounts) 27¾ in. Inscribed on base: Amore Resurgam (May I be reborn by love).
Coll.: Ravensworth Castle, England.
Ref.: K. Lankheit in *München Jahrbuch der Bildenden Kunst, 1956*, VII 192, and in *Walters Art Gallery Journal*, XIX-XX, 1956-57, 9ff.; *Age of Elegance*, Baltimore Museum, 1959, no. 229; *Gothic to Baroque*, Allentown Art Museum, 1960, no. 34; K. Lankheit, *Florentinische Barokplastik*, Munich, 1962, pp. 138-39.

Klaus Lankheit has shown how the distinctive style of Soldani's groups is directly related to his training as a medalist. This *Venus and Adonis* group—which should probably be dated shortly after 1700—is conceived like a relief, from a strictly frontal point-of-view, and shows Soldani's peculiar emphasis upon parallel diagonal lines and planes.

The decorative rhythm of the composition, the punctilious craftsmanship of the surface finish, and the funerary symbolism expressed in the appliques of the base—with the elks' skulls, the garlands of ivy and the inscribed cartouche—give this group the character of a Baroque "conceit" in visual form. A highly refined *objet d'art*, it reflects the taste of the literary minded and sophisticated courtly circles of Soldani's times. [O.R.]

V. *Milan*

Giovan Battista Crespi, called *IL CERANO*
1575 Cerano near Novara—Milan 1633

The outstanding talent among the Milanese artists, Cerano, apart from his principal activity as painter, was also architect, sculptor, writer, engraver and intimate of the intellectual circle of the Borromeo family. Cerano was the official painter to Cardinal Federigo Borromeo, and celebrated the family saint, the Archbishop of Milan, Carlo Borromeo (1538-1584), with fresco cycles in the Duomo. His patron and client by 1601, Federigo made Cerano the first director of his academy founded in 1620.

Cerano's early life is still poorly documented. His style was developed under the guidance of Barocci's paintings in Milan and the great late Mannerist fresco cycles that he became familiar with on his trips to Rome in the 1590s: the Oratory of the Gonfalone Confraternity painted in 1572 by Federico Zuccari and Cesare Nebbia (also well known to Cardinal Borromeo); the official decorative schemes of the pontificates of Sixtus V and Clement VIII, the Sistine Chapel in Sta. Maria Maggiore, the Sistine Library in the Vatican, and the transept of St. John Lateran.

Cerano never abandoned completely the decorative types of late Mannerism, but his style steadily developed an emotional intensity and a painterly breadth that is wholly Baroque, heightened by a certain refined elongation and elegant contortion: a residuum of late Mannerism.

134. *The Madonna and Child with St. Francis*

Mr. and Mrs. Paul H. Ganz, New York, N. Y.

Canvas, 46 x 37 in.
Ref.: Rosci and Brizio, *Mostra del Cerano*, Novara, 1964, no. 112; M. Valsecchi in *Paragone*, 1964.

This is an example of a standard devotional type produced by Cerano and his workshop. Easel pictures with similar compositions and subjects were especially frequent in the early 1620s. Valsecchi cited two versions, one in Florence and the other at Sotheby's in London. There are also a *bozzetto* (Castello Sforzesco, Milan; [*Mostra*, no. 113]), and variants (Milan, Coll. Uggè [*Mostra*, no. 111]; Pavia, Certosa, *Madonna with SS. Carlo and Ugo of Grenoble* [*Mostra*, no. 108]; *Madonna with SS. Siro and Anthony*, Pavia, Cath. [*Mostra*, no. 123: dated c. 1625]). In *SS. Siro and Anthony* the figure of St. Francis becomes St. Anthony, but the pose and the Christ Child are the same. Indeed the Ganz picture must depend upon this altarpiece, and so should be dated c. 1625. The New York picture and its related compositions are all closely connected with Raphael's various Madonnas with saints. The *Foligno* (Vatican), the *Holy Family under a Palm Tree* (London, Bridgewater House), the *Alba Madonna* (Wash., Nat. Gall.), and the *Belle Jardinière* (Louvre) are pertinent reminding one that the Carracci looked to Raphael to revitalize their art, an attitude not usually connected with the Milanese School. [F.C.]

Pier Francesco Mazzucchelli called *MORAZZONE*

1573 Morazzone near Varese—Piacenza 1626

His principal teacher was Ventura Salimbeni. Early in his life, he was in Rome where his frescos in S. Silvestro in Capito can still be seen. By 1602 he had returned to Lombardy where he executed frescos in the Ascent to Calvary Chapel and the "Ecce Homo" Chapel of the Sacro Monte in Varallo. He was particularly able in organizing the execution of grand series of frescos to be carried out by a large workshop.

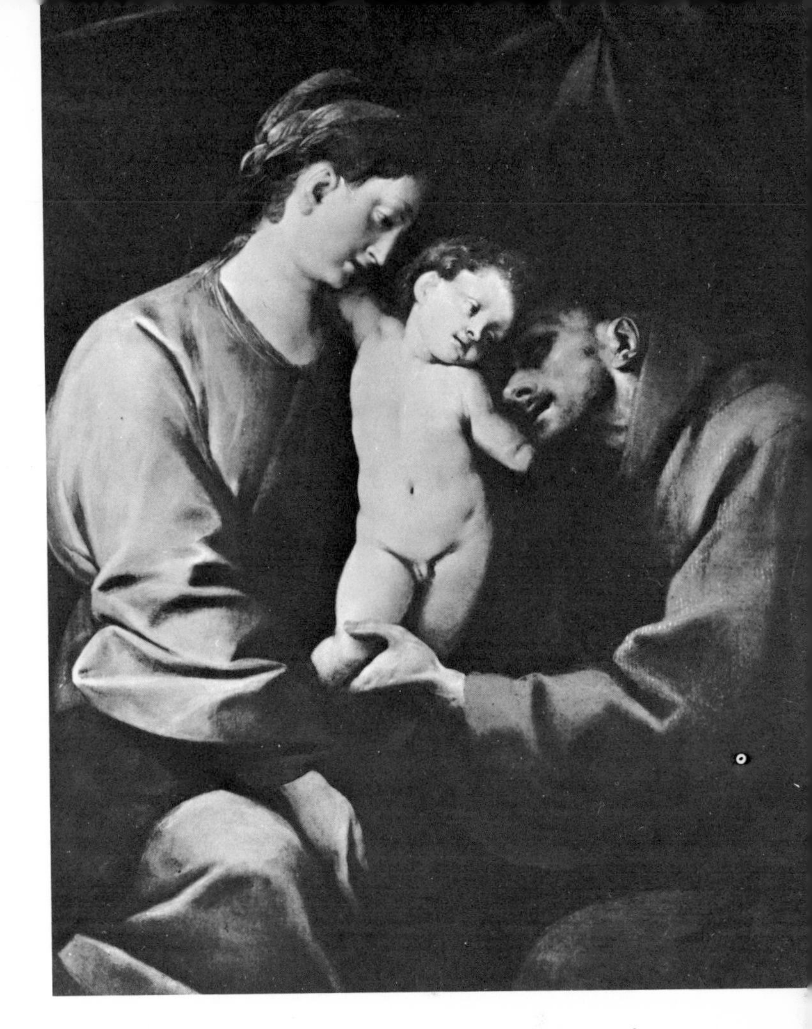

His compositions and even the special psychology of his character reflect a heightened emotionalism that recalls medieval mystery plays and Morazzone's own experience of the works of Gaudenzio Ferrari. Morazzone went further than his contemporaries in promoting a popular, illusionistic realism in fresco by using contemporary architecture extending into the observer's space, contemporary costumes, and genre elements in close connection with religious events. These paintings recall Morazzone's interest in Venetian painting and remind one of the note by Borsieri (*Supplimento della Nobilità di Milano*, Milan, 1619, p. 64), that he copied numerous compositions by Tintoretto.

135. *The Flagellation of Christ*

The special reference in this *Ecce Homo* presented in the guise of a *Flagellation of Christ* is revealed by the appearance of St. Peter on the lower right clasping his hands and kneeling in penitence. The keys of the Saint are almost hidden in shadow.

Mr. and Mrs. Paul H. Ganz, New York, N. Y.

Canvas, 47½ x 50 in.

Coll.: Robert Vose Gallery, Boston.

Ref.: M. Rosci in *Bolletino d'Arte*, 1959, pp. 151-57; R. Longhi in *Paragone*, VIII, 1957, no. 87, p. 68; M. Gregori and R. Longhi, *Il Morazzone*, Milan, 1962, no. 47.

This picture, one of the most important Milanese paintings in America, was attributed to Daniele Crespi by Bode in 1911. G. Constable relegated it to the Circle of Crespi and others called it simply Genoese School, Longhi, in 1957, was the first to recognize the painting as an important work by Morazzone. It has been dated around 1616 and associated with an *Ecce Homo* completed by the artist on June 7, 1616, for the Podesta of Novara, Gregorio Ambelli (Gregori and Longhi, p. 221). This *Flagellation* is significant within Morazzone's career because it bridges a gap to his late style as illustrated in the so-called *Quadro di Tre Mani* (Brera, Milan), generally dated around 1620. The association with the *Ecce Homo* of 1616 is supported on stylistic grounds by the pronounced and forceful anatomy of the principal figure and by the almost monochromatic, sombre color. The ascetic, generally brown color reveals a gravity dependent on Caravaggio, coupled with an emotional intensity deriving from late Mannerism and perhaps ultimately from a deep strain of medieval emotionalism remaining in Milan—the qualities of the Milanese School at its best. The painting has been related to a print recorded by Campori (*Raccolta di Cataloghi*, 1870, p. 455). [F.C.]

136. Madonna and Child with St. John

Robert and Bertina Suida Manning, New York, N. Y.

Brush and brown ink, heightened with white on gray-brown paper, 7¾ x 7¾ in.
Coll.: P. & D. Colnaghi, London.
Ref.: Colnaghi, *Old Master Drawings*, London, 1951, no. 24; M. Gregori and R. Longhi, *Il Morazzone*, Milan, 1962, no. 55.

The attribution to Morazzone was made by Popham with a verbal agreement by Pouncey. Arslan, on the other hand, has doubted the attribution. However, the figure style of the drawing, the arrangement of the figures in a shallow foreground space making a linear and decorative design close to the surface and their types are those of Morazzone. Moreover, the technique is confirmed as Morazzone's by comparison with *The Assumption* (Brera inv. no. 138) and *The Coronation of the Virgin* (Uffizi inv. 744E; Gregori and Longhi, no. 11). Both drawings also exhibit the chiaroscuro technique in which dark washes, almost acid-like in their tendency to eradicate even important forms like faces and heads, appear. These rich areas of shadow are brightened and given form by the introduction of white applied with the brush in broad and thin strokes, widely separated from each other, forming screens of long and rhythmic hatching. The drawing belongs to Morazzone's late style about 1618-20. [F.C.]

137. Figure Study

Possibly a study for an apostle.

Janos Scholz Collection, New York, N. Y.

Brush, brown ink over black chalk on a paper trimmed irregularly, 9¾ x 11¾ in.
Coll.: Zatzka.
Ref.: Alfred Neumeyer and Janos Scholz, *Drawings from Lombardy and Adjacent Areas*, Oakland, 1956; M. Gregori and R. Longhi, *Il Morazzone*, Milan, 1962, no. 57.

Arslan has not accepted the attribution of this study to Morazzone. However, its haunting beauty leads one to persist in valuing it as an important drawing closely related to the master. [F.C.]

GIULIO CESARE PROCACCINI
1574 Bologna—Milan 1625

One of the three foremost painters in Milan in the early seventeenth century, the other two being Giovanni Battista Crespi (Il Cerano) and Morazzone, he was also the most gifted of his family. Born in

Bologna, he settled in Milan around 1590. He was trained and began his career as a sculptor with the reliefs on the façade of SS. Nazare e Celso in Milan, and about 1600 he turned to painting. In 1610 after his stay in Modena, he was commissioned to do six of the *Twenty Four Miracles of San Carlo Borromeo* in the Cathedral of Milan. Between 1613 and 1616, he came strongly under the influence of Correggio and Parmigianino introducing a softness and sweetness into his art which had been lacking in his earlier style and which does not appear in the other members of the Milanese School. In 1618 he traveled to Genoa where he saw works by Rubens introducing a new influence and change into his late style.

138. The Flight into Egypt

See no. 161.

Maestro Francesco Molinari Predelli, Bologna, Italy.

Canvas, 36¾ x 49¾ in.
Coll.: Frederick Mont, N. Y.; Maestro Predelli, 1964.

This fresh and broadly handled picture is certainly the most important and most beautiful painting by Procaccini to appear in America in recent years. The elongated strokes covering the surface reveal his reliance on the palette knife to obtain an interwoven series of iridescent hues. This broken color technique can be seen in the modello of the *Madonna and Child* in the National Museum in Naples (N. Pevsner in *Rivista d'Arte*, 1929, p. 335, fig. 7). The use of angels to frame the principal motif, to animate the composition, and to confirm and amplify psychological attitudes is a hallmark of Giulio Cesare's art and is used here to great effect.

The masterly use of this technique is best seen in the *Pietà* in Sant' Angelo in Milan (Pevsner, 1929, p. 339, fig. 9). The elaborate landscape, rare in his works, and the pure and lyrical color suggest a date in the middle of the second decade. [F.C.]

CAMILLO PROCACCINI
c. 1551 Bologna (?)—Milan 1629

Camillo was the elder brother of Giulio Cesare Procaccini. A pupil of his father, Ercole the Elder, he studied works by Correggio and Parmigianino and became a member of the painters' guild in Bologna in 1571. Around 1585-86 he was mentioned in Milan, the stage of his extended activity. He received commissions for paintings in the Collegio di Spagna in Bologna, in the Collegiata di S. Prospero in Reggio, in the Cathedral of Piacenza, and in the Palazzo Doria in Genoa, among others. His frequent journeys between cities are characteristic and give us a hint of the habits of this artist and his contemporaries who went where there was work to be done. In 1590 Camillo was painting the organ wings in the Cathedral of Milan, and he was occupied in that city for the greatest part of the decade. He was particularly fond of warm tones and bright color, complicated compositions, technical tour de force and inexhaustible fantasy. These special interests keep him very much within the Mannerist taste of the sixteenth century.

139. The Madonna and Child

Janos Scholz Collection, New York, N. Y.

Red chalk, brush and brown ink, heightened with white, on paper toned light brown, 8⅞ x 7³⁄₁₆ in.

Coll.: Savoia-Aosta (Lugt suppl. 47a).

Ref.: Janos Scholz Collection exhibitions: Hamburg, Germany, 1963; Cologne, Germany, 1963-64.

This nervous, brilliant drawing makes a particularly happy comparison with the *Flight to Egypt* by Camillo's brother (no. 138). Giulio Cesare's broad painting manner carried out in repeated strokes of the palette knife is here seen transferred to a drawing executed with the brush in varicolored strokes to form the kind of "phosphorescent splendor" of which Wittgen spoke in characterizing Procaccini's style. A similar drawing with an old attribution to

Camillo was sold in Zürich (October 28, 1943, no. 139). [F.C.]

Antonio d'Enrico, called *TANZIO DA VARALLO*
1575 Riale d'Alagna—Varallo 1635

One of the most temperamental and violent of Milanese artists, Tanzio reflects the somewhat medieval, religious climate that lingers on into the seventeenth century in Milan. His style reveals the impact of Caravaggio whose works he may have known in Rome sometime between 1610 and 1615. This sets Tanzio's work apart from that of say Giulio Cesare Procaccini in whom the sweetness, color, and broad treatment of Parma were to take a firm hold. The ascetic "realism" of Caravaggio coupled with Tanzio's highly mannered figures produces a figural type of ecstatic character, an effect heightened by a certain crudeness produced by archaizing means.

140. St. John the Baptist in the Wilderness

"For this is he that was spoken of by the prophet Esaias, saying, The voice of one crying in the wilderness, Prepare ye the way of the Lord, make his paths straight. And the same John had his raiment of camel's hair, and a leathern girdle about his loins; and his meat was locusts and wild honey." (*Matthew* III, 3-4.)

Samuel H. Kress Collection, Philbrook Art Center, Tulsa, Oklahoma.

Canvas, 63¾ x 43¾ in.

Coll.: Comm. Enrico Marinucci, Rome; Samuel H. Kress Collection, 1939.

Ref.: G. Testori, *Tanzio da Varallo*, Turin, Museo Civico, 1959-60, no. 13; R. Longhi in *Proporzioni*, I, 1943, 53n; Samuel H. Kress Foundation, *Art Treasures for America*, London, 1961, fig. 128.

Roberto Longhi was the first to recognize Tanzio da Varallo's authorship of this painting (previously attributed to Velasquez). It has also been attributed to Tanzio by G. Fiocco, F. M. Perkins, W. Suida, and A. Venturi. A sheet of drawings in the Pinacoteca in Varallo (Testori, no. 54) has been related to it in a somewhat forced way. This superb painting in Tanzio's best style is certainly his most important work in America. It should be dated around 1625. [F.C.]

140A. Kneeling Franciscan Monk

Janos Scholz Collection, New York, N. Y.

Red and white chalks on red tinted paper, 9¼ x 6¼ in.

Ref.: Testori, *Tanzio da Varallo*, Turin, Museo Civico, 1959-60, no. 44.

This fine drapery study by a draughtsman whose works are very rare indeed has been associated by Testori with a sheet in the Pinacoteca in Varallo (Testori, 1959-60, no. 43, Pl. 140) which prepares for a lost altarpiece showing the Virgin adored by Franciscan saints. The present sheet formed part of a large group of drawings which appeared on the Zürich art market from an unknown North-Italian source. [F.C.]

FRANCESCO DEL CAIRO

1607 Santo Stefano in Brivio—Milan 1665

Brought by his father to Varese at an early age, del Cairo may have studied with Morazzone in Milan. By 1633 he was court painter to Vittorio Amedeo I Duke of Savoy at Turin, who distinguished him as Cavaliere di S. Maurizio in 1632. He journeyed to Rome in 1638-39 and later to Venice. In 1648 he settled at Milan. His travels in northeastern Italy brought him under the influence of Guido Reni and the Venetians, and his vigorous and original early style with its febrile sensibility gave way to the imposing influence of his towering contemporaries in Bologna and Venice. This Goethe-like development proves less interesting visually than intellectually for, as Wittkower has noted, del Cairo's later work became "languid, thin, and classical." Perhaps it was the very tension between his romantic temperament and the violence and intensity of the Milanese tradition that assisted him to produce the gripping compositions of his early period which prepare for Magnasco and Goya.

141. Herodias

This fragment is probably an Herodias who has just been presented with the bloody head of St. John the Baptist on a charger formerly below her right hand (see no. 151). Figures of almost identical type and ecstatic mood were employed by del Cairo for Lucretia, St. Agnes, and Cleopatra.

Mr. and Mrs. Paul H. Ganz, New York, N. Y.

Canvas, 28½ x 24½ in.

Testori has referred to the "black and tragic poetry of del Cairo." A saint swooning in ecstacy by lamplight or preferably by moonlight (del Cairo was as aware as any romantic of the power of moonlit landscapes to set the mood of ecstacy) was one of his favorite subjects. The swooning Herodias is found in at least three other works by del Cairo (Vicenza, Pinacoteca; Boston Museum; Sabauda Gallery, Turin). The Ganz picture is closest to that in Vicenza. Both date before 1635 during his first and best period when he was court painter at Turin. The macabre subject and lighting are Caravaggesque but with a softness, an intricacy, and a trancelike quality suggestive of Morazzone's late style. [F.C.]

DANIELE CRESPI

1598/1600 Milan 1630

Trained in the tradition of, if not by, Cerano and Procaccini, by 1619 Daniele was assisting Moncalvo (Guglielmo Caccia) in frescoing the dome of S. Vittore in Milan. The same year he received an independent commission to decorate the Annunciation chapel of S. Eustorgio. His principal undertaking, a fresco cycle for the Certosa of Garegnano, Milan, is signed and dated 1629. Crespi's precocious and successful talent was cut short by the plague during the course of work in the Certosa of Pavia. Wittkower has noted that Crespi's best works "combined severe realism and parsimonious handling of pictorial means with a sincerity of expression fully in sympathy with the religious climate at Milan" (1958). The influence of Rubens and van Dyck is evident in his work, and he may have known Zurbaran's.

142. Death of a Warrior or Saint

Janos Scholz Collection, New York, N. Y.

Pen and brush, brown ink heightened with white on green-gray paper, 9¾ x 10½ in.
Coll.: Vallardi (Lugt 1223) album no. 595.
Ref.: Janos Scholz Collection exhibitions: Oakland, 1956; Columbia, S. C., 1961; Hamburg, Germany, 1963, Cologne, Ger., 1963-64.

Philip Pouncey first gave it to A. Tiarini but, after examining the original drawing, has agreed with an attribution to Daniele Crespi. [F.C.]

STEFANO MARIA LEGNANI
called Legnanino
1660 Milan 1750

A pupil of his father Ambrogio (or Cristoforo) Legnani, Stefano also probably studied under Cigoli in Bologna and Maratti in Rome. He worked in the Duomo of Milan (1690s), in S. Filippo, Genoa (1712), and also in the Piedmont. Although he was the outstanding artist in late 17th century Milan, still very little is known about him. His late style is thoroughly of the eighteenth century, exhibiting smoky azures, roses and grays, and a refined morbidity worthy of Pellegrini. (Arslan, *Duomo*, Milan, 1960, pp. 88, 90.)

143. Kneeling Nun

Museum of Art and Archaeology, The University of Missouri, Columbia, Mo.

Red and white chalk on tan paper; 14⅛ x 10 in. Male nude (verso). Coll.: Tilla, Milan. Verso, unrecorded collector's mark in Gothic script "BF" (?), stamped in purple. Sold as Morazzone at the Dorotheum, Vienna (3-4 June 1938, lot 278); Rockman Prints, New York, 1963.

This drawing was identified as Legnani on the basis of its relationship to *Christ Placing the Crown of Thorns on the Head of St. Catherine* (Monastery of St. Anthony Abbot, Cathedral, Milan; E. Arslan, *Le Pitture del Duomo di Milano*, Milan, 1960, pl. 167). The painting is dated by Arslan around 1690. Anthony M. Clark verbally agrees with the attribution to Legnani but believes the drawing does not prepare for the *St. Catherine* at Milan. [F.C.]

VI. *Naples*

JUSEPE DE RIBERA
called Lo Spagnoletto
1591 Jativa—Naples 1652

Ribera went very young to Italy and after visiting the North settled before 1615 in Rome where he was influenced by Caravaggio's works. By 1616 he had settled in Naples, and he stayed there the rest of his life, becoming the dean of Neopolitan painters and achieving an international reputation during his lifetime. He did no frescos, although he carried out some decorative cycles in oil. From his Spanish background and his responsiveness to Caravaggio he developed a personal style, which at different times was influenced by sixteenth century Venetians, notably Veronese, and by the seventeenth century Bolognese school.

144. Saint Jerome

One of the four Fathers of the Latin Church and the translator of the Vulgate Bible, St. Jerome (347-420) was often represented as a cardinal (although he was not), sometimes accompanied by a lion and sometimes by an angel; generally he appears as a scholar, usually with pen, ink pot, books and skull as his attributes, and frequently semi-nude to indicate he was a hermit. In this instance, Ribera, who represented him a number of times, has eliminated all but the most essential attributes to characterize him as a severe ascetic.

Ponce Art Museum (Luis A. Ferré Foundation), Ponce, Puerto Rico.

Canvas, 48 x 39⅛ in. Signed and dated lower left (on book): 1649.
Coll.: W. J. Gwynn, Lypiatt Park, Gloucester, England.
Ref.: *Blanco y Negro*, 1962, LXXII.

This fine picture shows Ribera at his most Caravaggesque and, except for the dated signature, would seem to have been painted no later than the early 1620s. The late dating of the painting is supported not only by the signature, but also by its similarity to a documented *Saint Jerome* (Naples, Capodimonte), commissioned for the Monastery of San Martino in 1638 but not signed until 1651. Despite a stiffer pose, fuller light and slightly more elaborate iconography, the Capodimonte painting is basically the same in conception as the Ponce version, which presumably either was painted in the 1620s but not signed and dated until later, or marks

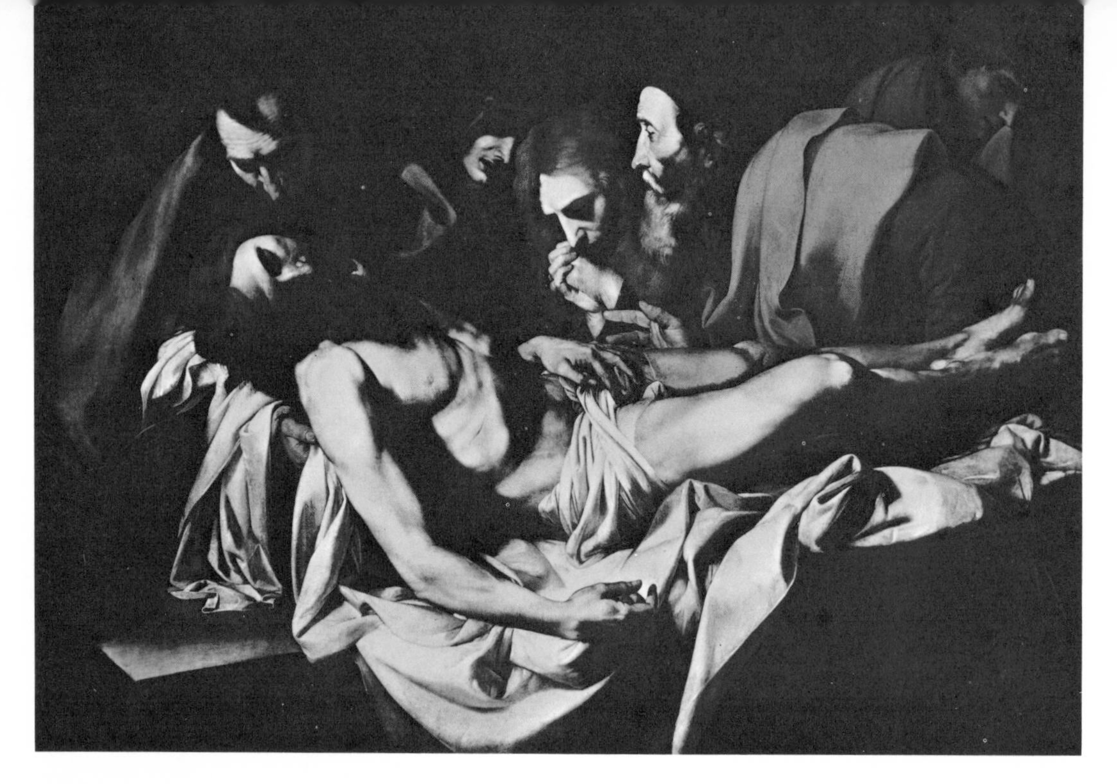

a late reappearance of Ribera's early intense Caravaggism. Ribera apparently derived his idea for the subject from Caravaggio's several versions, but by eliminating the discreet halos with which Caravaggio emphasized the old man's sainthood, created an image which is more strictly terrestrial. In fact, Ribera seems here to have achieved perfectly Caravaggio's ideal of representing sacred figures as belonging to mankind; Ribera's *St. Jerome* is memorable not because of any hints of divine inspiration but because of his austere and evidently commanding human personality. The painting might be considered a kind of portrait: its point is less sacred legend or doctrine than character. [A.M.]

145. The Entombment

Traditionally important as one of the events of Christ's Passion, this subject attracted Caravaggio (Pinacoteca, Vatican) and his followers. Because it presented the death of the Savior beautifully as demanded by the Council of Trent, offered the display of the venerated body of Christ, and allowed a diversity of intense dramatic responses, it appealed to many facets of the seventeenth century mind.

Bob Jones University Collection, Greenville, S. C.

Canvas, 51½ x 71¼ in.
Coll.: Weitzner, 1961.

Ref.: *Bob Jones Collection*, Greenville, 1962, no. 204; *Man: Glory, Jest and Riddle*, M. H. de Young Museum, San Francisco, 1965, no. 120.

The painting illustrates a significant amount of Caravaggism in the intense patterns of deep shadow relieved by brilliant green-white highlights suggesting in an all-too-palpable manner the presence of death. In the 1962 catalogue it is dated in Ribera's mature years 1635-40. [F.C.]

GIOVANNI BATTISTA CARACCIOLO
called il Battistello
c. 1580 Naples 1637

The city's first memorable native 17th century painter, Caracciolo was a pivotal figure in the history of Neapolitan painting. He was originally trained by a mediocre late Mannerist, Fabrizio Santafede, with whom he was still collaborating on frescos during the 1620's. Nevertheless, a decade or more before, Caracciolo had brought his style of oil painting up to date, particularly in response to Caravaggio's visits to Naples between 1606 and 1610, and also probably as the result of a trip to Rome (and perhaps to North Italy) about 1616 or shortly thereafter. Thus by 1620 Caracciolo not only had become Caravaggio's first and closest Neapolitan follower, to whom all later Caravaggesque painters in the city were indebted, but, in addition, was establishing along with Ribera the foundations of Neapolitan 17th century painting.

Too often Caracciolo has been mistakenly considered a mere imitator of Caravaggio. In fact, his canvases were always markedly personal and, particularly during the last fifteen years of his life, he developed a distinctively independent and original style. Furthermore, throughout his career he was an accomplished fresco painter in a generally non-Caravaggesque style which had a substantial influence on his younger contemporaries.

146. Mary Magdalen at the Foot of the Cross

The Magdalen is seated at the foot of the cross in a kind of stupor, her head against it, her left hand lightly caressing it, while her right hand touches an ointment jar concealed in shadow. She customarily appears in the group of attendants at the Crucifixion at the foot of the cross.

Robert Enggass has suggested that the subject "derives ultimately from the Caravaggio *Magdalen* at the Doria." It should be noted also that Caravaggio's lost *Magdalen in Ecstasy* was in Naples in 1612 when Finson made the signed and dated copy of it now in the Musée des Beaux-Arts, Marseilles.

Mr. and Mrs. Paul H. Ganz, New York, N. Y.

Canvas, 39 x 29½ in. Inscribed above to right on leg of cross with monogram (CAB).

Coll.: Denstone College, England; Thomas Agnew and Sons, London.

Ref.: Gilbert, *Baroque Painters of Naples*, Ringling Museum, Sarasota, 1961, no. 6; Enggass in *Burlington Magazine*, CIII, 1961, 199; Manning, *Neopolitan Masters*, Finch College Museum, New York, 1962, no. 1.

In the Busiri-Vici Collection, Rome, is another signed *Mary Magdalen* (seated full-length) a variant is at Capodimonte, Naples. Both can be dated during the late 1610s. Creighton Gilbert dates the Ganz painting 1620-1630; a considerably earlier date would be indicated by the crowding of the figure into limited space, if this effect were not probably the result of the canvas having been at some time cut down. Nonetheless, despite the amplitude of the

forms, the sharp line of the neck (reminiscent of Caravaggio's Doria *Magdalen*), and the complexity of the drapery folds, all of which are consistent with Gilbert's dating, the painting seems to fit best between the artist's Roman trip of ca. 1616-1618 and his masterpiece of 1622, the *Lavanda* (Naples, Monastery-Church of San Martino). Supporting this dating are not only the Busiri-Vici work but also the *Via Crucis* (Naples, Santa Maria del Popolo agli Incurabili), which was apparently painted while his experiences in Rome were still fresh. The Magdalen's left hand is almost identical to one on the cross in the *Via Crucis*, and the physiognomy is similar. [A.M.]

147. David with the Head of Goliath

The subject enjoyed a particular popularity among Caravaggio's followers, and this draughtsman seems to have been familiar with Caravaggio's picture in the Galleria Borghese. Quite apart from the almost parodied giantism of Goliath's head and the sword, the pose

of the David is as restless and alert as Caravaggio's is calm and contemplative.

Janos Scholz Collection, New York, N. Y.

Pen and brush, brown-grey ink on white paper. 10 11/16 x 7⅞ in.
Coll.: Piancastelli (Lugt 2078a); Brandegee (Lugt 1860c).

The attribution of this drawing originates from an inscription on the old mount in the Piancastelli-Brandegee Collection, which according to the owner, dates back to the very early 18th century; very possibly this drawing, like many other Neapolitan drawings in the Piancastelli Collection, came from the collection of Bernardo De Dominici, the principal historian of 17th century painting in Naples.

Only one painting representing *David* has been attributed to Caracciolo (exhibited Galerie Heim, Paris, 1955), and other Caracciolo drawings known to me are in chalk, so authentication of this drawing seems difficult. Nonetheless, the pose so reminiscent of Mannerism, the linear technique, and the consistent agitation throughout are in keeping with Caracciolo's painted work, particularly after c. 1625. [A.M.]

MASSIMO STANZIONE
1585 Orta di Atella—Naples 1656

Stanzione started to study music, according to Dominici, but when he was 18 entered Santafede's studio to learn painting. He was influenced by Caravaggio, by Ribera, and particularly by Caracciolo. During 1617-18 and probably during 1623-25, Stanzione sojourned in Rome, where he was successful enough to gain a knighthood, and where he felt the influence of the Bolognese, particularly of Guido Reni. When Artemisia Gentileschi went to Naples about 1630, she also influenced him, as did the work of Vouet and van Dyck. About 1630, Stanzione achieved maturity and, until his death of the plague (which decimated the ranks of Neapolitan painters and marked the end of their first Baroque phase), he was one of the leading and most influential painters in the city.

148. Martyrdom of Saint Sebastian

One of the most popular early Christian martyrs, St. Sebastian was a centurian in the First Cohort in the time of the Emperor Diocletian. When he refused to abjure Christianity, Diocletian condemned him to death at the hands of archers. Left to die pierced by so many arrows that according to St. Ambrose he resembled a hedge-hog, Sebastian was rescued by the widow Irene, who nursed him back to health only to have him once again challenge the emperor who this second time guaranteed his death by having him beaten to death. The subject was much repeated in the Renaissance because it provided artists the opportunity of representing the youthful heroic male nude in the tradition of classical antiquity, and this popularity increased, if anything, after the Council of Trent. The subject has also a symbolic reference to the plague.

Nelson Gallery-Atkins Museum, Kansas City, Mo. (Gift of Dr. and Mrs. Hanns Schaeffer).

Canvas, 39¼ x 31½ in. Inscribed lower left: MSE.
Ref.: *Nelson Gallery Bull.*, 1958, I, 11; *Art Quarterly*, 1959, XXII, 85; Gilbert, *Baroque Painters of Naples*, Sarasota, 1961, p. 13.

Moving as this small painting is, the attribution to Stanzione is open to question. Although he did paint single figures of saints,

and sometimes included landscape settings in his larger paintings, he rarely if ever utilized a format quite like this; in fact, the format is very close to that used by Domenico Gargiulo (called Micco Spadaro) in his *St. Sebastian* (Corsini Gallery, Rome), the source for which seems to be Cavallino. Specifically to be noted is the same detailed emaciation in the musculature of Cavallino's *Healing of St. Sebastian* (Rome, Galleria Corsini). No record appears of Stanzione's having painted a *Martyrdom of St. Sebastian;* his only relevant subject is the very dissimilar *Healing* of the saint (Musée des Beaux-Arts, Lyon).

The signature is far from convincing. The elements of the monogram are arranged in a manner nowhere duplicated in Stanzione's many signed paintings. The stiff ridged drapery also seems different from any to be found elsewhere in Stanzione's work, and the rather clumsy handling of the breastplate at the saint's feet is entirely contradictory of the artist's usually suave handling.

Finally, dramatically and emotionally effective as the representation of the saint may be, it is so powerful as almost in itself to eliminate the painting from Stanzione's *oeuvre*. The artist could create effects of real passion, as he did for example in the *Preaching of St. John the Baptist* (Madrid, Prado), but even in such paintings, his style maintained a grace and rhythmic ease which is a far cry from the awkward anguished angularity of the *St. Sebastian*. Probably it does belong in Naples, at Stanzione's time and somewhere in the periphery of the great number of painters, most of them as yet relatively unknown, in his circle; but at present it seems impossible to establish an unquestionable attribution for it. [A.M.]

149. Massacre of the Innocents

King Herod, angered by the failure of the Magi to betray the

infant Christ to him, had all children of two years or less in Bethlehem slaughtered, thus fulfilling the prophecy of "Rachel weeping for her children," but failing to destroy Christ who had been taken in flight to Egypt. (See *Matthew* 2:16-18).

Janos Scholz Collection, New York, N. Y.

Pen and brush, brown ink over black crayon, on white paper, 7¼ x 5¾ in. Inscribed upper left: "Stanzione" (in a later hand)
Coll.: Piancastelli; Brandegee.
Ref.: Scholz in *Art Quarterly*, 1960, pp. 62, 68; Vitzthum, in *Burlington Magazine*, 1961, p. 314; Hamburg, *Italienische Meisterzeichnungen*, 1963, no. 149.

According to Scholz this is the right half of a larger composition. A painting of the subject by Stanzione is in the Harrach Collection, Vienna. The drawings now attributed to Stanzione do not form a consistent body of work, as Vitzthum has pointed out. This drawing however, although much freer, is not contradictory of another (also in the Scholz Collection) representing Apollo and Daphne. [A.M.]

MATTIA PRETI
called Il Cavaliere Calabrese
1613 Taverna—Malta 1699

Born in Calabria, Preti with his brother Gregorio went north to Rome about 1630, almost surely stopping en route in Naples where he must have had contact with Caracciolo. Although Rome was his headquarters for the next quarter century, he traveled extensively, to Modena and Venice and possibly even into France. De Dominici says he went to Cento to study with Guercino, but this is almost certainly false. Preti was a leading artist in Rome around 1640-55. After a spectacular failure in frescoing the ceiling of the nave of Sant' Andrea della Valle, in 1656 he returned to South Italy. First he went to Naples and then to Malta where, as a member of the Knights of St. John, he settled there for the rest of his life. He is often considered a Neapolitan painter; but despite the number of his paintings and his influence on later artists in the city, he spent only a few years there.

150. Martyrdom of St. Catherine of Alexandria

St. Catherine, a legendary lady of Alexandria in Egypt, was a kind of early Christian intellectual who not only confounded the arguments of the local pagan philosophers but also refused to abjure Christianity. As a result she was subjected to a series of tortures (including that of the wheel, her standard attribute) before she was finally martyred by being put to the sword.

Robert and Bertina Suida Manning, New York, N. Y.

Canvas, 40 x 29 9/16 in.
Coll.: David M. Koetser, New York.

Ref.: Manning, *Neapolitan Masters*, New York, 1962, no. 21.

A *bozzetto* for a ceiling painting in the series of 1656-61 in San Pietro a Maiella, Naples, this richly impastoed canvas represents the mature Preti's style, a kind of Full Baroque Caravaggism in which the drama of sharply contrasting light and dark is fused with virtuosic handling and brilliantly decorative composition and color. The soldier behind St. Catherine is clearly derived from the work of the influential but underestimated and neglected Pietro della Vecchia with whom Preti had contact in Venice.

The finished ceiling painting (much of it the work of assistants) is based on this sketch, but has been reoriented to a horizontal axis. The very low horizon line and the angle of vision of the sketch, suggestive of a *sotto-in-su* effect, indicate the artist's anticipation of the placement of the work overhead as a part of a great decorative cycle consisting of ten oil paintings set in a richly carved architectural-sculptural framework.

Other versions of the subject by Preti are in the Girosolimitana, in Santa Caterina d'Italia and in the Grand Master's Palace in La Valletta, Malta.

The composition was utilized by Solimena for a central episode in his *Massacre of the Giustiniani Family* (Genoa, Palazzo Ducale) which was destroyed by fire in 1777 but is known through a preparatory oil study (Naples, Capodimonte). This *Massacre* was a companion painting of the *Columbus Landing*, represented in this show by a drawing (no. 167). [A.M.]

151. The Feast of Herod

See no. 82.

The Toledo Museum of Art, Toledo, Ohio, gift of Edward Drummond Libbey.

Canvas, 70 x 92 in.

Coll.: Ferdinad van den Einden; Prince Belvedere Caraffa, Naples (?); Prince Colonna di Stigliano, Naples.

Ref.: B. N(icolson) in *Burlington Magazine*, CIII, 1961, 195; J. Russell in *Sunday Times*, London, 21 May 1961; *Illustrated London News*, 3 June 1961, p. 939; L. Frohlich-Bume in *Weltkunst*, 15 June 1961, p. 13; *Pantheon*, IV, July-Aug. 1961, lxx f.; *Burlington Magazine*, CV, 1963, 296; *Gazette des Beaux-Arts*, LXIII, 1964 (Feb. sup.) 57; *Toledo Mus. News*, VII, 1964, 91; O. Wittmann in *Apollo*, LXXXI, 1965, 28; A. Frankfurter in *Art News*, LXIII, Jan. 1965, 1, 5, 24.

A revelation of the breath-taking power of Preti's color and the festive virtuosity of his brush, this masterpiece was inspired by Rubens' *Feast of Herod* (Edinburgh, Nat. Gall.), which created a sensation in Naples when brought there by the Flemish merchant and banker Gaspar de Roomer about 1640 (see Haskell, *Patrons and Painters*, London, 1963, pp. 206 ff.). The wealth of psychological nuances and the sumptuousness of Rubens' *Feast* were on a far grander scale than anything previously seen in Naples, which had been conditioned to the careful draughtsmanship and psychological

directness of Caravaggism. The sadistic brutality of Rubens' Herodias, who pricks St. John's tongue with a fork, must have appealed to the silenic de Roomer whose taste is reflected in works subsequently acquired by his Neapolitan associates.

Preti's *Feast of Herod* probably was commissioned or purchased by a member of de Roomer's circle who desired the subject depicted by Rubens. A likely person would be Ferdinad van den Einden, his business partner, who ordered several large pictures of Preti after the success of the *Marriage at Cana* painted for de Roomer on Preti's return to Naples in 1656. This would give a dating for the Toledo work of around 1656-61 when Preti was in Naples. [F.C.]

152. Belisarius Receiving Alms

As reported by the Byzantine historian Procopius and embellished by popular legend, General Belisarius (505-565), after having achieved extraordinary victories both East and West for the Emperor Justinian, fell afoul of his patron, was stripped of rank, wealth and titles, blinded, and turned out into the streets of Constantinople as a beggar. Recognized by one of his former soldiers who took pity on him and arranged for him to live in peace and comfort, Belisarius became in later years a symbol of the fallen mighty and the passing of earthly triumphs, of charity, and by implication of the ingratitude of autocrats.

Collection of Walter P. Chrysler, Jr.

Canvas, 60 x 78 in. Inscribed upper right (on column): "Obbulum Bilisari" (Alms for Belisarius).

Coll.: Venetia Buddicom, Penbedn Hall, Flintshire; Vitale Bloch, Paris; Colnaghi, London; Julius Weitzner, New York.

Ref.: Colnaghi, *Paintings by Old Masters*, London, 1953, no. 12; *Burlington Magazine*, 1953, XCV, 286; B. Suida Manning, *Paintings Collection Chrysler*, Portland (Ore.), 1956, p. 31; *Colnaghi's 1760-1960*, London, 1961, pl. 16; Manning, *Neapolitan Masters of the Seventeenth and Eighteenth Centuries*, New York, 1962, no. 20.

The *sfumato* handling of the group on the left seems to suggest a date after Preti's withdrawal to Malta in 1661; but the head of Belisarius is strikingly reminiscent of what have been hypothetically recognized as the Venetian works of Pierfrancesco Mola (1612-1666) in which the traces of Caravaggio's influence—or to be more exact, of such of his followers as Mola's *landsmann* Giovanni Serodine (1600-1630)—are particularly evident. The simplification of light and shadow areas into two sharply contrasting values is certainly reminiscent of Caravaggio; but the replacement of the plasticity which Caravaggio's forms maintain, by surfaces which are so brightly illuminated as to become brilliant patches or light accents, belongs to a much later and more dynamic phase of the Baroque. In fact, in this tendency, in his use of a blurring atmosphere, and in his brilliant colorism, Preti shows himself to be at least as much a decorative painter as one of dramatic and pathetic narrative. [A.M.]

SALVATOR ROSA
1615 Naples—Rome 1673

Rosa's training was Neapolitan—first with his uncle, Domenico Antonio Greco, and his brother-in-law, Francesco Fracanzano; later, between the ages 17 and 20, with Ribera and Aniello Falcone. In 1635 he went to Rome where, except for the years 1641 to 1649 spent in Florence, he passed the rest of his life. Not only a painter, he was also a poet, playwright and musician, whose romantic individualism was highly popularized during the 19th century, and whose picturesque landscapes were very influential on later artists.

153. Self-Portrait

M. Knoedler & Co., Inc., New York, N. Y.

Canvas, 29½ x 24 in.

Presumably this mirror-image is Rosa's preparatory study for his larger and more elaborate *Self-Portrait as a Warrior* (Siena, Palazzo Chigi-Saraceni). The pose and features are identical; the physiognomy is recognizable as the artist's by comparison with the self-portraits in the National Gallery, London, and the Metropolitan Museum, New York. The Metropolitan Museum painting is signed in such a manner as to imply a date of 1659, but the other three portraits were probably all painted about 1640, shortly after Rosa's arrival in Florence. The late 17th century Florentine writer Baldinucci noted that Rosa used his own features not only in self-portraits but also in such paintings as the head of a battered and weary mature man (London, Denis Mahon). Whether portraying himself as himself or using himself as a model, Rosa was particularly interested in characterization. In this portrait he has represented himself as dashing and mysterious—a kind of Byronic desperado, creating an image which might be conceived as an imaginary portrait of Manfred: "I know thee for a man of many thoughts/and deeds of good and ill, extreme in both,/Fatal and fated in thy sufferings." [A.M.]

154. The Finding of Moses

To escape an edict of Pharoah requiring that all male Hebrew children be killed at birth, Moses' mother placed her baby in an ark made of bullrushes, and hid him near the bank of the river. Pharoah's daughter, coming with her handmaidens to bathe, found the baby, took compassion on him, and gave him to a Hebrew woman to raise, not knowing that the woman was, in fact, his own mother. (*Exodus* 2, 3-10).

The Detroit Institute of Arts, gift of Mr. and Mrs. Edgar B. Whitcomb, 1947.

Canvas, 48½ x 79¾ in.

Coll.: One of four paintings done for Don Lorenzo Onofrio Colonna, two of which, representing *St. John the Baptist Preaching* and *St. John in the Desert*, are still in the Colonna Gallery in Rome; in the Palazzo Colonna, Rome, until the late 18th century, when it and the companion *Mercury and the Dishonest Woman* (now in the National Gallery, London) were purchased by an English gentleman-dealer, William Young Ottley; sold at Christies', 1801, to the third Earl Temple, later the Marquess of Buckingham; inherited by his son, the first Duke of Buckingham and Chandos, and kept at Stowe; sold, 1848, to a Mr. Farrar; then belonged to Lord Ward, later Lord Dudley, from whom it passed in 1892 to the McCormick family of Chicago. Purchased from Durlacher Bros., New York, in 1947 for the Detroit Art Institute as a gift of Mr. and Mrs. Edgar B. Whitcomb.

Ref.: Mentioned by many 18th century English visitors to Rome, including Smollett, Lady Somerset, Mariana Stark *Letters from Italy* (1790s); Ottley, *Italian School of Design*, London, 1823, p. 71; Lady Morgan, *Life and Times of Salvator Rosa*, London, 1824, II, 107-8; Buchanan, *Memoirs*, London, 1824, II, 20, 27, 381; Waagen, *Treasures*

of Art in Great Britain, London, 1854; Manchester, *Art Treasures Exhibition*, 1857, no. 757; Mireur, *Dictionnaire des ventes d'arte*, Paris, 1901-12, VI, 313-14, Grigaut, *D.I.A. Bull.*, XXVII, 1948, 63; New York, Durlacher Bros., *Paintings by Salvator Rosa*, 1948; Oberlin, Allen Memorial Art Museum, *Italian Paintings of the Seventeenth Century*, 1952; *Catalogue of the Whitcomb Gifts*, Detroit, 1954, pp. 98-99; Salerno, *Salvator Rosa*, 1963, no. 84, p. 135.

This painting might more exactly be called *Landscape with the Finding of Moses*. Although the figures provide the religious and literary pretext for the painting and form one of several visual focal points, they are fundamentally subordinate to the natural setting, which is obviously Rosa's primary interest. More than a little reminiscent of the seacoast in Campania where the artist was born, raised and trained, nonetheless the scene is clearly not observed directly from nature but a fabrication of the imagination in the studio. The three centers of interest—the figure group, the rocky excrescence on the left, and the distant city—function like three gigantic steps into an almost endless space, ultimately disappearing into a clouded horizon. It is an extraordinarily animate landscape, as though the agitation of the figures, the flutter of the birds, the anthropomorphically clutching profiled foliage, the sweep of the bay, the suggestion of wind and the piling up of the clouds, all were manifestations of a single natural vitality with which the rhythmic exercise of its different forces achieved a flowing cosmic order. A late work, it must have been done during the last decade of the artist's life, when he had perfectly achieved the means of integrating figures and landscape.

A detail of the two women with the basket containing the baby was engraved by the Abbé de Saint-Non in 1770. Two other versions were once in English collections but have now disappeared, although one is known through a color stipple engraving by John Baldrey 1785 (Nagler, vol. XIII, 378). Still other versions of the subject, but very different, were paintings formerly in a Roman private collection (Salerno, 145) and in the Giovanelli Collection, Venice (Ozzola in *Bollettino d' Arte*, XIX, 1925-1929, 29-33). [A.M.]

155. Baptism of the Eunuch

156. St. John the Baptist Preaching in the Wilderness

Salerno notes that the subject of the *St. John Preaching* is a "clear allusion" to the name of the patron, Giovanni Battista Costaguti. The companion painting also can be taken as referring to Msgr. Costaguti, because it too represents an act of baptism. The source of its subject matter is *Acts* 8,27, recounting the conversion, in the desert on the road from Jerusalem into Gaza, by the Apostle Philip of the eunuch who was treasurer to Candace, the Queen of Ethiopia.

Collection of Walter P. Chrysler, Jr.

Canvas, each 79 x 48 in. The *Baptism* is signed with monogram.

Coll.: Painted for Msgr. Giovanni Battista Costaguti (—1704), these two paintings have never been separated; by 1746 no longer in the Costaguti family collections; 1781, collection of Humphrey Morice, Lord Warden, at the Grove near Chiswick; 1786 (or before) collection of the second Earl of Ashburnham (*sale*, Sotheby's, London, 24 June, 1953); David M. Koetser, New York.

Ref.: Baldinucci, *Notizie*, Florence, 1681 (1773 ed., XIX, 12); Pascoli, *Le Vite*, Rome, 1730, I, 67; De Dominici, *Le Vite*, Naples, 1742-1743 (1844 ed., III, 456); Baldinucci, *La Vita di Salvator Rosa*, Venice, 1830, p. 35; Walpole, *Walpole Society Publications*, Oxford, 1928, XVI, 77; Lady Morgan, *Salvator Rosa*, London, 1824, II, 368; Ozzola, *Salvator Rosa*, Strasbourg, 1908, pp. 159, 182; B. S. Manning in *Chrysler Collection*, Portland (Ore.), 1956, p. 32, no. 36; Gilbert, *Baroque Painters of Naples*, Sarasota, 1961, p. 28, no. 25.

In these two paintings Rosa has fused figures and landscape so that neither seems to dominate but each supports the other. The landscape exists not merely as the setting for the narrative but also with its suggestions of blustery weather and of restlessness, as evocative of the expressive mood of the scenes. Although both scenes represent dignified religious subjects, nonetheless there is something of the "raffish and piquant effect" of Rosa's smaller paintings, as Creighton Gilbert has pointed out. Specifically to be noted is Rosa's debt to the Venetian Pietro Muttoni (called Pietro della Vecchia) for such figures as the soldiers in both paintings.

Like the *Finding of Moses* (number 154), these are works of Rosa's full maturity, done during the last decade or so of his life. A preparatory drawing for the *Baptism of the Eunuch* is in the Morgan Library, New York (Vitzthum in *Burlington Magazine*, 1961, p. 324 no. 14). [A.M.]

157. Rocky Landscape with St. Anthony Abbot and St. Paul the Hermit

St. Anthony Abbot, born c. 250 in Egypt, as a youth began his hermit's life, suffering the temptations which have inspired so many artists. His meeting with St. Paul, who is also known as Paul of Thebes where he was born c. 230, took place when both were old men. St. Anthony had thought that he was the first hermit, but guided according to legend by a centaur and a satyr, he discovered St. Paul who had lived in solitude for sixty years, fed daily at noon by a raven bringing him bread. After St. Anthony left, he had a vision of two angels carrying the soul of St. Paul, and returning to the older saint's refuge found his body there, in an attitude of prayer, the moment here represented.

Denis Mahon, Esq., London.

Canvas, 26½ x 19½ in., *pendant (Desolate Landscape with Dead and Splintered Trees*, Mahon Collection, London) Signed *SR*.

Coll.: Edward Harley, Earl of Oxford (acquired, together with its *pendant*, at the latter's sale in 1741-42 by the Duchess of Bedford; Dukes of Bedford (chiefly at Woburn Abbey) until 1951, when both acquired by the present owner.

Ref.: Royal Academy, *Italian Art and Britain*, London, 1960, no. 405; Salerno, *Salvator Rosa*, 1963, p. 127, no. 56; Pilo, *Mostra di Marco Ricci*, Bassano del Grappa, 1963, no. 1.

This beautiful little painting is typical of the small fantastic landscapes for which the artist is now most admired. Its theme is more than the landscape itself, for the figures of the two little saints suggest a philosophical meaning: man helpless in an irrational and uncontrollable natural world. Dwarfed by the massive and precarious rock formation and the gigantic and menacingly anthropomorphic foliage, the two saints might well be intimidated by the frightening force of tempestuous nature. The source of this theme can be found in late medieval art in Northern Europe; it was taken up from Rosa by Alessandro Magnasco.

The figure of St. Paul is similar (although not by any means identical) to the life-size hermit *St. Onophrius* recently acquired by the Minneapolis Art Institute. Like the St. Onophrius, this painting and its signed companion work (also in the Mahon Collection) should be dated from the last decade of the artist's life. Salerno associates the Mahon paintings with the two canvases in the Chicago Art Institute representing the life of Policrates. Significantly, he notes a "moral content" in Policrates' history—"no one in this world can consider himself happy before death"—and surely something of this transcendental pessimism can be detected within this painting as well. [A.M.]

158. Soldier Standing

The subject is related to the paintings of battles and of little groups of soldiers, bandits and other adventurers which form a distinctive part of the artist's *oeuvre*.

Janos Scholz Collection, New York, N. Y.

Red chalk on white paper, 9½ x 6½ in.

Coll.: Piancastelli; Brandegee.

Ref.: Gilbert, *Baroque Painters of Naples*, Sarasota, 1961, no. 66; Scholz in *Art Quarterly*, 1960, XIII, 62; Hamburg, Kunsthalle, *Italienische Meisterzeichnungen*, 1963, no. 139.

The forthright observation of the living model in this drawing seems more typical of Aniello Falcone than of Rosa; an attribution to Paolo de' Matteis has also been suggested. However, the attribution to Rosa is supported by a black chalk study of figures in the *Cabinet des Dessins* of the Louvre. A comparison of the linear devices by means of which the folds of drapery are represented, indicates that both drawings are by the same hand, although the Scholz drawing utilizes more shading for chiaroscuro, and is much more vigorous in graphic means and in characterization. Presumably a work of the 1630s, done while Rosa was under Falcone's influence. [A.M.]

159. *Figure Studies*

Obviously this sheet of figure studies is a series of sketches for a painting, probably a religious subject, perhaps set in the Near East, and representing a miracle, a martyrdom, a divine apparition, or some sort of apotheosis.

The Metropolitan Museum of Art, New York, Dick Fund, 1938.

Pen and brown ink and brown wash on paper, 8 x 5 9/16 in.
Coll.: Dan Fellows Platt, Englewood, N. J.

Datable during the 1660s on the basis of similarity to the pen and wash *St. George* (École des Beaux-Arts, Paris) which was done about 1668. Such a subject as is indicated by the poses would be relatively rare in Rosa's *oeuvre;* perhaps some slight affinity can be recognized to the poses and drapery in the *Jonah Preaching to the Ninevites* (Copenhagen, Statens Museum for Kunst) of 1661. [A.M.]

ANDREA DE LEONE
1610 Naples 1685

Reported by De Dominici as having been trained by Corenzio first, De Leone owed much more to his brother-in-law, Aniello Falcone, in whose studio he worked together with Salvator Rosa, learning to paint battle-pictures. Presumably his first contact with Castiglione was in 1635, when he visited Naples. De Leone collaborated with Andrea Vaccaro in a

group of works at the Church of San Paolo Maggiore. Forced to leave Naples by the revolt of Masaniello in 1647, De Leone went to Rome, where he must have renewed relations with Castiglione and established contact with Poussin. It is not known exactly when Andrea De Leone returned to Naples; apparently he was there by 1656, and remained the rest of his life.

160. Tobit Burying the Dead

The source of the subject is Tobias 1,18-21, relating how Tobit, acting against the command of Sennacherib, buried the bodies of the Jews whom the king had had killed outside the walls of Nineveh. Tobit's hooded figure left of center is making a gesture almost of benediction; it seems to be answered by the gesture of the similarly costumed figure silhouetted on the far upper right. This second hooded figure probably represents the spy who informed Sennacherib of Tobit's disobedience of the royal interdiction.

Mr. and Mrs. Paul H. Ganz, New York, N. Y.

Canvas 49 x 65½ in.

Coll.: Marquis de Gourvenet, Paris (*sale*, Paris, 1775 [as Sebastian Bourdon]); Czernin, Vienna (as Poussin); Frederick Mont, New York, 1962.

Ref.: Mariette, *Abecedario*, 1854-1856, III, 205; Blunt in *Warburg Journal*, 1939-40, III, 142-47; Manning, *Neapolitan Masters*, New York, 1962, no. 9.

Blunt's definitive analysis of the painting demonstrates its composition is derived from Castiglione studio drawings (Chatsworth; ex-de Vries Collection, Cleveland; Witt Collection, London). Although the pen and bistre drawing (London, Victoria and Albert Museum), which Blunt recognizes as specifically preparatory for the painting, is reminiscent of Castiglione, it is more classicistic and closer to Poussin. Blunt therefore assumes that the painting was done in Rome about 1648 when De Leone, Castiglione and Poussin were all there, and that De Leone at that time had access to Castiglione's studio.

In this respect, De Leone's contacts with Rosa (who returned to Rome from Tuscany in 1649) should be emphasized as in the treatment of foliage and landscape, and Tobit's heavy drapery. The corpses are also revealing of De Leone's sources: the one in the center is van Dyckian; but the frank realism with which the two in the lower right corner have been represented surely refers back to Falcone. Perhaps some trace of this continued realism is to be discovered also in the triumphal arch which is similar (but not identical) to the so-called Arch of Drusus in Rome.

Altogether, the elements of the painting seem fully to justify Blunt's conclusion that it typifies the tendency to create "out of Poussin's gentle romanticism . . . a style which can be properly called picturesque." One might add that from Poussin's lofty and sometimes austere idealism there also evolved a kind of historical narrative which was basically anecdotal. [A.M.]

BERNARDO CAVALLINO
1616 Naples 1656

Cavallino, the son of a painter, apparently spent his whole life in Naples. Working only in oil, he was a pupil of Caracciolo, a friend of his father, and primarily through him had contact with Caravaggism. Cavallino was also a pupil of Stanzione, by whom he was introduced into the more luxurious and decorative world of the fully developed Baroque. He seems also to have been led into this world by Artemisia Gentileschi and by the works in Naples of van Dyck. Finally, Cavallino may have had contact with Velasquez who visited Naples in 1630; and he surely was influenced by Aniello Falcone and his lively, small-scale genre paintings. The result of this diversity of sources was not an eclectic art, but one which, during a sadly brief career, went through a succession of phases, from early, intense Caravaggesque drama to late Baroque, decorative lyricism. Cavallino's paintings are consistently filled with a kind of impassioned elation, almost miraculously synthesized with the refinement in color, types and atmospheric effects and the delicacy of touch which have earned him characterization as the Italian Vermeer.

161. The Flight into Egypt

Warned by an angel who appeared to him in a dream of King Herod's plot to murder the infant Christ, Joseph took the Holy Family to Egypt where they remained until Herod was dead and it was safe to return to Galilee. (*Matthew* 2,13-15) The angel leading the Madonna and Child and the two accompanying angels are gratuitous additions by the painter, following the standard practice of representing the subject.

Wadsworth Atheneum, Hartford, Conn., The Ella Gallup Sumner and the Mary Catlin Sumner Collection, 1942.

Canvas, 40 5/16 x 49 3/4 in.

Coll.: Anonymous sale, Christie's, London, 1931; Sir Kenneth Clark, London; Durlacher Brothers, New York.

Ref.: London, Burlington House, *Exhibition of XVIIth Century Art*, 1938, no. 312; Northampton, Mass., Smith College Museum of Art, *Italian Baroque Painting*, 1947, no. 6; Hartford, Conn., Wadsworth Atheneum and Sarasota, Fla., Ringling Museum, *A. Everett Austin, Jr.: A Director's Taste and Achievement*, 1958, no. 16a; Bridgeport, Conn., Museum of Science, Art and Industry, *Twenty Top Treasures from Connecticut Museums*, 1962, no. 1.

This painting, combining a pastoral landscape with a stage-lighted nocturnal representation of the Holy Family in flight, is distantly recollective of such Venetian sources as Tintoretto's very differently composed version of the subject at the Scuola di San Rocco. But the immediate source is Stanzione, such figures as the angel-guide being as Stanzionesque as any in Cavallino's career. Significantly enough, Cavallino seems to have chosen a relatively Caravaggesque phase of his master's *oeuvre* as his inspiration: the lighting, as though from a flood light on the left, is a favorite device of Cavallino's, and is reminiscent not only of Caracciolo but also of Caravaggio's *Flagellation* (then and now in the Monte della Misericordia, Naples); and the St. Joseph certainly is kin to Ribera's middle-aged bearded men.

Very similar in detail to a number of Cavallino's works (particularly, in landscape, physical types, and sharp division of light from dark, to the *Salvation of Moses*, formerly collection of Dr. Paolo Wenner, Naples), this painting must date from relatively early in the artist's career, after such strikingly Caravaggesque works as *Judith* (Naples, Capodimonte), but well before his only dated work, *Saint Cecilia* (1645, formerly Dr. Wenner's Collection). [A.M.]

162. St. Agatha

There is no attribute in this painting specifically characterizing St. Agatha, rather than any other of the pretty, young Christian martyrs who were so appealing to Baroque taste. In fact there is nothing specifically indicating that it represents a saint, rather than merely an intense and rather neurotic young lady. As for St. Agatha herself, she was a Sicilian girl of the third century who died preserving both her chastity and her allegiance to Christianity.

The Detroit Institute of Arts, gift of Mrs. Standish Backus, 1945.

Canvas, 27⅛ x 22¾ in.
Coll: A. F. Mondschein, New York.

The direct source for this painting is no doubt the representations of female martyrs by Stanzione and his followers; specifically this painting can be compared to the famous *St. Agatha* (Capodimonte, Naples), formerly attributed to Stanzione, but now given to Francesco Guarino, which it resembles not only in the general arrangement but also in the animation and the impasto of the drapery as well. But the sharp contrasts between light and shadow on the face, and the linear contour of the left side of the neck and head are strikingly reminiscent of Caracciolo. The physiognomy is rather less sweet and smiling than Cavallino's customary types. [A.M.]

LUCA GIORDANO
1634 Naples 1705

Originally a pupil of Ribera (whose works he imitated—and so sometimes faked—throughout his life), Giordano became Naples' first great Seicento native fresco painter, primarily as a result of a long trip to Rome and North Italy which he made during his late teens and which profoundly affected his whole career. Particularly responsive to Venetian painting and to the works of Pietro da Cortona in Rome and Florence, Giordano, who earned the nick-name of "fa presto" for the virtuosic speed with which he carried out vast fresco cycles, was a brilliant colorist, gifted with an incredibly rich and fertile decorative imagination. He was active during his maturity not only in Naples but also in North Italy, which he visited again possibly in the late 60s and early 70s and in 1682-1683, and in Spain where he went in 1692 for a decade of strenuous activity before returning to Naples. The distinction which Neapolitan painting achieved in the latter 17th century depends primarily on Giordano and Solimena.

163. The Adoration of the Shepherds

The nocturnal scene is of course canonical. Angels appeared to shepherds in the fields to announce the birth of Christ, whom the shepherds then went to find lying in the manger. (*Luke* 2, 8-20) The *motif* of the "radiant babe" has a long history in pictorial representations; perhaps the most famous prototypes for Giordano's use are Correggio's so-called *La Notte* (Dresden) and Rubens' altarpiece at the Church of San Filippo Neri in Fermo in the Abruzzi.

The Detroit Institute of Arts, gift of the Founders Society, 1944.

Canvas, 27⅝ x 20⅞ in.
Coll.: Dr. Fritz Haussmann, Berlin.
Ref.: Voss in *Zeitscrift für Bildenen Kunst*, LXV, 1931-32, 168; G. Delogu, *Rivista Mensile Illustrata d'Arte e di Cultura*, Dec. 1935; New York, Schaeffer Galleries, *Gems of Baroque Painting*, 1943, no. 18; Richardson in *D.I.A. Bull.*, XXIII, 1944, 36-37.

This small painting is presumably a sketch for an altarpiece, either lost or never completed. It shows considerable influence of Pietro da Cortona, but probably dates from Giordano's maturity around 1665-1670. [A.M.]

164. The Song of Miriam

The Prophetess Miriam sang a song of triumph after the safe crossing of the tribes of Israel and the destruction of the Pharoah of Egypt's pursuing army in the Red Sea. (*Exodus* 15, 21)

Bob Jones University Collection, Greenville, S. C., gift of Harry and Oscar Dwoskin, 1961.

Canvas, 60⅛ x 91⅛ in.
Coll.: Alcazar, Toledo.
Ref.: *College Art Journal*, 1959, p. 353; *Bob Jones University Collection*, Greenville, 1962, I, 153, no. 85; Milkovich, *Luca Giordano in America*, Memphis, 1964, no. 22.

According to the catalogue of the Bob Jones University Collection, Denis Mahon has suggested that this painting is a sketch for a fresco which Giordano did at the Church of San Lorenzo in the Escorial during his visit to Spain and which the Spanish historian Palomino described (*El Museo Pictorio*, 1724, II, 47). Two other versions of the subject exist: one is no. 159 (Prado, Madrid); the other, a small study of the central figures, was in the art market during the 1950s.

The painting itself is more than a little reminiscent of the work of the great Roman decorator, Giovanni Lanfranco, who was in Naples during the 1630s and 1640s, and with whose work there and in Rome Giordano must have been thoroughly familiar. [A.M.]

FRANCESCO SOLIMENA
1657 Nocera or Canale di Serino—Barra near Naples 1747

Originally trained by his father, Angelo, who was a painter active in Nocera, Solimena with his younger brother, Tommaso, went to Naples in 1674. There he stayed, except for occasional trips into the surrounding areas, for the rest of his life. Although the young Solimena was very independent, he collaborated with the Neapolitan master of still-life painting, Giuseppe Recco (1634-1695), and was influenced by the works in Naples of Lanfranco and Preti. But it was to the great Luca Giordano that he responded most profoundly—so profoundly in fact that he made of himself, in succession to Giordano, Naples' leading decorative painter, whose frescoes covered acres of church and palace walls and ceilings in the city, whose oils were sought hardly less abroad than at home and whose reputation and influence were literally international.

165. *Alexander the Great Sacrificing to Jupiter Ammon*

After the battle of Issus and his conquest of Syria and Phoenicia, Alexander the Great (356-323 B.C.) moved on to Egypt which he took without opposition. He spent the winter of 332-331 there, and made an expedition to the oasis of Siva, deep in the Libyan desert, to consult the oracle of Zeus-Ammon; the oracle flatteringly hailed him as the son not of Philip of Macedonia but of a god, an idea which Alexander found very pleasing. Ammon, an ancient Egyptian god originally localized at Thebes, was eventually established as a universal god, and in later times was associated with Zeus. Solimena has represented his image with the traditional attributes of Zeus.

The Detroit Institute of Arts.

Canvas, 71¾ x 82½ in.
Coll.: Purchased in 1965 through Colnaghi's, London, from an Italian collection.

Although at first glance lacking some of the characteristic features of Solimena's style, this painting is in fact fairly typical of his work of the early 1690s, which was still very much influenced by Luca Giordano. Despite the difference in subject, the composition is surprisingly close to that of the *Nativity of the Virgin* (New York, Metropolitan Museum), formerly attributed to Giordano but now generally accepted as by Solimena. The similarity in the conception of the two pictures—with a crowd of figures in the foreground, an important detail in the left middleground, and recessive architecture fading into atmosphere in the background—indicates a relation between them which might not have been deliberate on the part of the artist. But such details as the heads of St. Anne and of Alexander, and the poses of the repoussoir figures in the lower left of both paintings, are so close (despite the exchange of sex in both pairs of figures) as to indicate the use of the same preparatory study drawings. Solimena apparently used these drawings a third time as the basis for a repoussoir figure in the same relative position and for a draped female figure comparable to the figure of Alexander, in his *Triumph of St. Ignatius Loyola* (Naples, Church of the Gesù Vecchio) which was mentioned by De Dominici and can be dated 1697 (see Bologna, *Solimena*, 1958, pp. 81-82); and, fascinatingly enough, he used one of them again for the very familiar repoussoir figure in the *Madonna and Child with Saints Januarius and Sebastian* (Naples, Pisani Collection), c. 1700.

It is however, important to observe that although Solimena was in his 40s when he painted the Detroit canvas, he had not as yet fully evolved what we customarily recognize as his personal style: the space is still rather crowded, the figures are close to the picture plane and are very large in relation to the dimensions of the whole canvas, and the architecture plays a subordinate role without serving the organizing, clarifying, unifying function it was shortly to fulfill; most striking of all, however, is the lack of the neo-Caravaggesque illumination which shatters the solids of Solimena's later paintings into jagged fragments of light and dark. Here areas of brilliantly intense color achieve an effect somewhat similar to that of the contrasting areas of light and dark typical of his later work. [A.M.]

166. *Rebecca and Eliezer*

Abraham's steward Eliezer, sent by his master back to Ur of the Chaldees to seek a wife for Abraham's son Isaac, encountered Rebecca at the well, was recipient of her cordiality, and chose her for Isaac's wife. The actual moment represented is Rebecca's departure from Ur, when she tearfully kisses the hand of her brother (and guardian) Laban, as Eliezer (on the steps on the right) would lead her away, on the journey back to Canaan. (See *Genesis* 24:10-26.)

The University of Michigan Museum of Art, Ann Arbor.

Pen and sepia with pencil underdrawing, 8 7/16 x 13 1/16 in.
Coll.: Purchased in 1954 from H. M. Calmann, London.
Ref.: Wunder in *Art Quarterly*, 1961, XXIV, 164.

This drawing, squared for transfer is preparatory for a painting (Musée Fesch, Ajaccio) which Ferdinando Bologna (*Solimena*, Naples, 1958, p. 247) dates c. 1715. A later version, c. 1729-30, was in the Harrach Collection in Vienna (Bologna, p. 281), and a copy is in the Pinacoteca Nazionale, Bologna. There are other preparatory drawings (Bologna, pp. 279, 283). An engraving was made by La Marra in 1792.

This drawing shows the characteristics of Solimena's fully mature style: many agitated figures, the most important set well back from the picture plane, in a vast space characterized largely by the monumental architectural setting, all animated by sharply contrasting areas of light and dark. [A.M.]

167. *The Landing of Columbus in the Indies*

On the *recto* Columbus is represented on the left in front of a group bearing a crucifix and a flag. Among other groups there are nude Indians. In the center a floating group of angels surrounds an allegorical figure of Divine Faith. On the *verso* a preliminary study.

The Cooper Union Museum, New York, N. Y.

Pencil, pen and brown ink with gray wash on white paper, 10 5/16 x 21 5/16 in.
Coll.: James Hazen Hyde, New York.
Ref.: Wunder in *Art Quarterly*, 1961, XXIV, 151-64.

This drawing is a preliminary study for a painting (known through Caylus' 1718 engraving of Jean François de Troy's copy) Solimena carried out as part one of a cycle of three for the Sala del Consiglio del Senato in the Palazzo Ducale, Genoa. The composition of the finished painting simplified that of the drawing considerably. Commissioned in 1715 and completed by 1728, the cycle represented the *Massacre of the Giustiniani Family at Chios*, the *Landing of the Relics of St. John the Baptist in Genoa*, and the *Columbus*. All three were destroyed by fire in 1777. (See F. Bologna, *Solimena*, Naples, 1958, pp. 111 and 285.) [A.M.]

VII. *Genoa*

GIOACCHINO ASSERETO

1600 Genoa 1649

According to Soprani (1674) Assereto was first the pupil of Luciano Borzone (1590-1645), and then of Giovanni Andrea Ansaldo. He went to Rome in 1639. Besides the influences of Genoese painters his style manifests his attraction to the Lombard school, particularly to Cerano. In addition to numerous easel paintings, Assereto also left a number of frescos, such as in the church of Santissima Annunziata del Vastato, Palazzo Granello (1634) and Palazzo Negrone (finished 1644). In 1647 he was commissioned to execute the façade decorations of Palazzo Granello with a Coronation of the Virgin, and Virtues. Assereto also had connections with Spain, where his works were particularly well received.

168. *Circe Mulling Wine*

Circe, a sorceress, whose story is told in Homer's *Odyssey*, lived in the island of Aeaea. When Ulysses landed there, Circe turned his companions into swine, but Ulysses resisted this metamorphosis by virtue of a herb called *moly*, given him by Mercury.

Mr. and Mrs. Elton F. MacDonald, courtesy The Dayton Art Institute, Dayton, Ohio.

Canvas, 29¾ x 35 in.

Coll.: Major Wellman, Clifton Park near Arklew, Eire; Hanns Schaeffer, New York.

Ref.: Manning in *Genoese Masters*, Dayton, Ohio, 1962, no. 3; L. Mortari in *Paragone*, 153, 1962, pp. 27-8; C. Gilbert in *Arts*, vol. 37, Jan. 1963, p. 59; P. Rosenberg in *Burlington Magazine*, CV, 1963, 209.

The extraordinary subject matter as well as the brilliant brushwork, showing strong evidence of Assereto's early connections with Lombard painting, characterize this work as a surprising and most attractive product of his early activity. Formerly attributed to Bernardo Strozzi, Hermann Voss was the first to identify this painting as a work of Assereto, an attribution subsequently made by Roberto Longhi, followed by Luisa Mortari. Gilbert and Rosenberg were not convinced of this attribution. [R.L.M.]

GIOVANNI BENEDETTO CASTIGLIONE
called Il Grechetto
1600/10 Genoa—Mantua 1665

Grechetto began his artistic education under Giovanni Andrea De'Ferrari and then attached himself to Anthony van Dyck. To widen his artistic horizon he went to Florence, where he received commissions to do a self-portrait and two mythological scenes for the Palazzo Pitti. He continued to Rome, Naples, Bologna and Venice. Upon his return to Genoa his activity intensified, but he acceded to the invitation of the Duke of Mantua to transfer to that city, where he remained from about 1639 to 1661. Once more he returned to his native city,

staying there until 1664, whereupon he went back to Mantua.

In his day Grechetto was esteemed one of the greatest Genoese painters. Without Grechetto, Gregorio De'Ferrari, Domenico Piola and even Gaulli become almost unthinkable. His style was a rich source of inspiration throughout Europe, spreading far beyond the confines of his own sphere of activity. He was an excellent engraver, able to conjure up light effects with his burin or in his etchings which recall Rembrandt and which must have appealed to the fancy of Tiepolo. He also invented the monotype, a technique which, after generations of neglect and oblivion, was taken up again toward the end of the last century. As a draughtsman Castiglione must be ranked among the most skillful, imaginative and tasteful of the entire 17th century. [B.S.M.]

169. An Offering to Pan

Pan is the Greek god of shepherds, hunters, fishermen, flocks, pastures, forests and their wildlife. The original seat of his worship was in Arcadia where he was supposed to wander through the forests attended by Nymphs playing the syrinx or "Pan's pipe" which are fabled to be his creation. He was usually represented with the head, chest, and arms of a man, and the legs and sometimes horns and ears of a goat. He was also regarded as causing sudden and groundless fear or panic.

The National Gallery of Canada, Ottawa.

Oil on canvas: 61 x 90 in.

Coll.: Sir Stuart Samuel, London (Sale, Christie's, London, 25 March 1927, no. 105 (as *An Offering to Hymen*).

Ref.: *Catalogue of Paintings*, National Gallery, Ottawa, 1948, p. 14, no. 3525; A Blunt, *Drawings of Castiglione and Stefano della Bella*, London, 1954, p. 28; R. H. Hubbard, *European Paintings in Canadian Collections: Older Schools*, Toronto, 1956, p. 156; Hubbard, *National Gallery Catalogue of Paintings and Sculpture*, I, Ottawa, 1961, p. 12; Manning in *Genoese Masters*, Dayton, Ohio, 1962, no. 24.

Among the drawings by Castiglione at Windsor Castle, Blunt (Fig. 4) reproduced *Oriental Figures Before a Herm*, which can be regarded as a preparatory study for this painting. Blunt also points out that the left-hand group has been engraved (Saint-Non, *Fragments des Peintures et Tableaux les plus intéressants des Palais et Églises de l'Italie*, IV, Paris, n.d., pl. 13). Chronologically, Blunt places the Windsor study among the water-colors of the early Genoese period, when Castiglione was strongly influenced by his Flemish masters, especially Roos. This would indicate an early date for the painting. [R.L.M.]

170. A Pastorale

"And Jacob said unto them, My brethren, whence be ye? And they said, Of Haran are we. And he said unto them, Know ye Laban the son of Nahor? And they said, We know him. And He said unto them, Is he well? And they said, He is well: and, behold, Rachel his daughter cometh with the sheep." (*Genesis* 29:4-6)

Robert and Bertina Suida Manning, New York, N. Y.

Canvas, 30⅜ x 33½ in.

Coll.: Anon., England; David M. Koetser, New York.

Ref.: *Exhibition of Italian Art*, Birmingham, Ala., 1958, p. 11, no. 5; Manning, *Genoese Masters*, Dayton, Ohio, 1962, no. 22; Manning, *Genoese Painters*, Finch College, New York, 1964, no. 44.

This is an imposing painting in which Castiglione represents a pastoral scene with Old Testament connotations—the subject matter is incidental. The chapters from *Genesis* relating the story of Jacob and Laban are not followed to the letter, but might well have been the inspiration for this virtuoso display of people and animals, copper basins and crockery jars. They are painted with painstaking care, true to nature, and yet imbued with a poetry which is entirely Castiglione's secret, going beyond what he may have absorbed from the Bassani or from any of the northern animal painters, such as Giovanni Roos, who was active in Genoa about the same time. Castiglione's pastorales were also touched by the exalted air of Titian's inventions which had also inspired Poussin, and sometimes brought the two masters to curiously related solutions. [R.L.M.]

171. Noah Entering the Ark

"And Noah went in, and his sons, and his wife, and his sons' wives with him, into the ark, because of the waters of the flood." (*Genesis* 7, 7)

The Metropolitan Museum of Art, New York, N. Y., Rogers Fund, 1962.

Brush, red-brown and blue-gray oil paint on paper: 15¾ x 22 in.
Coll.: Giuseppe Vallardi (Lugt 1223); M. le chevalier A. D. de Turin (?)
Ref.: *Emporium*, CXXXVIII, Aug. 1963, 88.

Grechetto's predilection for the story of Noah's ark is attested by a large number of paintings and drawings from all periods of his activity. This subject, perhaps more than any other, offered this great painter of animals the opportunity to portray many of them. How marvellously well he could paint both man and beast is fully evident in this superb brush drawing of the latest phase of his early period. [B.S.M.]

172. Bacchanale: A Bacchante and Three Figures

A favorite theme, inspired by his contact with the Romanizing classicism of Poussin during his Roman and Mantuan periods, Castiglione's great predilection for this subject is attested by numerous drawings, paintings, and an engraving of 1648.

Robert and Bertina Suida Manning, New York, N. Y.

Pen and brush, brown ink on slightly yellowed paper, 6 7/16 x 8 3/16 in. Vallardi stamp, lower left corner.
Coll.: Giuseppe Vallardi (Lugt 1223); Dan Fellows Platt, Englewood, N. J. (Lugt Suppl. 2066b and 750a); Princeton Univ. Art Museum, Princeton, N. J.; Dr. Hanns Schaeffer, New York; Dr. Wilhelm E. Suida, New York.
Ref.: Wunder in *Art Bulletin*, 1960, XLII, 222.

This drawing, dated by Wunder c. 1640-50, is related to several others with the same theme (Cooper Union Museum, New York; Biblioteca Trivulziana, Milan; Albertina, Vienna). Several paintings crystalize the idea: the painting in the Galleria Sabauda, Turin (G. Delogu, *G. B. Castiglione*, Bologna, 1928, pl. 24) appears to follow closely the Cooper Union sketch, whereas one, in a Private Collection in Genoa (C. Marcenaro, *Dipinti Genovesi del XVII e XVIII Secolo*, Turin, 1964, pl. 26), appears to be based on

the present drawing. Furthermore, the same idea appears in a painting (Paul Ganz, New York) related to the engraving (Bartsch 16), for which there is a preparatory drawing in red chalk (Uffizi, Florence). [B.S.M.]

173. Melancholia

The iconography seems to derive from the North, rather than

from the description in Cesare Ripa's *Iconologia* (Padua, 1618, p. 319), where *Melancholia* is represented as an old woman in poor clothes, seated upon a bare stone by a dried-up tree without foliage, indicating that state of soul brings out nothing fruitful. It is infinitely closer in spirit to the iconography of Dürer's famous engraving which has been linked by C. G. Carus to the Faust psyche—man's lonely search for superhuman wisdom.

Philadelphia Museum of Art, Philadelphia, Pa., PAFA Collection.

Brush with sepia on paper, 10¾ x 15¾ in. Inscribed lower right corner: Castiglion #211; on mount, lower right: Castiglioni.
Coll.: Vallardi (stamp lower left; Lugt 1223).

The present drawing appears closely linked (even though there are several compositional differences) to Castiglione's etching of the subject (B. 22). Another drawing is listed by A. Pigler (*Barockthemen*, 1956, II, 478) in the Darmstadt Museum (no. 33), in crayon and pen, as a preparatory drawing for the engraving, with the remark that the subject might rather be Circe, which is absolutely incorrect. Stylistically the present drawing appears to fit with the group of drawings at Windsor, which Prof. Blunt dates 1645/55, particularly no. 45, in which certain Rembrandtesque techniques reveal themselves in much the same manner. [B.S.M.]

174. The Vision of St. Bernard of Clairvaux

St. Bernard (1090-1153) was remarkable for his devotion to the Virgin; the Missum Est was composed in Her honor as the Mother of the Redeemer; and in eighty sermons on texts from the Song of Solomon, he set forth Her divine perfection. Accordingly, the Blessed Virgin regarded her votary with special favor. Once, when he was writing his homilies, almost too ill to hold his pen, She graciously appeared to him and comforted and restored him by Her presence. (Jameson, *Legends of the Monastic Orders*, New York, 1892, pp. 180ff.)

The present representation of the Vision of St. Bernard of Clairvaux corresponds in most points to the traditional representation known in paintings by Perugino, Fra Bartolommeo, etc. The feature of the raven in the lower left-hand corner is a curious allusion by Castiglione to the patriarch of the reformed Benedictines: St. Benedict of Subiaco and Monte Cassino.

Museum of Fine Arts, Boston, Mass.

Brush, with olive-green, rose, ochre and gray oil washes on white paper; 16¾ x 11 in. Issuing from the lips of the Virgin an inscription alludes to the God-given nature of the Order; a second inscription, on a scroll carried by two angels, refers to the Saint's particular devotion to the Virgin.

Coll.: John Skippe.

Ref.: *Christie Sale*, London, 20-21 Nov. 1958, no. 72; *Boston Mus. Bull.*, LX, no. 318, 1962, 133-35.

Stylistically the present drawing, which is of great freshness and coloristic refinement, fits into Castiglione's mature years, datable 1648-55. [B.S.M.]

175. The Adoration of the Magi

See *Matthew* 2, 11.

Robert and Bertina Suida Manning, New York, N. Y.

Red-brown oil colored with blue on white paper, 13⅝ x 9⅝ in. Inscribed lower right in pencil: Genoa/Ben Castiglione.

Coll.: Dr. William E. Suida.

Ref.: Manning, *Genoese Masters*, Dayton, Ohio, 1962, no. 74; Manning, *Genoese Painters*, Finch College Museum of Art, New York, 1965, no. 56.

This late brush drawing, 1655-60, was most probably executed at about the same time as another drawing of the subject at Windsor Castle, which Prof. Blunt (*Drawings of Castiglione*, London, 1954, p. 40) described as having a great fluency, which sometimes leads to a lack of definition of form; also, color is in general more freely used in this and numerous other late drawings which are executed in a combination of reddish-brown and blue coloring. [B.S.M.]

176. Abraham Commanded to Dwell in the Land of Canaan

The identification of the subject, as is frequently the case with a Castiglione's pastorale with Old Testament overtones, is a tentative one. Instead of an image of the Lord there appears here an Angel directing Abraham. (*Genesis* 13, 14-15)

Philadelphia Museum of Art, Philadelphia, Pa., PAFA Collection.

Brush with brown and greenish oil wash on paper, 15¼ x 21¼ in.

Coll.: Vallardi (Lugt 1223); Pacini (Lugt 2011).

This belongs among Castiglione's late brush drawings, showing particular affinity to *The Sacrifice of Noah* (Windsor Castle; Blunt no. 163), in which the figure of Noah is reminiscent of Abraham. A second drawing of the same subject, with some compositional changes, probably of a somewhat earlier date, is also in the PAFA Collection. [B.S.M.]

177. *Moses and the Children of Israel Offer Gifts for the Tabernacle*

Moses stands in supplication before the altar, above whose sacrificial fires there appears the figure of God supported by angels; surrounding the altar there are kneeling figures of men and women bringing the offerings ordained by God for the building of the tabernacle; further offerings are being brought on mule-back from the right background. (See *Exodus* 35:4ff.)

Fogg Art Museum, Harvard University, Cambridge, Mass., bequest of Charles A. Loeser, 1932.

Red crayon and bistre wash with touches of blue, pink, white and red oil paint on buff-colored paper, 10⅞ x 16⅛ in.
Ref.: A. Mongan and P. J. Sachs, *Drawings Fogg Museum of Art*, Cambridge, 1940, no. 239.

This admirable drawing certainly belongs to the very latest period of Grechetto's creative activity. Its style agrees completely with drawings at Windsor which Prof. Blunt groups under the heading, "Brush Drawings of the Last Period (c. 1660-65)." The present work could not be better characterized than in Prof. Blunt's words pertaining to this group: "A small group of particularly impressive drawings may be assigned to Castiglione's very last years because of the likeness to the monotype dated 1660 (No. 216 below). In these drawings there appears a revival of the artist's interest in Rembrandt. It no longer, however, takes the form of direct imitation of his style or technique but of a much deeper understanding of the true dramatic quality of his work. A slight technical device—the curious shorthand drawing of the features—also links these drawings together and seems to be a development from the manner of the works in group XI C." (*Drawings of Castiglione and Stefano Della Bella at Windsor*, London, 1954, p. 42). [B.S.M.]

VALERIO CASTELLO
1624 Genoa 1659

Son of the Cambiasesque painter Bernardo Castello, Valerio received his first training in a highly artistic and cultural environment. His father was the friend of the poets Torquato Tasso, Cavaliere Marino and Chiabrera. His brothers Gerolamo and Giambattista were most capable miniaturists. As a boy he learned by working on drawings of his father. Later Valerio entered the studio of Fiasella with whom, according to Ratti, he was not satisfied, and transferred to the studio of Giovanni Andrea de Ferrari, but could not get along with him either. From the works left in Genoa by Procaccini, Valerio found nourishment and incentive for his own formation. According to Soprani, he followed this inspiration to the source, going to Milan, where he copied Procaccini's most beautiful works. Nonetheless the result was splendid. Actually there are few Genoese artists who have such a clear-cut personality as Valerio's. It should be noted that the above cited influences do not suffice to explain the stylistic heredity of Valerio's pictorial style—one must here consider Titian as well as Tintoretto and Rubens.

Flaming color, sparkling in an intensity which does not fear the strongest contrasts, coupled with highly dramatic agitation in the figures, mark the summit of Valerio's art.

178. *Diana with Nymphs*

Diana, an ancient Italian deity, was goddess of the moon and of hunting and protectress of women—all attributes beautifully exemplified in this painting. Her worship, early widespread throughout the peninsula, was brought to Rome by the Tarquins. With the introduction of the Greek Apollo and Artemis, Diana was identified with Artemis as a huntress.

Norton Gallery and School of Art, West Palm Beach, Florida.

Canvas: 65 x 99 in.

Coll.: Francis Bartlett; Herbert M. Sears; E. and A. Silberman, New York.

Ref.: Manning in *Paintings Collection Chrysler*, Portland, Ore., 1956, p. 33; Manning, *Genoese Masters*, Dayton, Ohio, 1962, no. 18; P. Rosenberg in *Burlington Magazine*, CV, 1963, 209.

For many years this painting was considered to be a work of Luca Giordano. In 1945 William E. Suida was the first to identify it and its pendant, *The Legend of St. Genevieve of Brabant* (Collection of Walter P. Chrysler, Jr.), as very important examples by Valerio Castello. [R.L.M.]

DOMENICO PIOLA

1628 Genoa 1703

Domenico's first teacher was his brother Pellegro (1617-40). After his death, Domenico entered the studio of Cappellino for a brief period. He then became fascinated by the works of Castiglione, whose style he soon learned to imitate to perfection (C. G. Ratti). For a time he worked with Valerio Castello. Domenico spent the greatest part of his life in his native city with only brief sojourns in Milan, Bologna, Piacenza and Asti, about 1685. His greatest rival was at the same time his best friend, Gregorio de Ferrari—both were in great demand and perhaps the most sought after painters of decorative frescos of their time.

Domenico's style, derived from Castiglione and Correggio, was carried to its fullest expression in monumental decorative painting, which found its great exponent in Rome in the person of another Genoese painter: Gaulli.

Domenico Piola left a large number of frescos in Genoese churches and palaces, many oils and drawings, and skilfully executed engravings. His sons Anton Maria, Paolo Gerolamo, Giovanni Battista, and a daughter Margherita were his pupils. [B.S.M.]

179. Bacchanal in a Garden

Influences not only from Poussin, but also Parmigianino and Correggio can be detected in this colorful composition which is suggestive of the fresco decorations executed by Piola in numerous

palaces in Genoa. One is also reminded of similar Poussinesque Bacchanals by the Veronese artist, Giulio Carpioni (1611-1674). The background architectural elements and the fountain give the impression that Piola has selected the garden of a Genoese villa as the setting for this frenzied event.

Robert and Bertina Suida Manning, New York, N.Y.

Canvas, 29 x 38⅞ in.
Coll.: Anon., Oxford, England; Arthur Appleby, London.
Ref.: *Paintings by English and Continental Artists*, Appleby Brothers, London, 1963, no. 21; R. L. Manning, *Genoese Painters*, Finch College, New York, 1964, no. 67.

Andreina Griseri was the first to identify this painting, which had previously been attributed to Jacques Blanchard, as a work by Domenico Piola. This attribution was later independently re-confirmed by Gian Vittorio Castelnovi. [R.L.M.]

180. Allegory of the Solstice

For this subject, very unusual in artistic representation, see: C. Ripa's *Iconologia*, Padua, 1618, Part II, pp. 482 ff. In the present drawing there are none of Ripa's symbolic allusions; however, the position of the sun permits us to identify the left hand portion as the Summer Equinox, the right hand portion the Vernal one.

Janos Scholz Collection, New York, N. Y.

Pen and brush, brown ink over black crayon on white paper, 11½ x 16¾ in.
Coll.: Piancastelli (Lugt 2078a); Brandegee (Lugt 1860c).
Ref.: Manning, *Genoese Masters*, Dayton, 1962, no. 91; Manning, *Genoese Painters*, Finch College, New York, 1964; Janos Scholz Collection exhibitions: Columbia, S. C., 1961; Hamburg, 1963, no. 115; Cologne, 1963-64, no. 115.

This fine drawing belongs to Domenico Piola's fully developed mature style. A scheme such as this lends itself well to decorative fresco painting. [B.S.M.]

BARTOLOMEO GUIDOBONO
"Il Prete di Savona"
1654 Savona—Turin 1709

Of Lombard origins, Bartolomeo's father Giovanni Antonio settled in Savona, working as decorator for the local ceramic factories and was his first teacher. His early interest in literature changed to a deep attraction for the church, and he was ordained a priest; still, his love for painting never subsided, and he decided to dedicate himself seriously to this art. He went to Parma where he spent a year and greatly

admired Correggio. Then he went to Venice for a prolonged stay. Upon his return to Savona, Bartolomeo at first decorated majolicas, as did his father before him. Several such works are preserved in the museum of Savona and at the Ospedali Civili, Genoa. Later he turned to painting, both easel and fresco.

Guidobono never lacked commissions from Genoa's noble families. About 1680, according to Ratti, he accepted the invitation of Duke Vittorio Amedeo di Savoia to the court at Turin. His brother Domenico continued painting in Bartolomeo's manner, but he was a much lesser artist.

Bartolomeo Guidobono must be ranked among the most charming artists of the Italian Baroque; his paintings show a certain pastel-like quality, where the lights appear as though filtered through nebulous clouds, extremely soft and sweet; the forms seem to float and the shadows are softened.

181. Lady Playing the Lute

This enchanting figure of a young girl, full-length, seated on the ground, playing a lute appears to be an idyllic genre-subject, reminiscent of certain Venetian 15th century representations, such as Paolo Veronese created in connection with some of his grandiose fresco decorations for Venetian Villas.

Janos Scholz Collection, New York, N. Y.

Pen and brush, dark brown ink over black crayon on gray paper, 6⅜ x 8⅛ in. Numbered and inscribed upper left: "69 Guido Buono".

Coll.: Brass, Venice.

Ref.: J. Scholz, in *Art Quarterly*, XXIII, 1960, 60-61; Manning, *Genoese Masters* Dayton, 1962, no. 86; Manning, *Genoese Painters*, Finch College Museum of Art, New York, 1965, no. 83.

Janos Scholz points out that the evidence of strong Emilian and Venetian influences on Guidobono's painting style can also be noted in the present drawing. [B.S.M.]

ALESSANDRO MAGNASCO
called Il Lissandrino
1667 Genoa 1749

Alessandro was the son of the painter Stefano Magnasco, who had been a pupil of Valerio Castello. After his father's death, Alessandro was sent in 1677 to Milan, where he became the pupil of Filippo Abbiati. According to Ratti, at that time Magnasco painted numerous portraits of excellent quality. Soon, however, he abandoned portraiture and began to paint landscapes with small staffage figures, the genre for which he became famous. He spent the major part of his life in Milan, with the exception of several sojourns in his native city and a stay in Florence between 1703 and 1711 as a guest of the Grand Duke Gian Gastone de'Medici. In 1735 he was called back to Genoa by his daughter and he remained there until his death.

During his lifetime Magnasco enjoyed great fame, but subsequently was completely forgotten. His so-called rediscovery occurred a few decades ago, when general interest in "Expressionism" in modern paintings lead to his re-evaluation. The formation of his style is rooted in the artistic heritage of Valerio Castello as well as Grechetto, from whom he inherited the dramatic tensions and the almost demoniac flashes of his illumination. To these are added Lombard elements (Morazzone and Crespi's pathos), as well as Venetian trends through Abbiati (who was after all Venetian) and Sebastiano and Marco Ricci whom Magnasco knew in Milan at the end of the 17th century. From these various, yet basically related backgrounds, combined with influences from Salvator Rosa, Stefano della Bella, and Callot, arose the artistic personality of Magnasco, breaking all connections, emerging completely individualistic and triumphant. In his imaginative and fantastic creations with their brilliant brushwork and subtle color harmonies, one can sense an extravagant fusion of qualities which, as Antonio Morassi has noted, run the gamut from memories of El Greco to Guardi, forshadowing Goya and certain aspects of Daumier.

182. Arcadian Landscape with Figures

At the end of the seventeenth century painters were freed from the necessity of painting purely religious subjects. Such a romantic landscape as the present one would hardly have been possible at an earlier date. Paint for its own sake with tricks of brush and fantasy of form became the rule and it was Magnasco who became the leader of this virtuosic bravura.

Collection of Walter P. Chrysler, Jr.

Canvas, 97¼ x 61½ in. Initialed in a cartello on an earth-mound in the center of the composition: A. M.

Coll.: Georg Schwarz, Berlin; Benedict, Berlin; Newhouse, New York.

Ref.: B. Geiger, *Magnasco*, Vienna, 1923, p. 48, no. 107; B. Geiger, *Magnasco*, Bergamo, 1949, p. 73; Manning, *Inaugural Exhibition*, Chrysler Art Museum, Provincetown, 1958, p. 23, no. 40; Manning, *Genoese Masters*, Dayton, Ohio, 1962, no. 41; Manning, *Genoese Painters*, New York, Finch College, 1964, no. 85.

Magnasco rarely signed his works, and then only with his initials. Among his entire known oeuvre only two paintings are dated. Both are works of his first Lombard period. One of them, a large landscape with figures (Duca Gallarati-Scotti, Milan) is signed and dated 1691; the other, a representation of the meeting of Quakers (Vigano coll.), is dated 1695. According to Benno Geiger (1949) the present painting also belongs to Magnasco's early Lombard phase. He ranks it justly among the master's finest creations, stylistically and chronologically very near to the large landscape in the Gallarati-Scotti Collection, Milan. [R.L.M.]

183. The Eruption of a Volcano

Magnasco frequently depicted the microcosm of the eternal battle of man against the fury of the elements.

Mr. William T. Hassett, Jr., Hagerstown, Md.

Brush and brown ink heightened with Chinese white over red chalk indications on light brown paper: 12½ x 8⅝ in. Numbered upper left: 3.

Janos Scholz has pointed out (verbally) the inscribed "3" indicates that it more than likely formed part of a series similar to others with which stylistically it well compares: one in the Palazzo Bianco (Genoa), one from the Santarelli Collection (Uffizi, Florence) and those from the Puccio-Prefumo Collection in Genoa. All represent individual figures or groups of figures engaged in some kind of action; the present drawing offers perhaps one of the most complete compositions among them. All these drawings belong to the early middle period of Magnasco and are related to paintings such as the *Fantastic Scene* from the Contini-Bonacossi Collection (Geiger, *Magnasco*, Bergamo, 1949, pl.54), showing strong reminiscences of the styles of Sebastiano and Marco Ricci, as well as Tavella who, according to Geiger, collaborated on the execution of the painting. The Hassett drawing was first identified as Magnasco by Scholz. [B.S.M.]

VIII. *Venice*

Jacopo Negretti, called *PALMA IL GIOVANE* *1544 Venice 1628*

Son of Antonio Palma, he was called *Il Giovane* to distinguish him from his better known great uncle, Palma Vecchio. He studied under various masters and was influenced by Titian, Tintoretto, and Salviati. In his early travels he was invited to Urbino by Guidobaldo, Duca di Urbino, and also went to Rome where he studied Raphael and Michelangelo. Returning to Venice in 1670 he entered the studio of Titian. Perhaps Titian's last painting, the *Pietà* (Accademia, Venice) was finished by Palma. His contemporaries thought of him as a rival of Tintoretto and Veronese, and after their deaths he became the leading painter in Venice. With Domenico Tintoretto and Alessandro Varotari, *Il Padovanino*, he continued a late Mannerist style during the first half of the seventeenth century.

184. Saint Sebastian

See no. 148.

Mr. and Mrs. Paul H. Ganz, New York, N. Y.

Canvas, 26¼ x 12⅛ in.

Coll.: Sir Herbert Cook, Copesham, Esher; Cook, Doughty House, Richmond, England.

Ref.: Brockwell, *Pictures at Doughty House*, London, 1932, p. 42, no. 187; R. L. Manning, *Venetian Paintings of the Sixteenth Century*, Finch College, New York, 1963, no. 35.

Executed around the turn of the century, there is little doubt that Palma turned to Michelangelo for inspiration for this St. Sebastian as well as another formerly in the Lazzaroni Collection, Nice (A. Venturi, *Storia*, IX, pt. VII, fig. 119). One is reminded particularly of the grasping figure on the lower left in Michelangelo's *Last Judgement*. The Cook catalogue cites another version in the Chateau de Gatchina, Russia. [B.S.M.]

Domenico Robusti, called *DOMENICO TINTORETTO*
1560 Venice 1635

The son of Jacopo Robusti (Tintoretto), Domenico gained great fame as a portrait painter at an early age. Having mastered a fair literary education by 1577 Domenico is mentioned as *sindaco* of the *Scuola dei Pittori*. During the years 1581-84 he worked with his father for the Doges Palace. Carlo Ridolfi ascribes to Domenico four of the twenty-one paintings in the Sala del Gran Consiglio. In 1588 he collaborated with his father on the execution of the great *Paradiso*. In his will Jacopo named Domenico as his heir and also stipulated that he should complete all paintings left unfinished at the time of his demise. Domenico collaborated very frequently with his father in the execution of Jacopo's compositions. He was in great demand as a painter of portraits which, indeed, are superior to his "histories". His field of activity was centered in Venice, but extended also to Reggio Emilia, Mantua and Ferrara. Despite the great similarity to his father's style, Domenico's own paintings show more extensive unbroken areas of color which tend to give a somewhat superficial and flattening

effect. They also lack Jacopo's refined *chiaro-scuro*. His signed portraits and smaller figural compositions show a careful and smooth technique which differs from his father's much more grandiose painterly approach.

185. Composition with Many Figures

The subject matter here is not at all clear. In previous collections this drawing had the title "An Episode from the Life of Hercules"; Tietze (1944, no. 1473) referred to it as an "Allegory of War and Peace"; M. Muraro (Venice, 1957, no. 23) expressed the assumption that it might actually represent a "Descent of Christ into Limbo."

Janos Scholz Collection, New York, N. Y.

Brush, various oil colors on gray paper, 11⅜ x 8¼ in.; inscribed lower right: "Giacomo Tintoretto" (old hand in pen).

Coll.: Cardinal Albani, Rome; Russell (Lugt. no. 2770a); Goudstikker, Amsterdam.

Ref.: Goudstikker, *Catalogue*, Amsterdam, 1929, no. 41 (as by Jacopo T.); H. and E. Tietze, *Drawings of the Venetian Painters*, New York, 1944, no. 1473 (as by Domenico T.); M. Muraro, *Disegni Veneti della Collezione Janos Scholz*, Venice, 1957, no. 23; Janos Scholz Collection exhibitions: Bloomington, Ind., 1958; Toronto, Canada, 1960; Hagerstown, Md., 1960; Staten Island, N. Y., 1961; Hamburg, Ger., 1963; Cologne, Germany, 1963-64; New Haven, Conn., 1964.

The present work should be compared particularly to the drawings in the "London Sketchbook," formerly incorrectly attributed to Jacopo Tintoretto. As M. Muraro pointed out, it is exactly in this almost expressionistic halucinatory manner of drawing that Domenico, more so than anywhere else, demonstrates his independence from his father. [B.S.M.]

186. The Adoration of the Magi

See no. 175.

Robert and Bertina Suida Manning, New York, N. Y.

Brush, brown ink on gray-brown paper, 10¾ x 14⅞ in. Signed (?) lower left: "Di Tintoreto Veneciano fecit." Vaughan monogram in pen lower right; no. 155 on verso.

Coll.: Henry Vaughan (Lugt 1380); P. & D. Colnaghi, London.

The composition of this work in Domenico's typical summary technique derives in a certain sense from Titian's *Adoration of the Magi* (Prado, Madrid). Domenico, unlike his father's exalted almost proto-Baroque visions, returns to the serene balance of the mid-cinquecento in the present drawing. It is related to Domenico's *Adoration of the Shepherds* in the Samuel H. Kress Collection (El Paso Museum of Art), formerly attributed to Jacopo. Mrs. F. R. Shapley points out (El Paso *Catalogue*) that its comparative lack of *élan* would mark it as a work by Domenico. [B.S.M.]

CARLO SARACENI
called Carlo Veneziano
1580/85 Venice 1620

The early activity of Saraceni, whose father was of Bolognese ancestry, cannot be ascertained prior to his Roman sojourn about 1602 or slightly later. After a brief apprenticeship with Camillo Mariani (1556-1611), who was of Venetian origin, Saraceni approached the disturbed world of surprising innovations created by Caravaggio; he was among the first followers of the great Lombard master. However, he was not merely a follower of Caravaggio but was also close to Orazio Gentileschi, who was linked ideologically to Adam Elsheimer, the German who came to Rome about 1600, bringing with him a new idyllic and romantic concept of landscape painting, with a preference for nocturnes. Certainly Saraceni was influenced by him so far that the two personalities became almost confusingly similar, as is the case for the mythological scenes in the Naples Museum, given to Saraceni, but also sometimes attributed to Elsheimer. After the death of both Caravaggio and Elsheimer in 1610, Saraceni developed his own kind of Caravaggism with a dramatic light suffused by Venetian sensibility which distinguishes him from Gentileschi.

In 1620 Saraceni was in Venice with the French painter Jean Le Clerc (c. 1585-1633), and made his will. He died three days later at about forty years of age of *febre pechia*. He had married a certain Grazia, who was in Rome at the time of his death. The fact that his wife stayed in Rome might indicate that Saraceni had not intended to remain permanently in Venice.

187. Susanna and the Elders

See no. 68.

The Detroit Institute of Arts, The William H. Murphy Fund.

Copper, 18 x 14 in.
Coll.: A. F. Mondschein.
Ref.: Richardson in *Art Quarterly*, 1942, V, 238-40.

In this rather late work Saraceni has done a popular Baroque theme on a copper panel, somewhat in a Northern miniature style. He combines influences from Caravaggio with those of Elsheimer, but still shows evidence of his early Venetian training. [R.L.M.]

ALESSANDRO TURCHI
called L'Orbetto
c. 1582/90 Verona—Rome c. 1650

A trip by Turchi to Rome has been connected with those of Marcantonio Bassetti and Pasquale Ottino around 1620. His personality has been clarified by Roberto Longhi in his fundamental study (1928) which pointed out the relationship of the "Trio Veronese" (Turchi, Bassetti, and Ottino) to the Roman environment of the second decade of the seventeenth century. Zannandreis (*Le Vite dei pittori scultori et architetti veronesi* [ed. G. Biadego], Verona, 1891) speaks of his first manner showing strength in the shadows in the Venetian taste of Tintoretto. In his subsequent style he becomes sweeter and abandons the dark tonality. Among the three Veronese Caravaggists, Turchi is the sweetest and most caressing—almost a slave to a certain Bolognese decorum, translated by him into a more Venetian manner. There is no doubt that he was familiar with Saraceni. He worked in Saraceni's studio in Rome and collaborated with him on certain paintings executed in Mantua.

188. Bacchus and Ariadne

See no. 121.

Mr. and Mrs. Paul H. Ganz, New York, N.Y.

Canvas.

Usually in representations of this theme, Bacchus himself is placing the crown on the head of Ariadne. Although there is no mention in the *Metamorphoses* of Venus, Turchi, in this rather unique composition, pictured her, with Amor, placing the crown on the head of the grieving Ariadne, while Bacchus, accompanied by the drunken Silenus, is offering his love and help. Tintoretto, however, had also depicted this theme with Venus placing the crown on Ariadne in one of a series of four canvases executed in 1578 for the Salotto Dorato of the Doge's Palace, Venice.

Another canvas of this subject by Turchi is in the Hermitage, Leningrad (*Catalogue de Peintures*, 1958, no. 123: 44⅞ x 58 in.). Bacchus is not as close to Ariadne and therefore his right hand is below her elbow. A third painting of *Bacchus and Ariadne* by Turchi is also in the Hermitage (no. 6960: 48 x 58½ in.). [R.L.M.]

DOMENICO FETTI

c. 1589 Rome—Venice 1623

Fetti (or Feti) started his training under Ludovico Cigoli and was drawn into the Caravaggesque ambient which flourished in Rome during the second decade of the seventeenth century. Though he never became a Caravaggist in the strict sense of the word, the influence became a lasting one throughout his brief but inventive activity. In 1613 his patron Cardinal Ferdinando II Gonzaga became duke and took Fetti to Mantua, appointing him court-painter and inspector of the galleries. In the summer of 1621 the duke sent him to Venice to purchase paintings and *objets d'art*. The impressions he received remained decisive for his future. In the autumn of 1622 he again went to Venice, never to leave. The experiences he gained from his Mantuan and Venetian sojourns brought him close to Venetian painters, especially Bassano, Tintoretto and Paolo Veronese, inspiring him with a luminous manner without outlines, submerged in light. Rubens and perhaps van Dyck, whom he could have met in Venice in 1622, may also have shared in the formation of the last phase of Fetti's stylistic development.

Fetti's brief but wonderfully intense and inventive artistic expressiveness, precipitated into works of exquisite refinement especially during his final months in Venice, became fundamental for the formation of such Venetian seicento artists like Sebastiano Mazzoni, Francesco Maffei, and (to a large extent) the German-turned-Venetian, Giovanni Lys. [B.S.M.]

189. The Pearl of Great Price

"Again, the kingdom of heaven is like unto a merchant man, seeking goodly pearls: Who, when he had found one pearl of great price, went and sold all that he had, and bought it." (*Matthew* 13, 45-46).

Nelson Gallery-Atkins Museum, Kansas City, Mo. (Nelson Fund)

Panel, 24 x 17⅜ in.

Coll.: Accademia delle Belle Arte, Venice; Sir A. Willert, Headington Hall, Oxford; David M. Koetser, New York; Dr. Hanns Schaeffer, New York.

Ref.: R. Oldenbourg, *Domenico Feti*, Rome, 1921, p. 14; R. Pallucchini, *I dipinti della Galleria Estense*, Modena, 1945, p. 229; *Nelson Collection*, Kansas City, 1949, p. 47; *Domenico Fetti*, Durlacher Bros., New York, 1950, no. 2; R. Pallucchini in *Arte Veneta*, IV, 1950, 184; *Tour of Famous Cities*, Columbus Gallery of Fine Arts, 1952, no. 15; P. Zampetti, *La Pittura del Seicento a Venezia*, Ca'Pesaro, Venice, 1959, p. 38; *Burlington Magazine*, vol. 102, 1960, Advertisement Supplement, pl. 5 (signed version with D. A. Hoogendyk, Amsterdam, from the Collection of the Earl of Pembroke, Wilton House); Oberhammer and Lhotsky, *Kunsthist. Mus. Gemäldegalerie*, I, Vienna, 1960, 49-50; P. Askew in *Art Bulletin*, XLIII, 1961, 45; *Connoisseur*, vol. 154, Sept. 1963, p. 42.

For Ferdinando, Duke of Mantua, Fetti painted twelve works based on parables and two on parabolic utterances in *Matthew* and *Luke*. *The Pearl of Great Price*, one of the series, exists in other versions: Vienna (Oberhammer no. 530); Modena (Pallucchini); D. A. Hoogendyk, Amsterdam (*Burlington Magazine*). The Vienna painting, which came from Mantua, is considered the first version among the four. In her chronological listing, Pamela Askew places *The Pearl of Great Price* as the final subject among the last six original versions, establishing a date between September 1621 and September 1622 in Mantua. She pointed out that the composition is peculiarly Venetian, suggesting trade with the East with its oriental turbans, feathered hats, and sumptuous brocades. She states regarding the present version: "It is clearer, lighter, and gayer in color at the same time less finely and meticulously worked in surface detail than the Vienna painting. Freely and fluently painted, it is a repetition by Fetti's own hand." [R.L.M.]

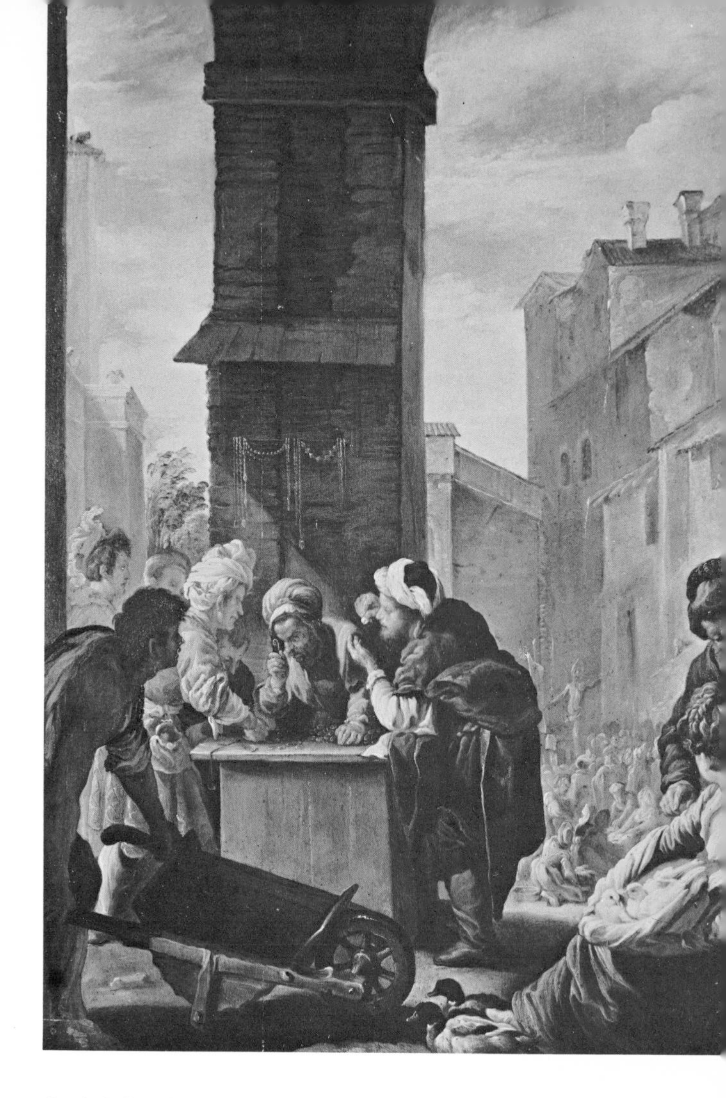

190. Jacob's Dream

See no. 73.

The Detroit Institute of Arts, gift of the Founders Society.

Panel, 23½ x 17 in.

Ref.: R. Oldenbourg, *Domenico Feti*, Rome, 1921, pp. 12-14; Newberry in *D.I.A. Bull.*, XIX, 1940, 69-71; *Domenico Fetti*, Durlacher Bros., New York, 1950, no. 5; *Art Digest*, vol. 24, no. 12, 1950, p. 10; R. Pallucchini in *Arte Veneta*, IV, 1950, 184; Arslan in *Arte Veneta*, VIII, 1954, 290-91; *La Pittura del Seicento a Venezia*, Ca'Pesaro, Venice, 1959, p. 165, no. 26 (related drawing); Oberhammer and Lhotsky, *Kunsthist. Mus. Gemäldegalerie*, I, Vienna, 1960, 49.

For this rather dramatic and pictorial rendition of an unusual subject from his Mantua period, Fetti seems to have turned to his early days in the studio of Cigoli for inspiration. Cigoli painted a "Dream of Joseph," which is monogrammed and dated 1598 (Musée des Beaux Arts, Nancy). Cigoli's painting was evidently based on Raphael in the Loggia of the Vatican; Fetti reversed Jacob's position and created an entirely new composition.

Oldenbourg lists four versions (Alton House; Hermannstadt; Pal. Corsini, Rome; Vienna), to which must be added the present one, another in a private collection in Lombardy, and an enlarged version in the Cleveland Museum. A drawing for the figure of Jacob is in Paris (Cabinet des Dessins, Louvre, inv. no. 3071). [R.L.M.]

191. Woman Sitting by the Fire

Michelangelo Muraro connected this figure with a hypothetical representation of the "Denial of St. Peter" (Luke 22, 56).

Janos Scholz Collection, New York, N. Y.

Black oil chalk with red and white chalk on gray paper, 11¾ x 7¾ in.

Coll.: Goldstein (Lugt 2823).

Ref.: M. Muraro, *Disegni Veneti della Collezione Janos Scholz*, Venice, 1957, no. 49; Janos Scholz Collection exhibitions: Mills College, Oakland, 1960; Staten Island, N. Y., 1961; Columbia, S. C., 1961; Hamburg, Ger., 1963; Cologne, Ger., 1963-64.

W. Stubbe and A. Hentzen (Hamburg, 1963) state that when this drawing was shown in Venice with the attribution by M. Muraro to Pietro della Vecchia, R. Pallucchini, followed by other scholars, reassigned it to the circle of Domenico Fetti. Indeed, the style of this drawing agrees rather well with certain drawings of the master's Mantuan period. [B.S.M.]

192. Christ Appearing to His Mother

Iconographically this drawing represents a most unusual scene: the Virgin, in an attitude commonly associated with the Annunciation, turns toward the right. She has a double "vision" of Her Son: one on earth, at the right, carrying the cross; the other toward the center background, carrying the banner of the Resurrection, either ascending to Heaven amidst other souls of the Blessed—perhaps angels—or ascending out of Limbo. There are certain curious figures at the upper right, such as a "horned" man, who might be identified with Moses (see no. 58). The derivation of this "vision" is not clear.

Robert and Bertina Suida Manning, New York, N. Y.

Red chalk on ecru paper, 15¼ x 12⅞ in. Inscribed lower left in pen in eighteenth century hand: "Fetti."

Coll.: William E. Suida.

Ref.: F. Davidson, *Domenico Fetti*, Durlacher, New York, 1950, no. 13; T. Pignatti in *Pittura del Seicento a Venezia*, Ca' Pesaro, Venice, 1959, no. 24.

This extraordinarily fluid drawing bears close stylistic relationship to signed a drawing of the *Trinity* in the collection of Mr. and Mrs. S. Schwarz, Larchmont, New York (Pignatti, no. 21), a relationship which confirms Dr. Suida's conviction of Fetti's authorship. [B.S.M.]

GIOVANNI LYS
called Pan
c. 1595 Oldenburg, Holstein—Venice 1629/30

Giovanni Lys is also known as Jan or Johann Liss. As a youth he went to the Low Countries, where he spent the years 1616-19, dividing his time between visits to Amsterdam, Haarlem and Antwerp. From there he went to Paris, then to Venice, where he arrived 1620/21. He made a brief sojourn in Rome (1622-24) and returned to Venice, to remain until his untimely death of the plague.

Lys had the faculty to open his eyes and his mind to the most diverse of artistic experiences: having lived in the Low Countries, he was able to absorb Caravaggism during his Roman sojourn and finally to become intimately acquainted with the great Venetian painters of the sixteenth century. At the same time he was also attracted by his own contemporaries, among whom he singled out particularly Domenico Fetti's magic brushwork, which greatly helped to liberate his own style from the shackles of his earlier education. His northern love for color blossomed forth within the Venetian environment into an exuberant luminosity. His early love for the representation of very liberal genre scenes, soon ceded to mythological and religious ones, painted in an ever freer and more

luminous airy style. Lys's strong attraction to the silvery tones of the great Paolo Veronese—a fact already known to Sandrart—enabled him to go beyond the taste of his contemporary Caravaggists to such an extent that we must recognize in his person the true precursor of a style developed later by Sebastiano Ricci and Tiepolo. [B.S.M.]

193. Cain and Abel

Genesis 4, 8-9.

Collection of Walter P. Chrysler, Jr.

Canvas mounted on panel, 34 x 28 in.

Coll.: Wentworth, Wentworth Castle, near Barnsley, York; Koetser, New York (1954).

Ref.: Oldenbourg, *Giovanni Lys*, Rome, 1921, p. 15; Steinbart, *Johann Liss*, Vienna, 1946, pp. 35, 61; *idem*, Berlin, 1940, pp. 99-101; *Pittura del Seicento a Venezia*, Ca'Pesaro, Venice, 1959, p. 152; *Baroque Paintings from Collection Chrysler*, Bowdoin College, Brunswick, Me., 1963, no. 28; Manning, *Venetian Baroque Painters*, Finch College, New York, 1964, no. 15.

A slightly larger version was cited by Oldenbourg and Steinbart (Helmut Zwez, Berlin-Neu-Westend; ex-Cassirer). Oldenbourg dated it around 1623/24, and Steinbart (1940) believed it was inspired by a Tintoretto of the subject mentioned by Ridolfi (1648). It is considered the first of several compositions by Lys based on Old Testament themes. The figure of Abel is related to that of the slave in Tintoretto's *San Marco Rescuing the Slave* (Accademia, Venice). Steinbart also noted that the powerful figure of Cain demonstrates Michelangelo's influence on Lys as interpreted by Titian in such works as *Abraham's Sacrifice*, *David and Goliath*, *Cain and Abel* (S. M. della Salute, Venice), and *The Forge of Vulcan* (engraving). [R.L.M.]

194. Allegory of Christian Belief

Iconographically, Lys does not adhere too strictly to any prototype in this *Fede*. It is rather a personal expression of his own sentiments. The inscription has led Prof. Steinbart to consider it a probable document for the Protestant Lys's conversion to Catholicism upon his arrival in the Eternal City. Were it not for the inscription and the crown at her feet, it would be rather difficult to identify this seated allegorical figure. Usually Christian Faith has as attributes a Cross and a Chalice; sometimes she also has a book. Ripa (*Iconologia*, I, Padua, 1618, p. 178) furthermore states that she is sometimes represented with naked shoulders and upper body (as is the present figure) because the preaching of the Evangelical texts should never be obscured by useless words, enigmas or words of double meaning, as are frequently used by heretics, but expressed with clear and simple words of great purity.

The Cleveland Museum of Art, Cleveland, Ohio, Dudley P. Allen Fund.

Pen and ink, and sepia wash on white paper, 6 x 3 11/16 in. Signed lower right: "Johan Lis/Mahler Holsatia/Zu Rom Den 19 Marti Ao 16 . . ."; above center "Alle Kunst undt Widtz ist/eitel staub./Hoch weisheidt ist ann./Christum gelaub."

Coll.: Dr. O. Feldmann, Brünn, Czechoslovakia.

Ref.: O. Benesch, *Beschreibender Katalog, Zeichnungen d. Deutschen Schulen*, Vienna, 1933, p. 71; K. Steinbart *Johann Liss*, Berlin, 1940,

pp. 83, 163; E. Schilling in *Festschrift Lohmeyer*, Saarbrücken, 1944, p. 30; K. Steinbart, *Johann Liss*, Vienna, 1946, pp. 13, 35, 61; *Cleveland Museum Bull.*, XL, 1953, 215-16; T. Pignatti in *Pittura del Seicento a Venezia*, Venice, 1959, no. 33.

According to Prof. Steinbart the date should be read as 1622, the date of his arrival in Rome. He also pointed out the striking connection with Domenico Fetti's *Artemisia* (Uffizi, Florence). Both compositions derive to a degree from Paolo Veronese's *S. Elena Dreaming of the True Cross* (National Gallery, London) which in turn is drawn from an engraving by Marcantonio Raimondi based upon Raphael. [B.S.M.]

195. The Judgment of Paris

The young shepherd-prince of Troy, urged by Mercury to pronounce judgment on the beauty of the three Goddesses, Venus, Juno and Pallas, hands the golden apple sent by Eris, the goddess of discord, to Venus. She rewards him with the possession of the most beautiful woman on earth, Helen, the wife of Menelaus, whom Paris has to first abduct, thus causing the Trojan War.

Fogg Art Museum, Harvard University, Cambridge, Mass., bequest of Charles A. Loeser.

Bistre, blue and pink wash over red crayon on white paper, 15⅝ x 18⅛ in.

A. Mongan and P. Sachs, *Drawings in the Fogg Museum of Art*, Cambridge, 1940, no. 80 (as late follower of Correggio); W. E. Suida in *Art Quarterly*, XXI, 1958, 397; K. Steinbart, "Johann Liss" *Storia dell' Arte*, Venice, 1959, pp. 205/6; *Pittura del Seicento a Venezia*, Ca' Pesaro, Venice, 1959, no. 32; C. Volpe in *Paragone*, 1959, no. 115, pp. 53-57.

This drawing, first assigned to Jan Lys by William E. Suida upon comparison with the *Toilet of Venus* (Uffizi), has been accepted by most scholars except Carlo Volpe, who unconvincingly attempts to give it to Annibale Carracci. The nude at the right derives from

Correggio's *Education of Cupid* (London, Nat. Gall.). There are certain reminiscences of Raphael (Mongan and Sachs) and Rubens, which Liss may have come by via his friend Domenico Fetti. [B.S.M.]

196. The Agony in the Garden

"And there appeared an angel unto him from heaven, strengthening him." (*Luke* 22, 43; see also no. 66).

Janos Scholz Collection, New York, N. Y.

Pen and brush, brown ink over preliminary red chalk on white paper, 5⅝ x 6⅝ in.
Coll.: B. (unidentified); Moscardo (Lugt 1920c).
Ref.: Scholz, *The Life of Christ*, Notre Dame, Ind., 1964.

This drawing is to be connected with the series of religious paintings Lys executed during his last years in Venice. It differs, however, from his small representation on copper of that subject (Steinbart, *Johann Liss*, Vienna, 1946, pls. 48,49), which is signed and dated 1628 (or 1629)—one of Lys's very last works, in which he painted a reprise of Paolo Veronese's superlative *Agony in the Garden* in the Brera, Milan. [B.S.M.]

FRANCESCO MAFFEI

c. 1600 Vicenza—Padua 1660

Maffei received his first artistic education in his native city in the school of Alessandro Maganza. The truly formative impact upon his style, however, came from the paintings of Paolo Veronese, Bassano, and perhaps El Greco. His first signed work (Oratorio, S. Nicolà da Tolentino, Vicenza) bears the date 1626. Twelve years later he was active in Venice, complet-

ing two paintings which Sante Peranda had left unfinished at the time of his death in 1638. Maffei did not remain long in Venice; he returned to Vicenza, and his activity radiated to Brescia, Rovigo, and from 1657 on he worked in Padua. Exciting, even violent brushwork, vast chromatic contrasts, daring compositions, bear testimony to a typical Baroque personnage. Regarding Maffei's oeuvre as a whole, his development seems perhaps slow, with reprise after reprise of sixteenth century elements. However, these reprises were resolved into a veritable explosion of original ideas.

197. The Last Supper

After Jesus had disclosed to His Disciples His knowledge that one amongst them shall betray Him, the disciples were greatly perturbed (see John 13, 22ff.).

Janos Scholz Collection, New York, N. Y.

Lead pencil on white paper, 6¾ x 11 11/16 in.

Coll.: Moscardo (Lugt 2990). M. Muraro, *Disegni Veneti Scholz*, Venice, 1957, no. 51; *Life of Christ Drawings*, Art Gallery, Notre Dame, Ind., 1964.

M. Muraro assigned the present drawing by stylistic analysis to Francesco Maffei's latest period. Maffei painted two versions of the *Last Supper*, a horizontal one (Castelvecchio Museum, Verona) and an upright, extremely "Baroque" one (Parochial Church of Verolanuova, Brescia) which shows Christ and His disciples grouped around a circular table. Our drawing appears to be independent of these painted versions. [B.S.M.]

SEBASTIANO MAZZONI

c. 1611 Florence—Venice 1678

Mazzoni was a pupil of Cristoforo Allori. His nature was so freedom loving that early he avoided entanglements. Thus Ivanoff's theory that he was attracted by the scenes of popular life which Giovanni da San Giovanni was painting at that time, appears acceptable. He was also attracted by the paintings of Francesco Furini and other painters active in Tuscany during his youth. Mazzoni was also a poet and had to flee from Florence because of certain stinging verses he had written. The exact date that he arrived at Venice is not known; however the first two paintings that he did for S. Benedetto are dated 1648. His early paintings in Venice show that he certainly had contact with Strozzi, but soon he left this and reached an altogether personal style. As a matter of fact, no other painter united by public strings to the culture of Venice of the second half of the seventeenth century created for himself such an independent style as did Mazzoni.

His chronology is sparse; other than the date of 1648 for the two paintings for the church of S. Benedetto, there is the date of 1660 for the "Banquet of Cleopatra" in Washington, and that of 1669 for the painting in the church of the Carmini. Dates are known for some of his literary works: "Il Tempo perduto" (1661), "Il buon viaggio scherzoso" and "La pittura guerriera" (both 1665).

Mazzoni's verses, far from being empty or only bizarre or grotesque, reveal a complex even though extravagant personality. His art too, rather than grotesque, appears intensely dramatic—painting for him becomes an essential expression of his spirit. This is certainly not placid or accommodating painting. He is an isolated and difficult to understand figure in seventeenth century Venetian painting.

198. The Sacrifice of Jephthah

Jephthah, the ruler of Galaad, sacrificed his only daughter in fulfillment of a vow that if he returned victorious over the Ammonites he would make an offering of whatsoever came forth to meet him on his return. (*Judges* 11, 30-40)

Nelson Gallery—Atkins Museum, Kansas City, Mo., Samuel H. Kress Collection.

Canvas, 46 x 59 in. Signed near lower left (on marble base): monogram SMF

Ref.: H. Voss in *Jahrbuch der Preussischen Kunstsammlungen*, LIII, 1932, no. 55; Gnudi in *Critica d'Arte*, IV, 1936, p. 181; W. Suida in *Art Quarterly*, XVII, 1954, p. 105; P. Zampetti, *Pittura del Seicento a Venezia*, Venice, 1959, p. 111, no. 172.

The relationship between the architecture and the figures, and

the architectonic elements as well, remind one of the *Feast of Cleopatra* (National Art Collection, Washington, D. C.), a painting dated by Mazzoni (1660). The fact that the present painting is executed in more detail and in a less sketchy manner than the Washington painting would indicate that it was probably painted a little earlier than 1660. Another version with some differences in the composition is in the Pedrocco Collection, Venice (Zampetti, no. 171). [R.L.M.]

BERNARDO STROZZI
1581 Genoa—Venice 1644

When fifteen years old, Bernardo entered the workshop of Sorri, a Sienese painter, then active in Genoa. At seventeen he became a Capuchin monk, but abandoned the monastic life (1610) in favor of becoming a prelate—accordingly he was at first called "Il Capuccino," later "Il Prete Genovese." When he refused to return to the monastery after the death of his mother he was arrested and imprisoned (1630). Regaining his freedom, he moved to Venice where he became a Monsignor in 1635.

At the beginning of his artistic career, Bernardo Strozzi underwent the most diversified influences: that of the Flemings, Rubens and van Dyck; the pupils of Cambiaso; the Sienese Barocci and the Mannerists; but above all the Lombard Cerano and the Bolognese-turned-Lombard, Giulio Cesare Procaccini. A painter of greatest native talent, he created a style which became fundamental not only for Genoese painting of the seventeenth century, but carried to Venice it became imbued with the luminous brilliance of the

great Venetians of the preceding century, to make Strozzi truly one of the founders of the Venetian seventeenth century painting style. [B.S.M.]

199. Street Musicians

William E. Suida has indicated that in works such as this, Strozzi demonstrates an ability, like that of Franz Hals, to paint figures so life-like that they almost seem to be in action.

The Detroit Institute of Arts, gift of Italian-Americans of Detroit, 1951.

Canvas, 43 x 61 in.
Coll.: Pietro Cardiello, Detroit.
Ref.: W. E. Suida, *Samuel H. Kress Collection*, San Francisco, 1955 pp. 58-59; R. Longhi in *Scritti Giovanile*, Florence, 1961, I, 489.

Roberto Longhi (1961) evidently published the first example of *Street Musicians* by Strozzi (Schönborn Coll., Pommersfelden). Some differences however can be noted—the man on the left has a much fuller beard and the colors of his costume seem to be different. A replica of the present version (Kress Coll., De Young Mus.) was destroyed by fire. Variants exist (Reval, Esthonia, formerly Liphart, Ratshof, near Dorpat; Signora Clementine Basevi Gambarana, Genoa). Morassi dates the Gambarana version in the last year of the Genoese period, the approximate date of the present painting. Around this time the Flemish master Jacob Jordaens painted a similar group of musicians called the *Serenade* (Rooses, *Jordaens' Leben and Werke*, Stuttgart, 1890, p. 89). It is possible that Jordaens may have known the work of Strozzi. [R.L.M.]

200. Saint Lawrence Distributing the Treasures of the Church to the Poor

St. Lawrence was educated at the University of Saragossa where he met Pope Sixtus II (257-58) who took him to Rome and created him an archdeacon in charge of the treasures of the Church. When Sixtus was condemned to death by the prefect of Rome because of his religion, Lawrence desired to die with him. On instructions from Sixtus, Lawrence agreed to wait three days during which he was to distribute to the poor the treasures of the church which the prefect had demanded. Following the three day period of distribution, Lawrence appeared with a great crowd of the poor and sick before the prefect to tell him that these people were indeed the treasures of the church. For this Lawrence was condemned to die on a gridiron and in the midst of his torture he shouted to the prefect: *Assatus est; jam versa et manduca.* (I am roasted, now turn me and eat me.)

City Art Museum of St. Louis, St. Louis, Mo.

Canvas, 48 x 64 in.
Coll.: Spinola, Genoa; Jacob Heimann, New York.
Ref.: *Golden Gate International Exposition*, San Francisco, Calif., 1940, p. 13, no. 166; *Three Baroque Masters*, Baltimore Museum of

Art, Baltimore, 1940, p. 24, no. 13. Worcester Art Museum Annual, 1946, V, 41; *Seicento Exhibition, Allen Memorial Bull.*, Winter 1952, no. 17; *Bull. City Art Museum,* St. Louis, XXIX, Nov. 1944, 1-2; L. Mortari in *Bollettino d'Arte*, 4, 1955, p. 327; *Fifty Masterworks from the City Art Museum,* Wildenstein Gallery, New York, 1958, no. 10.

The Cathedral in Genoa, Strozzi's birthplace, is dedicated to St. Lawrence and possibly for that reason the present subject appealed to him so greatly that he painted it in varying compositions throughout his career. Luisa Mortari places the present painting from Strozzi's Genoese period second in her chronological listing of the varying compositions, preceded by the example in the Palazzo Reale, Genoa. The other compositions which follow in sequence are in the Galleria d'Arte Antica, Rome; the Brass Collection, Venice; the Samuel H. Kress Collection, Portland Art Museum, Portland, Ore. (other versions with Marchesa Rosetta Gropallo De Ferrari, Sarzana, Italy and a third formerly with Mrs. M. H. Drey, London); and S. Nicola Tolentino, Venice. Mortari also mentions two school paintings of this subject, one in the Museum of Caracas, Venezuela, and the other (a copy of the S. Nicola Tolentino version) in the Church of S. Lorenzo, Fiumicello. [R.L.M.]

201. *The Holy Family—Vision of the Trinity*

A most unusual representation of the Holy Family and an angel adoring the Christ Child, placed by the Virgin upon an altar-like table below the Dove of the Holy Ghost and the blessing God the Father who holds a cross in his left hand: the position of the Infant Christ upon the altar as well as the presence of the cross expand this Vision of the Trinity to allude to the Crucifixion.

Robert and Bertina Suida Manning, New York, N. Y.

Pen and brush, sepia on *ecru* paper: 15½ x 11 in.
Coll.: W. E. Suida.
Ref.: L. Mortari in *Bollettino d'Arte*, 1955, p. 313; T. Pignatti in *La Pittura del Seicento a Venezia*, Ca Pesaro, Venice, 1959, p. 171, no. 42; Manning in *Genoese Masters*, Dayton, 1962, no. 99; Manning, *Genoese Painters*, Finch College, New York, 1964, no. 32.

This drawing is considered the earliest known one by Strozzi (Dr. Mortari, Prof. Pignatti and Prof. Fiocco). It combines influences from the Sienese masters, notably Salimbeni with certain Cambiasesque elements—characteristic traits for the early works by this master. [B.S.M.]

202. *The Stigmatization of St. Francis*

In a rocky wilderness St. Francis kneels with uplifted gaze and outspread hands in devout ecstasy. Above him hovers the mystic Seraph. In the background is Friar Leo, friend and disciple, who is recorded to have been present when St. Francis received the stigmata: the physical manifestation of the awe-inspiring spiritual infusion of the Holiest of Holies into his existence. (Mrs. Jameson, *Legends of the Monastic Orders*, Boston and New York, 1892, pp. 290-91).

Janos Scholz Collection, New York, N. Y.

Pen, gray-brown ink heightened with white chalk on gray-brown rough paper, 14¼ x 11⅛ in.

Coll.: Prayer (Lugt 2004); Goldstein (Lugt 2824).

Ref.: J. Scholz, in *The Art Quarterly*, XXIII, 1960, p. 61; Janos Scholz Collection Exhibitions: Oakland and San Francisco, 1960; Staten Island Museum, New York, 1961; Columbia, S. C., 1961; Hamburg and Cologne, Germany, 1963-64; Yale University, New Haven, 1964.

Janos Scholz assigns the present drawing to Strozzi's early Genoese period; indeed, the types, reminiscent of G. B. Paggi, but developed in Strozzi's more precocious and bold manner confirm it. [B.S.M.]

203. Head of a Woman

Possibly a preparatory sketch for the head of the Virgin in a vibrantly painted small *Annunciation* (Budapest Museum of Fine Arts).

Robert and Bertina Suida Manning, New York, N. Y.

Black chalk on gray paper, 8⅞ x 6¼ in.

Coll.: Dr. William E. Suida.

Ref.: Mortari in *Bolletino d'Arte*, 1955, p. 323; Pignatti in *La Pittura del Seicento a Venezia*, Venice, 1959, no. 43; Manning in *Genoese Masters*, Dayton, 1962, no. 98; Manning, *Genoese Painters*, Finch College Museum of Art, New York, 1964, no. 33.

Dr. Luisa Mortari assigned this drawing to Strozzi's late Venetian period (1630-40), relating it to the Budapest *Annunciation*, a small painting in which the master seems to consciously return to elements known from his earlier Genoese years, particularly comparable to another *Annuniciation* (Convento delle Interiate) in which he achieved a moment of greatest freedom during his Genoese period. [B.S.M.]

204. Minerva or Bellona

Although this drawing as well as the painting for which it

evidently served as a preparation (the painting too is in the Cleveland Museum of Art) have always been referred to as representing Minerva, the Roman equivalent for Pallas Athena, the goddess of Wisdom who sprang fully grown from the head of her father Zeus (Jupiter), there are several factors which cause us to question the iconographical identification. The emphasis on helmet, cuirass (barely indicated in the lower left foreground, but fully represented in the painting), and shield, plus the absence of the owl as Minerva's sacred animal, would indicate an identification rather with Bellona, goddess of war, sister of Mars. Certainly Strozzi's Bellona is a very non-bellicose Goddess of War. She is seated at rest, seemingly listening with a rapturous expression (very much like that of Strozzi's female saints in ecstasy) to the dictum from above—shall it be war or peace? Loosely she appears in readiness, holding on to her shield and plumed helmet—her cuirass not far away. However, in the painting her anti-war like spirit appears even further emphasized than in the drawing by her sumptuous maidenly attire and the charming ribbon in her hair. The seventeenth century knew several such pacifist representations of War, the classic example being Velazquez's tired Mars, represented as an aging warrior who appears to have fallen asleep. Rembrandt's sumptuously dressed Bellona may also be cited in this connection.

The Cleveland Museum of Art, Cleveland, Ohio, John L. Severance Fund

Black and red chalk on buff-pink paper, 14⅝ x 10$\frac{5}{16}$ in.
Ref.: H. Francis in *Cleveland Mus. Bull.*, XLIII, 1956, 123-26; H. Comstock in *Connoisseur* (Am. ed.), vol. 138, 1956, pp. 211 f.

This drawing, extremely close to the painting for which it was prepared, certainly dates from Strozzi's late Venetian period. The painting shows his fully mature art, blending his Genoese heritage, touched by the breath of Rubens, with the sumptuousness of form and color of the Venetians. Stylistically the drawing appears related to the beautiful head of a woman (no. 203) as well as to a series of twenty others, mainly representing details of hands, draperies, etc., done on the same kind of buff-pink paper (Palazzo Rosso, Genoa). The Cleveland work is the first full-scale drawing for a known composition by Strozzi to have come to light. [B.S.M.]

MARCANTONIO BASSETTI

1588 Verona 1630

Bassetti started his training under Felice Brusasorci.

Soon he went to Venice where he became thoroughly acquainted with the art of Tintoretto, which he interpreted in a calm and systematic manner, not dissimilar from Palma Giovane's. From about 1615 to 1620 Bassetti went to Rome, where he was near Saraceni, and apparently also had contact with Borgianni. His style became tempered through acquaintance with the works of both the Carracci and the Caravaggists, notably Lionello Spada. He also undoubtedly knew the work of Domenico Fetti, whose style he approached more and more, especially in his full maturity. While in Rome his Venetian-Tintorettesque style becomes transformed into a serene naturalism. He is the most famous painter among the Veronese triad: Bassetti, Turchi and Ottino. Bassetti's death of the plague at the age of forty-two ended a flourishing career.

205. The Eucharist

In the presence of God the Father, the Holy Ghost, Angels and Seraphim, an angel holds the chalice of the Eucharist signifying the presence of the third personnage of the Trinity. This is a rare representation of an allegory of the Trinity whereby the Sacrifice of Christ, symbolized by the chalice containing His blood, is made the physical as well as the spiritual center of the entire concept.

Janos Scholz Collection, New York, N. Y.

Pen and brush, brown ink heightened with white over preliminary work with black crayon on blue paper, 5⅞ x 6¾ in.
Coll.: Moscardo (Lugt 1920c).
Ref.: T. Pignatti in *La Pittura del Seicento a Venezia*, Ca'Pesaro, Venice, 1959, no. 15.

Pignatti has pointed out that this very exciting and beautiful drawing shows many stylistic connections with other drawings by Bassetti, such as the beautiful series at Windsor (Blunt, *Venetian Drawings at Windsor Castle*, London, 1957, p. 25), although it deviates entirely from his habitual technique of using oils on prepared paper. The design of the figures made luminous by stripes of light recalls effects achieved by Bassetti in several other works. [B.S.M.]

Pietro Muttoni, called
PIETRO DELLA VECCHIA
1603 Venice 1678

He received his curious nickname because of his unusual ability to restore as well as imitate paintings by masters of earlier generations. Melchiori and others testify to this ability and also relate that he had restored Giorgione's *Madonna of Castelfranco*. He received his artistic formation in the studio of Padovanino, where he worked side by side with Pietro Liberi and Girolamo Forabosco. Soon he also established contact with the innovators of the Venetian seventeenth century: Fetti, Strozzi and Lys. He married Clotilde, one of the beautiful daughters of the French painter Nicolo Regnier who had settled in Venice. Pietro Vecchia painted principally in Venice and is mentioned as member of the *Fraglia* from 1629-39. Boschini admired his great ability in imitating Giorgione; Moschini and Zanetti praised his beautiful light effects. Lanzi states that he was so proficient at imitating that many of his works were circulated as originals by Giorgione, Licinio and Titian. He loved to paint bizarre subjects, such as armed men in the taste of the sixteenth century (Giorgione and Romanino) of which there are a large number. Via Saraceni he acquired a Caravaggesque sense for chiaroscuro which he superimposed upon the inherited culture of the Venetian cinquecento, bringing a novel vision of color and form. Despite his uncanny ability to imitate others, Pietro Vecchia's style is extremely personal.

206. Allegory of Poverty, Mother of the Arts

The subject is clarified by Ripa's *Iconologia* (1613, II, 160). The figure with the raised winged left arm, who is chained at the feet, is the symbol of the poverty of a human being of genius. Theocritus said to Dofonto: "It is only the poor man who is successful with the arts." The broken chains at the feet of the female figure and the winged genius, who arrives bringing crowns, enrich the composition with new significance (M. Muraro, 1957).

Janos Scholz Collection, New York, N. Y.

Pen and brush, brown ink on white paper, 7⅞ x 11½ in. Signed near center; inscribed below to left, "Piero Vechia"; Bateson stamp, lower left. On *verso* geometrical calculations.
Coll.: William Bateson, London (Lugt Sup. 2604a).
Ref.: Bateson Sale, Sotheby, London, 1929, no. 121; M. Muraro,

Disegni Veneti della Collezione Janos Scholz, Venice, 1957, no. 48; N. Ivanoff, *I Disegni Italiani del Seicento*, Venice, 1959, pl. 20; T. Pignatti in *Pittura del Seicento a Venezia*, Ca Pesaro, Venice, 1959, no. 50; Janos Scholz Collection exhibitions: Mills College, Oakland, 1960; Columbia, S. C., 1961; Hamburg, Ger., 1963; Cologne, Ger., 1963-64.

According to Prof. Pignatti this drawing, together with the Madonna and Child (Dresden) published by Ivanoff, are the only two securely attributable drawings by Pietro Vecchia because of the signatures they both bear. Despite differences in technique this allegory is related stylistically to the group of drawings given to Pietro Vecchia in Florence. Furthermore, Pignatti points out the still life of musical instruments, etc., which seems to confirm some contact with Caravaggism as well as with the "verism" of the Lombard, Evaristo Baschenis. [B.S.M.]

PIETRO LIBERI

1614 Padua—Venice 1687

Before leaving for Constantinople in 1628, Liberi moved to Venice to pursue his studies of art. Most likely at this time he had his first contact with Varotari, who is said to have been his first teacher. Romantic adventures of all sorts took him within a span of eleven years throughout the Mediterranean area and elsewhere. He was in Rome from 1638-1641 to "see all" from Raphael and Michelangelo to the Carracci and Pietro da Cortona. In Florence he fres-

coed the ceiling of the Oratorio of San Filippo Neri. In Parma he saw works by Correggio, through the mediary of Lanfranco, whom he had seen in Naples and Rome. In Bologna he admired the works of Tibaldi and Niccolo dell'Abbate. After his return to Venice in 1643, for eight years he was somewhat of a forger, painting sometimes in the style of Reni, at other times in the style of Titian. After 1653 his status improved and he received commissions to decorate the Loggia of the Campanile and the Ducal Palace. His late Venetian works show a thorough acquaintance with those of Luca Giordano, Sebastiano Mazzoni and Gregorio Lazzarini. They influenced Antonio Bellucci, Paolo Pagan, and Antonio Pellegrini.

207. The Adoration of the Shepherds

Luke 2, 15-17

Janos Scholz Collection, New York, N. Y.

Pen, brown ink, brown and red washes over preparatory red chalk on white paper, 9¼ x 6⅛ in.

Coll.: Moscardo (Lugt 1920c).

Ref.: *La Pittura del Seicento a Venezia*, Ca Pesaro, Venice, 1959, p. 175; Scholz in *Art Quarterly*, XXIII, 1960, 56; Scholz, *Life of Christ Drawings*, Notre Dame, Ind., 1964.

The present drawing stylistically approaches Francesco Maffei (cf. *Martyrdom of St. Peter*, Uffizi 1666E). Ivanoff attributed a similar drawing in the Scholz Collection, exhibited at Venice (1959), to Liberi and compared it to others (Galleria Estense, Modena). [B.S.M.]

GIOVANNI BATTISTA LANGETTI

1625 Genoa—Venice 1676

Langetti at first studied with Pietro da Cortona in Rome, then went to Venice, where he remained permanently and worked with his compatriot Giovanni Franceso Cassana (1611-1690). Langetti was the second major Genoese painter to settle in Venice, following Strozzi's leadership. He exercised a significant influence on the development of Venetian painting during the second half of the seventeenth century. Like Maffei, he was influenced by Strozzi, from whom he acquired his taste for thick impasto brushwork. However, his choice of subjects was determined rather by the naturalism of the Caravaggesque painters, above all by Ribera, whose drastic realism he so frequently approaches. He differs from the Roman and Neapolitan Caravaggesque painters in that his choice of color is much more brilliant and intense, dark in the shadows, but luminous, sometimes even iridescent in the lights. He left a prodigious number of works.

208. The Vision of St. Jerome

St. Jerome (340-420) was one of the four Doctors of the Church. Among his many writings the most famous is his translation of the Bible into Latin, known as the Vulgate. For four years he retired to a desert in Chalcis, on the confines of Arabia, to study, meditate and do penance. There, according to legend, he befriended a lion by removing a thorn from his paw.

"In one of his distempered visions, he fancied he heard the last trumpet sounded in his ear by an angel, and summoning him before the judgment-seat of God. 'Who art thou?' demanded the awful voice. 'A Christian', replied the trembling Jerome. 'Tis false!' replied the voice, 'thou art no Christian; thou art a Ciceronian. Where the treasure is, there will the heart be also' . . . This is a common subject, and styled 'The Vision of St. Jerome.' " (A. Jameson, *Sacred and Legendary Art*, Boston, 1895, I, 281/90)

The Cleveland Museum of Art, Cleveland, Ohio, Delia E. and L. E. Holden Funds.

Canvas, 78¾ x 58¾ in. Signed lower left: LANGETI FAC.at

Coll.: Palazzo Conti, Vicenza; Brass, Venice.

Ref.: *Mostra della Pittura Italiana del Seicento e del Settecento*, Florence, 1922, p. 112, no. 559; G. Fiocco in *Dedalo*, III, Oct. 1922, 275-86; *Pittura Italiana del Seicento e del Settecento*, Milan, 1924, p. 177; F. Baumgart in *Bollettino d'Arte*, Sept. 1931, p. 104; H. S. Francis in *Cleveland Museum Bull.* XXXIX, Feb. 1952, pp. 24ff; Manning, *Genoese Masters*, Dayton, Ohio, 1962, no. 40.

Even though the major portion of Langetti's activity was centered in Venice, in this painting his Genoese heritage (including even reminiscences of his contemporary, Valerio Catello) shows itself, particularly in the fluttering angel *putto* near the van-Dyckish angel with the trumpet. The saint himself evidences certain similarities in general concept to the art of Ribera. Langetti's colors, are however more intense and richer. [R.L.M.]

GIULIO CARPIONI

1611 Venice 1674

According to tradition he began in the studio of Padovanino but his early work is unknown. A lunette, *The Apotheosis of Vincenzo Dolfin*, for the *Palazzo del Podestà* documents Carpioni in Vicenza for the first time in 1647. He probably came a year earlier after a hypothetical sojourn of two years in Padua. In 1648 he painted a second lunette for the *Palazzo del Podestà* and his first recorded altarpiece *The Martyrdom*

of St. Catherine for the church of the same name. This group of paintings shows Carpioni, not yet forty years of age, breaking beyond the art of Padovanino and his circle—there are no nostalgic reminiscences of Titian or Veronese. This breaking away from tradition, according to Fiocco, was stimulated by Carpioni's acquaintance with the graphic works of Pietro Testa and perhaps also some aspects of Poussin; also certain influences from other artists such as Francesco Ruschi and Niccolo Renieri who were active in Venice at that time (c. 1640). For about twenty-five years he worked in Vicenza perfecting an entirely original artistic vocabulary.

209. The Death of Leander

The legend of the two lovers, Hero and Leander, is the subject of a late Greek poem attributed to Musaeus. Hero was a priestess of Aphrodite at Sestos on the Hellespont, and Leander, who lived at

Abydos, swam the strait nightly to visit her. One night he was drowned, and Hero in grief cast herself into the sea.

Mr. and Mrs. Paul H. Ganz, New York, N. Y.

Canvas, 24 x 32 in.

Ref.: Manning, *Venetian Baroque Painters*, Finch College, New York, 1964, no. 31.

Evidently a subject of great appeal to Carpioni since he painted a number of closely related variations on this theme which are in the following collections: Viancini Collection, Venice (formerly); Museo Magnin, Dijon; Donzelli, Florence; Museum of Fine Arts, Budapest; and Coll. Emo-Capodilista, Civic Museum, Padua (G. M. Pilo, *Carpioni*, 1961, figs. 72, 101, 102, 105, 172). A drawing for the Padua version is with Dr. V. L. Braga, Vicenza. [R.L.M.]

JOHANN KARL LOTH
called Lotto or Carlotto
1632 Munich—Venice 1698

From his father, Ulrich, who had studied with

Saraceni, he acquired a tendency toward Caravaggism. He worked in Germany for Leopold I, and after periods in Vienna, Florence, Milan, and Verona, he settled in Venice. He had visited there in 1660 becoming a member of the *Fraglia dei pittori veneziani*—until 1687. He was particularly attracted to the art of Langetti and the naturalistic current, reinterpreted with crude realism and violence of coloring. Loth in turn influenced his compatriots, Hans Adam Weissenkirchner (1646-1695) and Daniel Seiter (1647/49-1705).

210. The Meeting of Rebecca and Abraham's Servant at the Well

See no. 166.

M. H. de Young Memorial Museum, San Francisco, Cal., purchase, 1947.

Canvas, 54 x 68 in.
Ref.: *Illustrations*, M. H. de Young Mus., San Francisco, 1950, p. 27; P. Zampetti, *Pittura del Seicento a Venezia*, Ca'Pesaro, Venice, 1959, p. 119.

Biblical themes appealed to Loth greatly and this work shows the rather personal manner in which he represented them. In the late evening the half nude figure of Rebecca stands out in contrast to the other figures clearly defined in the shadow—an attempt at *tenebroso*—demonstrating his tendency towards Caravaggism. Only the mountain silhouetted against the sky gives some feeling of space to the crowded composition. The bracelet, jeweled belt, and the box of jewels carried by the bearded servant add a Venetian touch. [R.L.M.]

ANTONIO BALESTRA
1666 Verona 1740

Antonio received his earliest training with the mediocre local painter Giovanni Zeffis. After the death of his father he abandoned an artistic career to become a merchant; however, he soon returned to a more intensive study of painting, going to Venice and entering the studio of Bellucci, whose influence remained of lasting significance. Thereafter he went to Rome, becoming the pupil of Carlo Maratti. In 1695, after a year of illness, he returned to Verona. Then he divided his time mostly between that city and Venice. He sojourned very briefly in Milan as well as certain cities in Emilia; in Bologna he developed a special attraction to the works of the Carracci. Balestra's style, calm and composed, could be characterized as neoclassical *avant la lettre*. [B.S.M.]

211. The Martyrdom of Saints Cosmas and Damian

Cosmas and Damian were, according to legend, Arabians reared by their widowed mother as Christians. They devoted their lives to charity, medicine and surgery to help the wounded and sick. All this they did for love, refusing to accept any reward. When Diocletian mercilously condemned Christians, Cosmas and Damian were cast into the sea, but were rescued by an angel. They were cast into a fire, but it would not burn them. They were stoned. The stones did not touch them but rebounded and killed many who threw them. The brothers were finally beheaded and their bodies were taken to Rome, where a church in the Forum was dedicated to them in 526 by Pope Felix IV. They are patron saints of the medical profession.

Mr. and Mrs. Paul H. Ganz, New York, N. Y.

Canvas, 44½ x 65¼ in.
Ref.: *Guida di Padova e della sua Provincia*, Padua, 1842, pp. 239, 242; Ballarin in *Arte Veneta*, XVI, 1962, 239; Manning, *Venetian Baroque Painters*, Finch College, New York, 1964, no. 48.

Executed very freely in rather reddish tones, this is an unusually large study or *modelletto* for a painting in the apsis (chapel 13) of San Giustina, Padua. Opposite (chapel 8) is the pendant in which Balestra portrays the scene in which Cosmas and Damian are removed from the sea by angels. The *Guida de Padova* describes them as in poor condition but says that they must be considered as the most imaginative creations by Balestra. [R.L.M.]

212. The Resurrection

All the Gospels speak of the discovery of the empty sepulchre by the Holy Women, but they do not describe the actual event of the Resurrection which, however, is abundantly illustrated in art.

Janos Scholz Collection, New York, N. Y.

Pen and brush, brown ink and gray washes over preliminary black crayon on white paper; 22¼ x 16 in. Inscribed below, "Balestra 6" (old attribution).
Coll.: Anon.; Venice; Sartori.

Mr. Scholz has pointed out that the status of drawings by Balestra

is rather problematic. Other drawings also bearing old inscriptions with attributions to this artist (Stockholm Museum) are quite similar in style as well as technique to the present one. [B.S.M.]

ANONYMOUS
c. 1650

213. A Theatrical Design

It is difficult to visualize the complicated machinery so indispensable for the success of Baroque theatrical performances, which featured not only affluent splendor in costuming but also the most elaborate stage settings. Operas as well as plays and ballets, usually allegorical in nature for the glorification of a monarch or a local ruler, or commemorative of such events as royal weddings, births or even deaths, demanded complex changes of scenery: physical transformations which took place on stage, such as a palace interior turning into a mountain, which in turn could become a ruin or even a gaping hellmouth such as the present one. Nearly all performances featured cloud-machines as well as descending or ascending deities.

Donald Oenslager Collection, New York, N. Y.

Pen and bistre with gray ink wash on white paper: 12¾ x 19 in.
Coll.: W. A. Freund, Berlin (Lugt 954).
Ref.: *Italian Architectural and Theatrical Design*, Este Gallery, New York, 1961, no. 60; D. Kelder, *Scenes and Spectacles*, Queens College, New York, no. 15; *Ballet Theater Designs*, Minneapolis Institute of Arts, 1963, no. 9; *Four Centuries of Theater Design*, A.F.A. Circulating Exhibition, 1963, no. 9.

According to Diane Kelder the present drawing of a hell-mouth is very close to Ludovico Burnacini's design for a scene for Francesco Sbarra (poet) and Marc Antonio Cesti's (composer) "Il Pomo d'Oro," an allegorical opera composed and performed for the glorification of the marriage of Leopold I of Austria and Infanta Margherita Theresa in 1668. As fantastic as the design appears at first glance, one can clearly determine the three side wings on either side of the gaping mouth. [B.S.M.]

LIST OF LENDERS

PRIVATE COLLECTORS

Mr. and Mrs. Winslow Ames, Saunderstown, Rhode Island, no. 69

Collection of Walter P. Chrysler, Jr., nos. 80, 81, 114, 118, 119, 152, 155, 156, 182, 193

Mr. and Mrs. Lawrence A. Fleischman, Detroit, Michigan, no. 111

Dr. and Mrs. Michael W. Freeman, Detroit, Michigan, no. 121

Mr. and Mrs. Paul H. Ganz, New York, New York, nos. 88, 93, 101, 110, 134, 135, 141, 146, 160, 184, 188, 209, 211

Mr. William T. Hassett, Jr., Hagerstown, Maryland, no. 183

M. Knoedler & Co., Inc., New York, New York, no. 153

Mr. and Mrs. Milton Lewine, New York, New York, no. 36

Mr. and Mrs. Elton F. MacDonald, Grosse Pointe Park, Michigan, no. 168

Denis Mahon, Esq., London, England, nos. 12, 19, 32, 66, 71, 72, 77, 78, 83, 98, 99, 157

Robert and Bertina Suida Manning, New York, New York, nos. 11, 37, 38, 50, 52, 53, 87, 109, 112, 126, 130, 136, 150, 170, 172, 175, 179, 186, 192, 201, 203

Mr. Frederick Mont, New York, New York, no. 90

Mr. Donald Oenslager, New York, New York, nos. 48, 213

Maestro Francesco Molinari Predelli, Bologna, Italy, no. 138

Mr. and Mrs. David E. Rust, Washington, D. C., no. 104

Janos Scholz Collection, New York, New York, nos. 7, 17, 20, 31, 35, 40, 58, 76, 79, 85, 94, 95, 108, 116, 124, 131, 137, 139, 140A, 142, 147, 149, 158, 180, 181, 185, 191, 196, 197, 202, 205, 206, 207, 212

Seiferheld and Co., New York, New York, no. 74

Mr. and Mrs. Eugene Victor Thaw, New York, New York, no. 24

Mr. and Mrs. A. D. Wilkinson, Grosse Pointe, Michigan, no. 15

Rudolf and Margot Wittkower, New York, New York, no. 75

INSTITUTIONS

The University of Michigan Museum of Art, Ann Arbor, Michigan, nos. 102, 166

Atlanta Art Association, Atlanta, Georgia, nos. 51, 70

Walters Art Gallery, Baltimore, Maryland, no. 133

Museum of Fine Arts, Boston, Massachusetts, nos. 100, 174

Fogg Art Museum, Harvard University, Cambridge, Massachusetts, nos. 84, 89, 107, 125, 177, 195

The Art Institute of Chicago, Chicago, Illinois, nos. 64, 67, 82

The Cleveland Museum of Art, Cleveland, Ohio, nos. 23, 41, 63, 103, 194, 204, 208

Museum of Art and Archaeology, The University of Missouri, Columbia, Missouri, nos. 129, 143

Columbia Museum of Art, Columbia, South Carolina, no. 113

The Dayton Art Institute, Dayton, Ohio, nos. 9, 168

The Detroit Institute of Arts, Detroit, Michigan, nos. 5, 8, 13-16, 21, 22, 25-27, 33, 44, 47, 61, 91, 132, 154, 162, 163, 165, 187, 190, 199

Bob Jones University Collection, Greenville, South Carolina, nos. 30, 54, 120, 127, 145, 164

Wadsworth Atheneum, Hartford, Connecticut, nos. 2, 6, 161

The Clowes Fund Collection, Indianapolis, Indiana, no. 4

Nelson Gallery—Atkins Museum, Kansas City, Missouri, nos. 3, 148, 189, 198

The University of Kansas Museum of Art, Lawrence, Kansas, nos. 43, 45

University of Louisville Art Collection, Louisville, Kentucky, no. 97

The Cooper Union Museum, New York, New York, nos. 122, 167

Samuel H. Kress Foundation, New York, New York, no. 128

The Metropolitan Museum of Art, New York, New York, nos. 57, 59, 73, 96, 117, 159, 171

The Pierpont Morgan Library, New York, New York, nos. 1, 28, 29, 39, 56, 86, 115

Allen Memorial Art Museum, Oberlin College, Oberlin, Ohio, nos. 18, 105

The National Gallery of Canada, Ottawa, Canada, nos. 10, 169

Philadelphia Museum of Art, Philadelphia, Pennsylvania, nos. 173, 176

Ponce Art Museum (Luis A. Ferré Foundation), Ponce, Puerto Rico, no. 144

Museum of Art, Rhode Island School of Design, Providence, Rhode Island, nos. 55, 62

North Carolina Museum of Art, Raleigh, North Carolina, no. 65

City Art Museum of St. Louis, St. Louis, Missouri, no. 200

M. H. de Young Memorial Museum, San Francisco, California, nos. 49, 210

Ringling Museum of Art, Sarasota, Florida, nos. 34, 68

Seattle Art Museum, Seattle, Washington, nos. 42, 60, 92

The Toledo Museum of Art, Toledo, Ohio, nos. 46, 151

Philbrook Art Center, Tulsa, Oklahoma, no. 140

Norton Gallery and School of Art, West Palm Beach, Florida, no. 178

Worcester Art Museum, Worcester, Massachusetts, no. 106

CONSULTING COMMITTEE

Chairman, Frederick Cummings, *Curator of European Art, The Detroit Institute of Arts*

Dr. Robert Enggass, *Art Department, Pennsylvania State University, University Park, Pennsylvania*

Dr. Olga Raggio, *Associate Research Curator, Western European Arts, The Metropolitan Museum of Art, New York, New York*

Bertina Suida Manning

Robert L. Manning, *Director and Curator, Finch College Museum of Art, New York, New York*

Dr. Dwight C. Miller, *Department of Art and Architecture, Stanford University, Stanford, California*

Dr. Alfred Moir, *Chairman, Art Department, University of California, Santa Barbara, California*

Dr. Donald Posner, Institute of Fine Arts, New York University, *New York, New York*

THE DETROIT INSTITUTE OF ARTS

The Arts Commission

Lawrence A. Fleischman, *President*

Douglas F. Roby, *Vice-President*

Mrs. Edsel B. Ford, Harold O. Love, Ralph T. McElvenny, Stanford C. Stoddard, Mrs. Harry L. Winston

Willis F. Woods, *Director*

William A. Bostick, *Secretary*

The Founders Society

William M. Day, *President*

Alvan Macauley, Jr., Edward E. Rothman, *Vice-Presidents*

John W. Shenefield, *Treasurer*

Mrs. Gaylord W. Gillis, Jr., *Secretary*

Willis F. Woods, *Executive Director*

Administrative and Curatorial Staff

Willis F. Woods, *Director*

William A. Bostick, *Administrator*

Francis W. Robinson, *Curator of Ancient and Medieval Art*

Frederick J. Cummings, *Curator of European Art*

Robert D. Kinsman, *Curator of Contemporary Art*

Charles H. Elam, *Curator of American Art*

Robert H. Tannahill, *Honorary Curator of American Art*

W. Hawkins Ferry, *Honorary Curator of Architecture*

William Peck, *Associate Curator of Ancient and Medieval Art*

Virginia H. Brose, *Curator in Charge of Education*

Jean Dodenhoff, *Assistant Curator, Education*

Nita L. Schwartz, *Assistant Curator, Education*

Audley M. Grossman, Jr., *Curator of Theatre Arts*

Carol Selby, *Librarian*

Harold T. Shaw, *Building Superintendent*

Joseph Klima, *Photographer*

Gordon H. Robertson, *Manager—Founders Society*

Edward T. Darling, *Public Relations Director—Founders Society*

Sarah Hackett, *Manager Museum Shop—Founders Society*

Honor Williams, *Activities Coordinator—Founders Society*

ITALY IN THE
SEVENTEENTH CENTURY
(boundaries approximate)
1. Piedmont (to Duchy of Savoy)
2. Lombardy (Duchy of Milan)
3. Duchy of Mantua
4. Venetia (Republic of Venice)
5. Liguria (Republic of Genoa)
6. Duchy of Parma
Turin
1
Milan
2
Brescia
4
Padua
Venice
3
Mantua
Parma
6
Modena
7
A
Bologna
5
Genoa
Lucca
Florence
Pisa
Urbino
B
Siena
8
Perugia
C
9
Corsica
Rome
10
Naples
D
E
Sardinia
F
Sicily
7. Duchy of Modena
8. Grand Duchy of Tuscany
9. Papal States
A. Emilia B. The Marches C. Umbria
10. Kingdom of Naples
D. Campania E. Apulia F. Calabria

SELECTED LIST OF BAROQUE EXHIBITIONS

PREPARED BY STEPHEN PEPPER

Berne, Switzerland, *Das Siebzehnjahrhundert in der Französischen Malerei*, ed. Boris Lossky, 1959

Bologna, Italy, Palazzo dell'Archiginnasio, *Maestri della pittura del seicento emiliano*, ed. G. C. Gnudi, et al., 1959

Bologna, Italy, Palazzo dell'Archiginnasio, *L'Ideale classico del seicento in Italia e la pittura di paesaggio*, ed. G. C. Gnudi, et al., 1962

Bordeaux, France, *L'age d'or espagnol: la peinture en Espagne et en France autour du Caravagisme*, ed. E. Lafuente Ferrari and René Huyghe, 1954

Bowdoin, Maine, Bowdoin College Museum of Art, *Baroque Paintings from the Collection of Walter P. Chrysler, Jr.*, 1963

Brescia, Italy, *Pittura a Brescia nel seicento e settecento*, ed. Emma Calabi, 1935

Cardiff, Wales, National Museum, *Ideal and Classical Landscape*, ed. P. J. Barlow, 1960

Cologne, Germany, Wallraf-Richartz Museum, *Italienische Meisterzeichnungen vom 14. bis zum 18. Jahrhundert aus amerikanischen Besitz: Die Sammlung Janos Scholz*, New York, ed. Wolf Stubbe and Horst Keller, 1963-1964

Columbia, South Carolina, Columbia Museum of Art, *Italian Baroque Drawings from the Janos Scholz Collection*, ed. A. Hyatt Mayor, 1961

Dayton, Ohio, Art Institute, *Genoese Masters, Cambiaso to Magnasco 1550-1750*, ed. Robert and Bertina Manning, 1962

Florence, Italy, Palazzo Pitti, *Pittura italiana del seicento e del settecento*, ed. N. Tarchini, et al., 1922

Genoa, Italy, Palazzzo Reale, *Pittori genovesi del seicento e del settecento*, ed. O. Grosso, et al., 1938

Hagerstown, Maryland, Washington County Museum of Fine Arts, *Four Centuries of Italian Drawings from the Scholz Collection*, ed. William T. Hassett, Jr., 1960

Hamburg, Germany, Kunsthalle, *Italienische Meisterzeichnungen vom 14. bis zum 18. Jahrhundert aus amerikanischem Besitz: Die Sammlung Janos Scholz*, New York, ed. Wolf Stubbe and Alfred Hentzen, 1963

Hartford, Connecticut, Wadsworth Atheneum, *Exhibition of Italian Painting of the Sei- and Settecento*, 1930

Kansas City, Missouri, William Rockhill Nelson Art Gallery, *Venetian Paintings and Drawings of the XVII Century*, 1937

London, England, Royal Academy of Arts, *Italian Art of the Seventeenth Century*, ed. O. Sitwell, 1925

London, England, Royal Academy of Arts, *Italian Art and Britain*, 1960

London, England, Royal Academy of Arts, *Seventeenth Century Art in Europe*, 1938

London, England, Royal Academy of Arts, *The Age of Louis XIV*, ed. A. Blunt, 1958

London, England, Wildenstein Gallery, *Artists in Seventeenth Century Rome*, ed. D. Mahon and D. Sutton, 1955

Milan, Italy, Palazzo Reale, *Mostra dei pittori della realta' in Lombardi*, ed. Longhi, et. al., 1953

Newcastle-on-Tyne, *Neapolitan Art of the Seventeenth and Eighteenth Centuries*, ed. Tony Ellis, 1962

New Haven, Connecticut, Yale University Art Gallery, *Italian Drawings from the Collection of Janos Scholz*, ed. Egbert Haverkamp-Begemann, 1964

New York, New York, Finch College Museum of Art, *Bolognese Baroque Painters*, ed. Robert Manning, 1962

New York, New York, Finch College Museum of Art, *Neapolitan Masters* of the *Seventeenth* and *Eighteenth Centuries*, ed. Robert Manning, 1962

New York, New York, Finch College Museum of Art, *Venetian Baroque Painters*, ed. Robert Manning, 1964

New York, New York, Finch College Museum of Art, *Genoese Painters, Cambiaso to Magnasco*, ed. Robert Manning, 1964

Notre Dame, Indiana, University of Notre Dame Art Gallery, *The Life of Christ, Drawings from the Janos Scholz Collection*, ed. Janos Scholz, 1964

Oakland, California, Mills College Art Gallery, *Drawings from Lombardy and Adjacent Areas, 1480-1620*, ed. Alfred Neumeyer and Janos Scholz, 1956

Oakland, California, Mills College Art Gallery, *Drawings from Bologna 1520-1800*, ed. Alfred Neumeyer and Janos Scholz, 1957

Oakland, California, Mills College Art Gallery, *Venetian Drawings, 1600-1800*, ed. Alfred Neumeyer and Janos Scholz, 1960

Oakland, California, Mills College Art Gallery, *Drawings from Tuscany and Umbria, 1350-1700*, ed. Alfred Neumeyer and Janos Scholz, 1961

Oberlin, Ohio, Allen Memorial Art Museum, *Italian Paintings of the Seventeenth Century*, ed. W. Stechow, 1952

Paris, France, Musée du Louvre, *Dix-septieme siècle français, chefs d'oeuvres des musées de Provence*, 1957

Paris, France, Musée du Louvre, *Dessins romains du XVII siècle: artistes contemporains de Poussin*, ed. J. Bean, 1960

Paris, France, Musée de L'Orangerie, *Peintres de la realité en France au XVIIe siècle*, ed. P. Jamot and C. Sterling, 1934

Paris, France, Petit Palais, *Le paysage français de Poussin à Corot*, ed. L. Hourticq, et. al., 1925

Paris, France, Petit Palais, *Le 17e siecle français*, 1958

Portland, Oregon, Art Museum, *Italian Paintings of the Late Renaissance and Baroque Period*, 1936

Portland, Oregon, Art Museum, *Paintings from the Collection of Walter P. Chrysler, Jr.*, ed. Bertina Manning, 1956

Poughkeepsie, New York, Vassar College, *Italian Baroque Paintings of the Seventeenth and Eighteenth Centuries*, 1940

Rimini, Italy, *Mostra della pittura del' 600 a Rimini*, ed. F. Arcangeli, et. al., 1952

Rome, Italy, Palazzo dell'Esposizione, *Il Seicento europeo*, ed. Luigi Salerno and A. Marabottini, 1957

Rome, Italy, Museo Nazionale d'Arte Antica, Palazzo Barberini, *Cortoneschi a Roma*, 1956

Rome, Italy, Museo Nazionale d'Arte Antica, Palazzo Barberini, *Paesisti e vedutisti a Roma nel '600 e nel '700*, ed. N. di Carpegna, 1956

Rome, Italy, Museo Nazionale d'Arte Antica, Palazzo Barberini, *Pittori napoletani del '600 e del '700*, ed. N. di Carpegna, 1958

Rome, Italy, Palazzo di Venezia, *Disegni delle collezione reali d'Inghilterra a Windsor*, 1961

Rouen, France, Musée des Beaux-Arts, *Nicolas Poussin et son temps*, ed. Pierre Rosenberg, 1961

São Paolo, Brazil, *Da Caravaggio a Tiepolo*, ed. G. Ronei, 1954

San Francisco, California, California Palace of the Legion of Honor, *Exhibition of Italian Baroque Paintings—Seventeenth and Eighteenth Centuries*, 1941

Sarasota, Florida, John and Mable Ringling Museum of Art, *Baroque Painters of Naples*, ed. Creighton Gilbert, March 1961

Staten Island, New York, Staten Island Museum, *Italian Drawings from the Janos Scholz Collection*, ed. Janos Scholz, 1961

Turin, Italy, Palazzo Madama, *Manierismo piemontese e lombardo del '600*, ed. G. L. Testori, 1955

Turin, Italy, *Barocco piemontese*, ed. A. Griseri, et al., 1963, 2 vols.

Venice, Italy, Fondazione Giorgio Cini, *Venetian Drawings from the Collection of Janos Scholz*, ed. Michelangelo Muraro, 1957

Venice, Italy, *La pittura del seicento a Venezia*, ed. P. Zampetti, 1959

Washington, D. C., The National Gallery of Art, *The Splendid Century—French Art: 1600-1715*, 1961

Wiesbaden, Germany, Nassauisches Landesmuseum, *Italienische Malerei des 17 und 18 jahrhunderts*, 1935

For further bibliography, see catalogue entries.

INDEX OF ARTISTS